TROUT STREAMS

The Ausable River, a fine trout stream.

TROUT STREAMS

Conditions that Determine Their Productivity and Suggestions for Stream and Lake Management

BY

PAUL R. NEEDHAM, PH.D.

Revised by Carl F. Bond

Oregon State University

HOLDEN-DAY

San Francisco, Cambridge, London, Amsterdam

Published by Holden-Day, Inc.
500 Sansome Street, San Francisco, California

FIRST EDITION PUBLISHED BY COMSTOCK PUBLISHING COMPANY, INC.
ITHACA · NEW YORK

Library of Congress Catalog Card Number 70-105668

Printed in the United States of America

Foreword

Biological fact, sound reasoning, and interesting opinion do not necessarily grow old or outdated even though they might have been set in print several years past. We need only to examine the state of the knowledge of scientific fisheries that confronted the late Paul R. Needham at the time he wrote *Trout Streams* in order to bring into perspective the reasoning, the fact, and the opinion he presented. For years artificial propagation had been considered not only a tool but, by some, as an end of itself, and the purpose had been forgotten in an effort to show great numbers of fish planted. Naturally there were critics of this procedure, and they promoted activity on several fronts.

During the late 1920's and the 1930's surveys of streams and lakes were conducted in order to learn about the environment into which the hatchery fish were being released. As knowledge of the fish, their habits, their food and other requirements grew, the realizations came that some streams did not need to be stocked, and that others could be made to support more trout by alteration of the physical environment.

Other activity was directed toward learning the fate of stocked trout, leading to the use of test streams and thorough creel census methods. The improvement of the hatchery product was receiving attention through selective breeding of domesticated brood stock, disease control and use of scientifically formulated diets.

Pollution was a problem but did not show the awesome potential we see now. Streams and lakes were being visited by brigades of anglers who only heralded the hordes to come. The major hydroelectric and water control systems were bringing huge rivers to bridle and there was uneasiness in some circles over our treatment of the environment.

Basic trout biology and the fundmentals of management were known, and in presenting his version of them, Dr. Needham was involved in a modicum of prophecy. But he did not passively wait for the field to develop along the lines he wrote of; he participated through his own efforts and those of his students, directing attention toward the systematics of trout, fate of planted fish and general stream ecology.

The past three decades have seen remarkable advances in understanding of stream ecology and the technology that eases that understanding. New concepts of biological productivity have helped us to learn what to expect from our waters. Close attention to the behavior of trout — their intra- and interspecific relationships — has enabled us to understand better how production and numbers are limited and regulated. Application of electricity to fish collecting has aided greatly in population research, and computer-aided biometrical studies have added confidence to what we have learned.

In the light of these and much other change, a few words in the text of this book have been changed, and several notes added to help the reader keep track of advances. New literature has been cited in case one wishes to look more closely into recent research. But the basic presentation and argument of the original text are left to speak for themselves.

CARL E. BOND

Oregon State University
October 1, 1969

PREFACE

THIS *book is an attempt to place in the hands of anglers, sportsmen, and conservationists reliable information relating to trout and to the streams in which they live. Many letters have been received asking where information could be found on trout, trout foods, and other aspects of stream biology. These led the writer to believe that a book bringing together and condensing the scattered information that has appeared in numerous journals within recent years would be of use in furthering the cause of stream and lake management. There are many facts of importance that are well-known to fisheries workers but are little known to sportsmen. If the support of anglers is to be obtained to put into effect more modern and better balanced conservation policies, these facts must be made available to them.*

We might now be said to be entering a new conservation era. In recent years fish and game research work has been greatly expanded by both federal and state agencies. The establishment of divisions of fish and game management in various universities and colleges gives further evidence of the new trend. These are hopeful signs. A working basis of facts is badly needed to replace guesswork in attempting to solve our problems in wildlife management.

Much of the material presented here is the writer's own; some of it is new, and some is drawn from previous publications. Portions have been borrowed from various sources; and while it is impracticable to make acknowledgment to all sources of data, credit is duly rendered to those persons whose contributions have been most useful. Acknowledgment is due to Field and Stream, National Sportsman, Westways, *and* California Fish and Game *for permission to use, either in whole or in part, articles by the writer that were published in these magazines. For making drawings of aquatic organisms, the help of Miss Laura Garnjobst of Stanford University, Miss Helen Zorsch of the University of Rochester, and Miss Virginia Thorsen of Burlingame, California, is gratefully acknowledged. Permission to reproduce illustrations was obtained from Dr. Anna H. Morgan of Mt. Holyoke College; from Dr. Myron Gordon, Professor J. G. Needham, and Professor P. W. Claassen of Cornell University.*

The United States Bureau of Fisheries has given permission to use much information obtained in the course of field work done under its auspices. Thanks are due also to the New York State Conservation Department, the New Jersey Board of Fish and Game Commissioners, and the California Division of Fish and Game for the use of much informa-

tion obtained from studies made in co-operation with these agencies, and to Stanford University for laboratory and library facilities.

Many persons have helped in the course of the preparation of this book. To my father, Professor James G. Needham of Cornell University, I am greatly indebted for much advice and criticism both as to subject matter and final organization of the manuscript. For critical reading of the manuscript I am also greatly indebted to Dr. G. C. Embody of Cornell University, Mr. Elmer Higgins and Dr. H. S. Davis of the United States Bureau of Fisheries, and Dr. L. P. Schultz, Associate Curator of Fishes, United States National Museum. To my wife, Dorothy Shorb Needham, I am grateful for much help in revision and editing of the manuscript.

PAUL R. NEEDHAM

Natural History Museum
Stanford University
June 1, 1938

CONTENTS

APPENDIX

INTRODUCTION

Cool clear-flowing streams are the domain of trout. Once such streams were to be found in all the uplands of North America. To help save such of them as remain, to help restore some of those that have been spoiled, and to report progress in knowledge of conditions that make for better fishing in all of them, are the main objectives of this book.

Fishing is the world's most nearly universal form of recreation. It is available to rich and poor, to young and old, to both sexes, at all seasons, and in most places where man himself has not spoiled it. People have always liked to go fishing and even today the greatest enjoyment of fishing is found in its most ancient form, fishing with hook and line.

Trout are the aristocrats of our inland waters because of their color and their gameness. Our "little waters" are our trout waters. Where people chiefly go for rest and recreation trout fishing is usually the major attraction.

This continent was once richly endowed with many native species of salmon and trout. In warmer waters other fishes, such as bass, pike, perch, muskelunge, and catfish afforded other kinds of fishing, and these may still be found in unpolluted lakes and streams near population centers; but good trout fishing nowadays is harder to find. Trout have been more affected by the economic development of the country. They have been forced to retire from portions of waters that they formerly occupied. But in spite of pollution, lumbering, road-building, and other conditions that have spoiled many trout waters, North American anglers are lucky in having some left; indeed, they are far luckier than they deserve to be, considering the lack of careful management of these resources.

An angler living in the eastern states, if he cannot find trout close at home, can drive to the upper reaches of hill and mountain streams that are populated with that old favorite, the eastern brook trout. Or he may go farther afield to the Sebago Lakes in Maine for landlocked salmon, or to the coastal streams of Maine and the Maritime Provinces of Canada for Atlantic salmon. If he prefers lake fishing, native lake trout and the introduced rainbow or steelhead offer good sport in some areas. In the eastern United States in many waters that were formerly inhabited by eastern brook trout, waters that have since become unsuitable by reason of high water temperature, the introduced brown and rainbow trout may be found in fair abundance. The former species was introduced from Europe, while the latter was originally found only on the Pacific Coast.

In the middle west he may also catch, aside from the native eastern brook and lake trout, the introduced rainbow and brown trout; in Montana, the grayling.

In the Rocky Mountain region a host of varieties of cutthroat or black-spotted trout are native. In the Yellowstone National Park the angler finds the graceful and agile Yellowstone cutthroat or black-spotted trout; in Utah, the Utah cutthroat; in the headwaters of the Colorado River, the Colorado River cutthroat. In addition to these native forms the introduced eastern brook trout, brown trout, and rainbow trout have been extensively planted.

In the intermountain and Pacific Coast regions, sea-run steelhead or rainbow trout, cutthroat or black-spotted trout, golden trout and kokanee (landlocked sockeye salmon) are native, and with the introduced eastern brook and brown trout, much excellent fishing is still to be found. In addition, five species of Pacific salmon occur from California to Alaska and of these, especially the chinook and coho* afford much splendid angling in the ocean, the estuaries, and the coastal streams during the spawning migrations. The Dolly Varden trout, a close relative to the eastern brook, may likewise be caught in cold streams from northern California northward, reaching its greatest abundance in Alaska.

Regardless of where trout may be found, their proper growth and reproduction are dependent upon good stream conditions. A multitude of interacting factors, biological, physical, or chemical in nature, are constantly present in any stream or lake, the total complex of which goes to form the environment in which any organism lives. Good ground cover and slow drainage make good trout water by maintaining even flows and temperatures. Lack of cover and rapid runoff produce the conditions existing today, when fertile soil is blown away or washed as silt into streams, destroying both terrestrial and aquatic resources. Our forested headwater tributary brooks, having small drainage basins, and fed by springs, snows, or glaciers, have not suffered unduly, but the main streams draining wide areas of deforested, semi-cultivated, or cultivated land have been greatly damaged.

The most evident characteristic of streams in general is their lack of stability. Constantly changing from day to day, from month to month, and from season to season, stream conditions offer a highly unstable and complicated pattern of interdependent influences each of which has its role to play for good or ill. Man has merely accentuated the instability of streams by destroying the ground cover of the land.

The primary needs of any animal are food, shelter, and fit conditions for reproduction. Besides clean water and pools in which to hide, the stream must furnish food. Any angler who has turned over stones in streams has noticed the great array of organisms that live submerged among them. They are of many colors, sizes, and shapes. Some build protective cases about their bodies. Some build cunning miniature nets

* In this book the terms chinook and king salmon will be used interchangeably, as will coho and silver salmon. Chinook and coho are now the most widely acceptable terms.

which they fasten on the stones for straining the water to catch food that is drifting downstream. Some are flat, limpet-like forms which lie closely appressed to the stones, perfectly adapted to life in the swiftest water. Others burrow in the bottom among stones and gravel, protected alike from hungry fish and from turbulent waters.

Insects are the most important single group inhabiting inland waters, both in numbers and in value as food for fishes. Other animal groups well represented in water and furnishing a substantial part of fish food are shrimp, scuds, sow-bugs, crayfish, small snails, and clams. There are many smaller organisms such as water mites, worms, and protozoans which, while not supplying food directly to fishes, do fill a large place in stream economy. Many of them turn plant food into flesh by utilizing aquatic plants, which are the primary source of food in water as on land.

On first approach, plant life appears to be absent from the swifter, colder trout streams. But this lack is more apparent than real. Unless abnormal conditions prevail, plants will usually be quite abundant—not many of the larger, rooted forms, to be sure, but a whole host of unicellular forms. Microscopic examination of surface growth on the stones on the stream bed reveals an amazingly large number of tiny plants belonging to four or five different groups. These minute forms are sometimes startlingly beautiful when seen under the microscope. They are able to live in both swift and slow water, and they coat the stones with slimy brown or yellowish ooze. Masses of these algae coating the stones make wading while angling a treacherous procedure in many streams. An angler met on the Ausable River near Lake Placid, New York, one day expressed it very well when he said wading this stream was "like trying to walk over greased cannon-balls." These minute forms are important biologically, for they are a primary source of food in streams. They are to the water what green leaves are to the land: they alone produce organic foods (starch-sugar) from inorganic raw products (carbon dioxide, mineral salts, etc.) by aid of the the energy of sunlight.

Among the larger plants visible to the unaided eye, various mosses, cresses, and pondweeds predominate. Swift waters of trout streams have no extensive weed-bed development and the pond weeds are restricted for the most part to long quiet pools where they can maintain a foothold. In stony riffles mosses will be found clinging to stones in the swiftest water. They are often associated with various filamentous algae which will be seen trailing their long, silken, green tresses downstream in the current. These great groups of underwater plants and animals are little known to anglers.

Better known to them are the adults of aquatic insects which leave the water in so-called "hatches," usually during early morning or evening in the summer time. Anglers try to imitate the hatching insects with wet or dry-flies patterned after insects present on the water. Wet-fly fishing is essentially fishing with imitations of the immature stages (nymphs, larvae, or pupae) that live in the water. The dry-fly imitates the adults of the same insects after they have left the water. Most of the flies commonly used by anglers have been devised by men interested enough to collect the actual living insects and to fashion more or less life-like imitations of them. In doing this only the commoner forms have been imitated, for as "Piscator," writing in the 5th edition (1856) of Ronald's *The Fly-fisher's Entomology,* says: "to an entomological collector the rarity of a species enhances its value; to a fly-fisher on the other hand, the frequent occurrence of a species, and its being widely dispersed or found upon all waters, constitutes the strongest reason for preferring it, because the fish feed upon such species more readily."

While it is true that many artificial flies imitate nothing that nature ever produced and are largely expressions of the fly-tier's imagination, a few offered for sale are fairly good imitations of living insects. There are various manuals giving descriptions of the natural flies and directions for tying good artificial ones; titles of some of these will be found in the bibliography at the end of this volume.

In this book we are less concerned with catching the fish, and more with having some fish to catch.

Management of our aquatic resources is a story of waste.* Our wilderness quickly vanished and with it went a large proportion of our game and fish, until today but vestiges remain. Power dams cut off the spawning areas from sea-run migratory salmon and steelhead; removal of forests exposed water to the sun's rays, sending water temperatures to fatal limits; and later, erosion wrought havoc with stream beds, destroying bottom life and spawning areas, and filling pools with trash. Overgrazing and forest fires, aided by lumbering operations, have denuded the soil of its protective cover until today seasonal changes bring floods and dust storms. Droughts and floods are not new to this country, as shown by past meteorological records. What has happened is merely that man has so changed conditions that when periods of flood or drought come now, with the ground cover removed by ill-conceived operations, the water and the wind work havoc.

In addition to such damage, both streams and lakes have been made the receptacles of all kinds of domestic and factory wastes, particularly in densely populated sections in eastern industrial areas. Sewage, oil, mine acids, creamery and paper-mill wastes are among the worst pol-

* As Gottlieb Boccius, one of the first conservationists, quaintly said in 1848 in his *Fish in Rivers and Streams:* ". . . Water is far more capable of producing abundance of food than any other element in the great laboratory of nature. Why then should such a source of plenty be neglected? . . . It is high time, therefore, for the naturalist to resort to art to restore our fisheries, or they must eventually become extinct."

luting substances. Conditions in many waters have become so bad as to drive out or kill off all species of game fish in thousands of miles of streams and lakes.

It is good to observe that, after many years of misuse of our lands and waters, the national conscience is apparently awakening. The various governmental agencies charged with responsibility for managing the natural resources in land and water are taking definite steps toward putting into effect scientific management programs. The various conservation and pollution bills proposed in Congress and in the various state legislatures in recent years are hopeful signs. They indicate recognition of the fact that present-day problems are the result of utter lack of foresight in the management of both public and private lands and waters, and realization that such mismanagement must be stopped for the future economical, recreational, and aesthetic welfare of this country.

Governmental aid to fish culture in this country has hitherto consisted mainly in the maintenance of hatcheries and in the distribution of their product. Artificial propagation was expanded rapidly after 1900, and today angling-license funds are spent mainly on purely propagative activities—but without commensurate results.* In spite of larger and larger sums of money spent annually on hatchery activities, fishing has generally continued to decline. The patient has not responded to treatment. We have in the main been blindly following old procedures.

Fish have been planted indiscriminately at the whim of either sportsmen, laymen, or politicians. Few facts have been available, and when available they have seldom been considered. To paraphrase a well-known motto, the policy of the past has been "millions for hatching, but not one cent for investigation." How long would a bank last that invested, say $500,000, without the slightest knowledge of what return it might expect annually from its investment? Just this sort of thing has been going on for years in the field of fish propagation. It is nobody's fault. Fisheries administrators lacked the facts, scientific workers did not have them; and there was no way of progress available except the old slow blundering method of learning by trial and error.†

But even so, we have learned some things as to the disposition of the product of the hatcheries. We have learned that for any given water native species are most dependable, being adapted by nature to it; that brown trout should not be planted in high cold lakes or very cold streams; that eastern brook trout do not do well in the warmer trout waters, and that they often do amazingly well in cold lakes. We have also learned that the indiscriminate mixing of warm-water spiny-rayed fish such as the perch, bass, and pike with trout often brings about disastrous results to the trout fishing, and without affording, in the long run, good fishing for the spiny-rayed fishes. We have also learned that stocking of fishless lakes with well-adapted species often brings about

* The efficiency of modern hatcheries and the improvement of the hatchery product, coupled with better knowledge and perspective within management agencies, have closed the gap between outlay and results. Invoved are improvements in diets, disease control, and stocking methods. See Butler and Borgeson (1965), Koski (1969), Senn and Noble (1968), and Worlund et al. (1969).

† Research to obtain the needed facts, and development programs to put them into use have been well-funded through legislation by the various states and the federal government. Many of the activities are cooperative in nature and involve acts such as The Federal Aid in Fish Restoration Program (Dingell-Johnson Act, 64 Stat-431); the Anadromous Fish Act, P.L. 89-304; and the Columbia River Fishery Development Program, P.L. 79-676.

phenomenal success. This has been demonstrated time and time again with the stocking of barren lakes throughout the United States generally.

Some state fish and game departments, believing that research had something to offer that would assist them in their management programs, have employed trained specialists to work on biological problems that needed solution. Often the biologist employed has been assigned to problems for which he was not trained (and no one person could possibly be trained for all the biological problems that are involved in fish culture); and often he has been loaded with far more jobs than anyone could adequately handle.

One hindrance to the union of science with practical fish culture in recent years has been the lack of continuity of both program and personnel. Research projects have often been started with high hopes and much promise, and then shifting ideas or personnel have necessitated stopping such investigations almost at a moment's notice and usually before any concrete results have been obtained. In so far as the production of facts that may aid the fisheries management is concerned, it is continuity of both program and personnel that counts; we cannot make much progress without both. Research is expensive; it is slow, and those who are going to employ it as a fact-finding method to aid in their problems must be willing to wait results. To quote Leopold (1937): "Facts, like pine trees, take not only rain, but time."

Given well-trained, competent personnel, proper equipment, capable permanent or seasonal aid, and sufficient time in which to work, research has paid big dividends in the past, and will continue to do so in the future.

If we compare agricultural research and what it has done for farming with aquicultural research and what it is doing for aquatic crops, it becomes at once evident that fisheries biology is many years behind the times. One reason for this is that aquatic problems are more difficult of solution. A farmer has only to walk out among his herd to count them, to observe their condition, to treat them when they are ill. They offer, therefore, much easier control because they live on land, and are not hidden below water.

Through agricultural research it has been determined, with fair accuracy, how many pounds of beef can be produced on certain types of range or pasture, or how many bushels of potatoes a certain type of soil can be expected to yield under given seasonal conditions. A detailed knowledge of the life history and habits of our game species will yield just as great returns in applicable facts for the use of fish managers as agricultural research has produced for farmers. A really effective program of trout management can be had only if the necessary facts are obtained, and only if these facts are applied in behalf of the fisheries concerned.

Most progressive conservation agencies, both state and federal, are approaching fisheries management problems through the following methods: (1) stream and lake surveys to develop initial fish-stocking policies; (2) detailed research investigations on special, critical problems demanding prompt solution; and (3) stream and lake improvements.*

Stream and lake surveys are the best means of opening up for further study major problems in any given drainage basin. Also, aside from furnishing the initial stocking policies, they are a means for determining the needs for stream and lake improvements. In other words, surveys are the opening wedge. Following survey work with the problems revealed, selection can be intelligently made for tackling those problems, the solution of which would have the broadest application and produce the greatest good in any given area.

Surveys and detailed investigations, together with practical improvement work conducted by highly trained and competent persons, will secure the greatest possible return for the angler's dollar.

Recently the investigation of trout stream problems has been seriously undertaken. Studies of the factors governing the distribution of trout, their foods, enemies, parasites, and other environmental conditions, have been made and a mass of new and highly desirable information has been accumulated. A digest of a portion of the results of this work will be attempted in the chapters that follow.

* As an extension of the three methods listed, the present conservation agencies are involved in special-purpose surveys and research into details of fish life history, physiology, and ecology. Habitat improvements are being considered on the basis of watersheds, not merely streams.

I

Trout and Salmon

DISTRIBUTION AND HABITS

THIS GROUP of fishes includes the most valuable of inland species. The Pacific salmon are of greatest commercial value, but of perhaps greater indirect value are inland trout (and related forms, such as grayling, land-locked salmon, and the western whitefishes); for millions of dollars are spent annually by fishermen in search of them. The songs in praise of good trout-fishing are rapidly becoming dirges because of the appalling depletion and spoilage of streams that has taken place in recent years. Commercial exploitation of our fisheries has paralleled the exploitation of deer, buffalo, elk, antelope, and other game animals. The only difference is that land game disappeared faster, because it was easier to find. There has been little husbandry practiced with either. Sustained yields were seldom considered until the specter of possible ultimate extinction reared its ugly head.

All trout and salmon belong to the family Salmonidae. They are, as every one knows, typical cold water fishes of north temperate and subarctic distribution. Both trout and salmon are migratory when living where climatic or geographic barriers do not prevent migration. Ocean-going salmon and steelhead trout feed in the ocean and breed in fresh water streams. Their migrations are more or less rhythmical movements between feeding and breeding areas. The Pacific salmon may live anywhere from one to eight years in the ocean before making their one spawning trip into fresh water.

The tendency of both salmon and steelhead is to return to the same streams in which they were hatched. A degree of straying from parent waters does occur, and must have occurred in the past: otherwise it would be impossible to account for their natural spread and distribution.

Aside from the larger size of salmon at maturity, the greatest practical difference between trout and Pacific salmon is one of habits, not of structure. All the Pacific salmon, so far as is known, die after spawning once. Trout, charrs, grayling, and other inland forms may spawn a number of times. However, steelhead that migrate hundreds of miles inland from the ocean may not survive the hardships of the long journey to spawn even a second time. Furthermore, the Atlantic salmon may spawn more than once.

One of the most interesting activities of salmon and trout is their spawning. All are nest-building species. The nests are mere shallow depressions made in gravel beds in streams. The females usually dig the nests by turning on their sides and making swift up-and-down movements of their bodies. They dislodge the bottom gravel and force it to one side until gradually the shallow nests are formed. Mating occurs over the pit of the nest. Milt from the male and eggs from the female are discharged at the same instant, fertilization of the eggs thus taking place in the water as they fall to the bottom of the nest. Nest building may require days or weeks, while the mating act is very brief. Immediately upon depositing a number of eggs, the female carefully covers them with gravel to protect them during incubation. "Redds" is a term often used to designate the spawning areas.

The spawning period may last from a few days to several weeks, depending upon water conditions, sexual maturity, and species of fish concerned. Once the eggs are deposited and covered no further parental care is given them. After hatching the fry may remain in the gravel until the food supply of the yolk sac is absorbed, or they may wriggle up out of the gravel prior to its absorption. However, once out of the gravel, and the food supply of the egg with which they began their earthly careers gone, they seek small prey in the shallow backwaters of pool and riffle, and a new generation has picked up the burden of independent existence.

PACIFIC SALMON

As noted in the accompanying table, five species of Pacific salmon fall into the group or genus *Oncorhynchus*. These are the kings of the family *Salmonidae*. They are noted for their vigor, size, and food value. A considerable amount of trolling is carried on by anglers in the Puget Sound region of Washington expressly for silver and king salmon. These fish rank above the steelhead both in general popularity and in numbers caught by sportsmen in this area. Their greatest value lies in their excellent canning properties. Extensive commercial fishing is carried on for them. The five species listed in Table I occur in waters of the Pacific coast, California to Alaska, reaching their maximum development in more northerly waters. Over-exploitation by commercial fishing and destruction by transportation, power, and irrigation projects have greatly reduced runs of these fish in coastal waters of northwestern United States.

Silver or coho salmon, king or chinook salmon, and steelhead trout are the dominant species of salmonoids surviving today in coastal waters of California. The once famous salmon runs up the Sacramento and San

TABLE I

PACIFIC SALMON*

Common Name	Scientific Name	Distribution in North America	Age at Maturity	Usual Weight Attained	Recognition Characters
Sockeye Red Blueback	*Oncorhynchus nerka*	Northern Calif. into Alaska	4 to 8 yrs.	5 to 7 lbs.	Gill rakers on first arch, 30–50.** Anal rays average 14 in number.** Young with large round parr marks, mostly above lateral line. Called kokanee (or silver trout) when landlocked. Black spots appear on back and tail fin as fish approaches sexual maturity.
Chum Dog	*Oncorhynchus keta*	Northern Calif. into Alaska	3 to 5 yrs.	8 to 12 lbs.	Gill rakers on first arch, 19 to 28. Anal rays, 13 to 15. Lacks black spots. With 19 to 24 scales above and 15 to 22 below the lateral line, fewer than in any other Pacific salmon.
Pink Humpback	*Oncorhynchus gorbuscha*	Northern Calif. into Alaska	2 yrs.	3 to 6 lbs.	Gill rakers on first arch, 27–35. Anal rays usually number 14 to 16. Easily recognized by large, oblong black spots on tail (nearly round in other species) and by its small and very numerous scales (170 to 231 oblique rows on side)** possessing more than any other Pacific salmon. Young lack parr marks.
Spring Chinook King Tyee Quinnat	*Oncorhynchus tshawytscha*	Central Calif. into Alaska	3 to 8 yrs.	16 to 30 lbs. Few up to 100 lbs. taken.	Gill rakers on first arch, 19 to 29. Anal rays, usually 15 to 17, a greater number than in any other Pacific salmon, first few rays not lengthened as in young silver salmon; tail and back with round black spots larger than in coho or silver salmon. Caudal peduncle more slender than in silver salmon, which it closely resembles. Young with parr marks wider than lighter colored interspaces.
Coho Silver	*Oncorhynchus kisutch*	Ventura River, Calif. into Alaska	2 to 7 yrs.	3 to 10 lbs.	Gill rakers on first arch, 19 to 25. Anal rays, usually 13 to 15; fish less than four inches long with first few anal rays whitish near tips and longer than those that follow, which tend to be pink in color. Black spots smaller than in king salmon. Caudal peduncle much stouter or deeper than on king. Teeth of adults arise from a white gum line.

* Modified after Jordan and Evermann (1896), Clemens (1935), and Schultz (1935, 1936).

** For method of making these counts, see footnote at bottom of Table II on p. 18

Joaquin Rivers have been greatly reduced. Overfishing, dam construction, irrigation, and pollution have played their destructive rôles. Clark (1929) says:

> The Sacramento and San Joaquin valleys cover a large part of the interior of California. Two rivers, by those names, drain the valleys and the surrounding mountains. The west side of both valleys is comparatively arid, while the east side is well supplied with streams, some of which are quite large. It is into these streams on the east side that the salmon run to spawn.
>
> It is estimated that there are (1928) 510 linear miles of stream beds suitable and available for spawning grounds. As nearly as can be estimated, previous to any obstructions in the streams, there were at least 6000 linear miles of stream bed suitable and available to spawning salmon. At least 80 per cent of the spawning grounds has been cut off by obstructions.

With only twenty per cent of the former spawning areas remaining available to king salmon, it is evident that this factor alone must have been of serious consequence in the depletion of these fish. At another point, Clark also says (1929) that without doubt extensive overfishing was the greatest single cause of decline in the runs of king salmon into the Sacramento-San Joaquin systems.* The introduction of striped bass into San Francisco Bay waters in 1879 may also have had bad effect on these runs, for the young salmon had to pass through striped bass feeding areas on their seaward migrations, and large striped bass are well known to be fish-eaters.

Chinook salmon, depending upon race and environmental conditions, remain as juveniles in fresh water from about three months to a year. They enter the ocean at sizes from two to four inches in the first year of life to five to eight inches in the second. Clemens (1935) says:

> In the sea they grow rapidly, maturing in three to eight years and reaching a very large size, a weight of 100 lb. being recorded. Tagging experiments have shown that they may travel long distances, as, for example, from the fishing-banks off Barkley Sound to the Sacramento River, California; from near Hippa Island off the Queen Charlotte Islands to Marshfield,† Oregon; and from Alaskan waters to the Columbia River. The commercial fishermen take them by troll, purse-seine, gill-net, and trap, and the sport fishermen by troll, as, for example, off Campbell River, where they constitute the widely known tyee-fishery.

Silver salmon, in contrast to kings, usually remain in freshwater for one year before going to the ocean, though a few may go to sea in their first year and a few after two years. After a year of stream life, before the exodus to the sea, many immature silver salmon are caught in streams by anglers. They are then between four and five inches in length, and as few anglers can tell the difference between trout and salmon with small fish of this size, they are usually called trout, which

* The relationship between the decline and overfishing was not as clear-cut as Clark supposed, judging from fluctuations that have occurred since 1929. There have been years of considerable abundance.

† Now Coos Bay.

they closely resemble. (See Table 2.) In the ocean growth is rapid and they usually mature at the end of their third year of life, when they make their return to spawning grounds in fresh water streams. The returned large-size adults offer much good sport in trolling, spinner, and fly-fishing.

Young hatchery-reared silver salmon planted in land-locked lakes will sometimes produce some excellent fishing. Intensively fished waters in which trout have been about depleted can be made to produce some good temporary sport this way. Of course the fish thus planted do not mature to spawn as they do in the ocean and hence offer only a temporary stock.* Continual plantings will be necessary to maintain the supply. On the other hand, in a few lakes in the northwest there is found a land-locked form of the sockeye or red salmon, *Oncorhynchus nerka,* known locally as kokanee and in some localities as "little redfish" or silver trout, which matures and spawns in fresh water. This occurs from Oregon to Alaska and inland to Montana (Schultz, 1935). Clemens (1935) says:

> The sockeye salmon is the most prized of the Pacific salmon because its high oil content, the colour of its flesh, and its rather uniform size make it an excellent fish for canning. The adults usually ascend those streams on which there are lakes and pass through the lakes to spawn in the tributary streams. A few spawn along the shores of lakes and a few in streams on which there are no lakes. Some young sockeye go to sea very soon after hatching, but the majority descend to the lakes, where they spend usually one, frequently two, and occasionally three years and eventually pass out to the ocean. They return as adults after three or four summers in the sea when they are thus four or five years of age. A few, for the most part males, mature at three years of age and are frequently referred to as grilse. A few mature at six years of age and fewer still at seven and eight years. While the weight at maturity is usually between 5 and 7 lb., weights as high as 12 lb. are recorded.

Pink and chum salmon do not migrate any great distance from the ocean as do kings, silvers, and sockeyes, but spawn rather close to tide-water. Most pink salmon mature at the end of their second year, whereas chums are usually four years of age at maturity. The young of both migrate to the ocean soon after spawning.

The young of all species of salmon, while in fresh water, feed on aquatic insects, crustaceans, molluscs, etc., or on foods that drop in the water from land as do trout. Therefore, when in fresh water they are competitors of resident stream trout for food.

In this connection it is interesting to note the contrast in rate of growth between sea-run trout and salmon, and trout that spend their entire lives in fresh water. Ocean-going fish grow at a tremendous rate and achieve weights of five or six pounds in only two years' time. Stream trout, on the other hand, usually weigh less than a pound in the same

* A remarkable exception is the establishment of coho in the Great Lakes. An initial plant of about 700,000 yearlings in Lake Michigan in 1966 produced an estimated 30% survival to the adult stage. Both natural and artificial propagation have been successful with these fish, although insecticide residues appear to have reduced the viability of the young.

Success of a lesser magnitude has been enjoyed by the chinook in Lake Michigan.

time under average stream conditions. The ocean offers far richer feeding grounds than freshwater streams. The latter are used largely for breeding, and not for feeding purposes by sea-run fish. In terms of pounds of fish produced, northwestern coastal streams are much more productive than streams having only resident trout. The ocean-feeding habits of the fish concerned make this possible.

One most remarkable habit of salmon is the long migrations they undertake on their spawning journeys. King salmon as noted by Jordan

FIG. 1.—A type of dam that completely blocks all upstream migration of trout, preventing access to small, cold, spawning tributaries above.

(1907) are known to travel as far as 2,250 miles up the Yukon River in Alaska. Sockeyes will migrate 1,800 miles up the same stream. Kings also travel to the headwaters of the Fraser, Columbia, Umpqua, Rogue, Klamath, Sacramento, and other Pacific Coast rivers. The end of the migration is not a pretty one. Weakened by the long trip from the ocean, by nest-digging and mating, scarred by fighting and covered with patches of dank gray fungus, they die in the shallows, or are killed by birds and other predators, once they have fulfilled their debt to nature.*

Migrations of both salmon and steelhead do not occur all at once in any given stream but occur in waves that fluctuate widely from day to

* The primary cause of the deterioration and death of Pacific Salmon has been determined by O. H. Robertson and his colleagues to be a severe hormonal imbalance. Accelerated aging is encouraged by over-production of secretions from the adrenal cortical tissue. Degeneration of many of the internal organs precedes death (Robertson, 1956; Robertson and Wexler, 1960).

day. A few fish will arrive at the estuaries of the coastal streams early and a few stragglers will arrive late after the peak of the run. The process is one of a daily ebb and flow to the maximum or peak, after which the numbers entering will decline daily until the run is ended. In the Klamath River in California this is well illustrated by the king and silver salmon and the steelheads that successively enter this stream each summer, fall and winter. About the middle of July king salmon begin entering the estuary; they reach their peak in August, after which the numbers entering decline steadily until by late October or November

Fig. 2.—Salmon attempting to ascend South Umpqua Falls (about 12 ft. high) during high water in spring near Roseburg, Oregon (photograph by courtesy of R. L. Harris, U. S. Forest Service).

the run has about ended. The kings are followed by silver salmon that begin entering the estuary in September and reach their peak about the middle of October, after which the number steadily declines. Steelheads follow silver salmon into California coastal streams as a rule, but in the Klamath a few early sea-run steelheads will enter the estuary about the same time as the king salmon and a few will be caught with the kings by trollers in August. But the heavy run of steelheads comes in late fall and winter after the king and silver salmon runs have ended. Snyder (1931 and 1933) notes that the pink and chum salmon also enter the Klamath but are seldom seen or recognized by fishermen.

Various types of fish ladders or fish lifts have been placed in and around dams and other obstructions to permit ascent of migratory salmonoids. Early experience of fish culturists was that ladders operated well only to heights of from fifty to sixty feet and were considered only partially successful. On the whole, early ladders were unsatisfactory because of variation in water flows from season to season, difficulties in locating entrances, and debris filling or clogging them. Each dam presents its own individual problems and ladders must be properly designed and not neglected after installation. Here, as in the matter of screens for irrigation ditchs, lack of workable designs drawn up on a basis of careful experimental investigation resulted in wasted funds and effort. In later years, however, the matter has received considerable attention from workers in many parts of the world.* A notable effort was the work of the United States Bureau of Fisheries in connection with Bonneville Dam on the Columbia River. Much factual information on the proper design and operation of both fish ladders and mechanical lifts is now available.

An equally important problem, unsolved to date, is that of determining the best method of permitting young seaward migrants to pass downstream without injury. Many young salmon and steelhead are killed on passing through power turbines on the way to the ocean. This phase of the problem is receiving equally intensive study by the United States Bureau of Fisheries.† Migrations of both large fish headed upstream or small fingerlings on their seaward journeys obviously must be protected and maintained or the runs of migratory fishes will become past history.

ATLANTIC SALMON

The Atlantic salmon, *Salmo salar salar,* is the only true, native salmon found on the east coast of North America. Pacific salmon have been introduced from the west coast to northeastern waters but it is doubtful if they become established. The Atlantic salmon likewise has been introduced into Pacific Coast waters, but it remains to be seen whether or not these fish will become acclimatized.*

Atlantic salmon are sharply distinguished from the Pacific salmon by cranial characters (Regan, 1914) and are apparently identical with the salmon of Europe except for minor differences. Regarding the evolutionary development of present-day salmonoids, Kendall (1935) says:

* See Clay (1961).

† Now the U. S. Bureau of Commercial Fisheries.

* Davidson and Hutchinson (1938) report that Pacific salmon have been successful only in a few waters in "New Zealand, Chile, the State of Maine, and the provinces of New Brunswick and Ontario." Huntsman and Dymond (1940) on the other hand, say that runs of pink salmon were maintained artificially for a number of years in east coast rivers, but state that there is no evidence of natural completion of their life cycle. Without this, these authors consider that Pacific salmon cannot properly be said to have become established in Atlantic waters. Coho salmon have been established in the upper Great Lakes. Anadromous runs of Atlantic salmon have not been established on the Pacific slope as of 1969.

The ancestral salmonoid may have occupied the Pacific, Arctic, and Atlantic Oceans, or it may have been restricted to the Arctic. Changes which were evidently initiated as early as the Miocene may have pushed some Arctic ancestors southward into the Pacific, if they did not already occur there. It is well established that in the Pliocene the Pacific was occluded from the Arctic by land connections between Alaska and Siberia. The salmonoids were then actually segregated into two groups, Pacific and Atlantic, with no possible means of intercommunication. With the closing of the Arctic-Pacific gateway, two independent lines of development began.

Evidence to support Kendall's statement is seen in the fact that the Atlantic salmon and the rainbow-steelhead trout of the Pacific are really very closely related forms. In a letter to the writer, Dr. L. P. Schultz has called the Atlantic salmon the "steelhead of the Atlantic." It is highly probable that these fish arose from a common ancestral salmonoid as Kendall suggests, and with the closing of the Arctic-Pacific gateway continued their development independently, eventually producing these two closely related types of fishes as they exist today.*

Atlantic salmon are now limited in their distribution in the United States to a few streams in northeastern New England. Even in these streams, pollution, lumbering, dams or other factors have about destroyed former splendid runs. Herein lies another story of virtually complete wastage of a rich natural resource.

These fish used to be fairly common from the Hudson River north. Large numbers were taken in the Hudson, Connecticut, and other rivers up which they would go in late summer to spawn. According to authentic accounts, the Atlantic salmon were very abundant in Lake Champlain's tributaries about 1800, after which they decreased rapidly in numbers and finally by 1850 had completely disappeared. Salmon up to 20 pounds were not uncommon and were taken usually with spears, nets, or seines; more rarely with rod and line for sport. The early settlers in the Connecticut Valley used to catch large numbers and salt them down in barrels for winter use. The demand quickly exceeded the supply and rivers flowing through populated districts soon had no more runs of salmon. An attempt was made in 1872 and 1873 to restock Lake Champlain with Atlantic salmon but apparently failed, as the fish were never heard of there again. These fish are now limited for the most part to the streams of the Maritime Provinces of Canada, to which the more affluent anglers go to fish for them.

The usual size of Atlantic salmon ranges between ten and twenty pounds. Numerous records show a good many fish between twenty and forty pounds and one is recorded as being eighty-three pounds in weight.

A species closely related to the Atlantic salmon, the landlocked or lake salmon, *Salmo salar sebago,* originally found only in the lakes of

* The relationship is greatest in life history. Systematically the Atlantic salmon is closely related to the brown trout and the steelhead to the cutthroat.

Maine, is a prime favorite with those who have angled for it with light fly-rod tackle. Many attempts have been made to introduce this fish into cold inland lakes and streams, but with little success. This species was introduced into several lakes of the east, but little evidence has been found that they have increased at all. Lake George and the Saranac Lakes in New York state have been stocked with scanty results, only an occasional landlocked salmon being taken there by anglers.

Landlocked salmon spawn in the fall in streams to which they migrate, and the young remain in the streams for two years before returning to deep water.

The Ouananiche of Lake St. John and the Saguenay River, *Salmo salar ouananiche,* is another very active close relative of the Atlantic salmon. Dr. Henry Van Dyke described this fish as the prince of all fighting game fish, the "sunburnt champion of the water-folk."

THE TROUT

In addition to the more evident characters of size, shape, and color, inland trout may be more certainly distinguished from the Pacific salmon by the critical characters listed in Table 2.

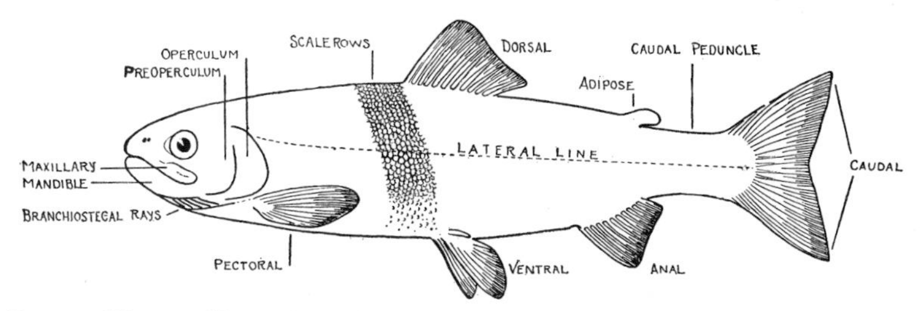

Fig. 3.—Diagram illustrating a few of the terms used in the description of a trout.

Artificial stocking from hatcheries has so modified the trout population of many streams that probably it will never be possible to determine for certain just what race, type, or species of trout originally inhabited them. In some cases the introduced forms have even completely replaced native species.

It is well known that color, spotting, size, shape, number of rows of scales, of vertebrae, and of fin rays, and the position and number of parr marks vary considerably, depending upon the environmental conditions under which trout have lived. Nevertheless proper identification is entirely dependent upon accurate measurement and comparison of these characters. Rapidly developing trout and salmon usually show fewer scales, fin rays and vertebrae than do those of slow embryonic development.

Ocean-going steelhead or rainbows grow rapidly; they usually show from 120 to 150 scales in the lateral line; golden trout, which normally live at altitudes around 10,000 feet and in very cold water most of the year, grow slowly, and scale counts in the lateral line will usually show from 160 to 200 present.

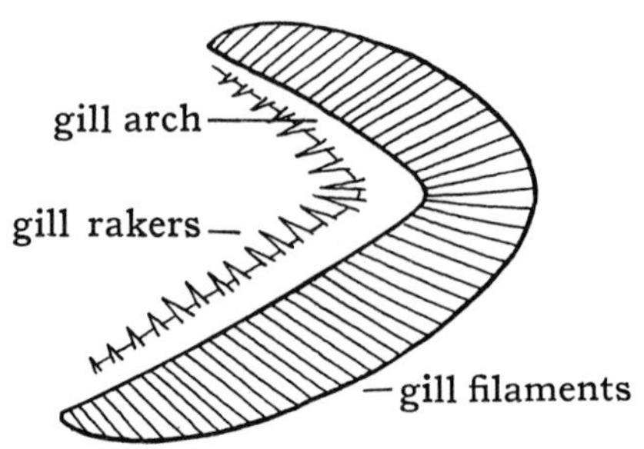

Fig. 4.—This diagram illustrates the approximate position of the gill rakers on the first gill arch located under the gill cover or operculum. The gill rakers, including all rudiments, are always counted on the first gill arch; those on the upper half of the arch are given first, followed by those on the lower half of the arch as 8 + 13 in the drawing (from Schultz, 1935).

It is a well known fact that the age of both trout and salmon can be read from rings on the scales, much as the age of a tree can often be determined by reading the rings on the stump after cutting. Rings or ridges are laid down on scales during the life of the fish, and record various occurrences in its life history. The rings are usually laid close together in periods of low food supply and of slow growth in fall or winter, while in spring or

TABLE II

Distinguishing Characters of Pacific Salmon and Trout

	Pacific Salmon	Trout and Charrs
Anal fin[1]	long, 13–17 rays	short, 9–12 rays
Gill rakers[2]	19–45 on first gill arch	20 or less on first gill arch
Branchiostegals[3]	10–19	10–12
Dorsal fin	seldom spotted in either young or adults	usually with many black spots in both young and adults

[1] Each fin except the fleshy adipose or "fat" fin between the dorsal and the tail fin on the back is supported by rods or rays of cartilage. The anal fin is located behind the vent on the belly. Short rays at front edge of this fin are not counted unless more than half the length of the longest ray found.

[2] Gill-rakers are found as stiff, comb-like spines on the inner sides of the gill arches that bear the gill filaments on their outer margins. Gill-raker counts are made on the first or outer arch on either side of the head; all rudiments are counted.

[3] The membrane that forms the lower margins of the gill covers below the head is supported on rays or rods of cartilage that are termed the "branchiostegals."

summer seasons, when growth is rapid, the rings will be more widely spaced* (See Fig. 6).

Many irregularities occur on scales and for this reason considerable experience is necessary for accurate interpretation of the age, rate of growth, or other history recorded on the scale surface. The scales of sea-run steelhead that survive to spawn two or three times usually show what are termed "spawning checks." Cessation of feeding and the hardships of the mating period usually cause some absorption or loss in the outer or growing edge of the scale. This in turn is recorded as a definite check that is usually quite characteristic of trout that have spawned one or more times. Stream life of young steelheads is recorded in the scales of adults by close-set rings in the nucleus or center of the scale, for growth is slow prior to their entering the ocean. Once in the ocean, growth is rapid, and the rings on the scales at once show a most characteristic wide spacing.†

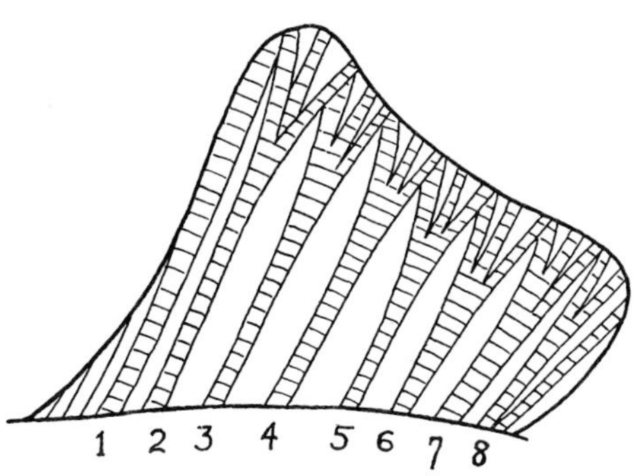

Fig. 5.—This diagram illustrates the method employed in counting the number of rays in the dorsal and anal fins. The first two or three short, unsegmented rays closely crowded together are not counted. The first ray counted is unbranched and extends nearly as far out as the first branched ray which follows. The last ray is usually "double branched" at the base, giving the superficial appearance of two rays, but is counted as one ray (from Schultz, 1935).

Scale studies to determine rates of growth are of fundamental importance as an aid in developing stocking policies. In the past, when fish populations became too large for available food supplies and the fish were stunted so that but few achieved legal size, the remedy usually applied was to plant more fish. This, instead of curing the situation, usually made matters worse. Scale studies offer a sound method for recognizing such problems, the solution of which is not to plant more

* This method of determining the age of fishes was first developed in Europe in work on the Atlantic salmon, and in the United States it was first applied by Dr. Charles H. Gilbert of Stanford University in his *Age at Maturity of the Pacific Coast Salmon of the Genus Oncorhynchus,* a study prepared for the United States Bureau of Fisheries in 1910-11.

† Recently in eastern California an angler caught a 6½ pound brown trout in Convict Lake and examination of the scales showed it to be in its eighth year. Three spawning checks showed it had spawned three times. Readers interested in obtaining further information on this phase of fisheries work are referred to papers listed in the bibliography.

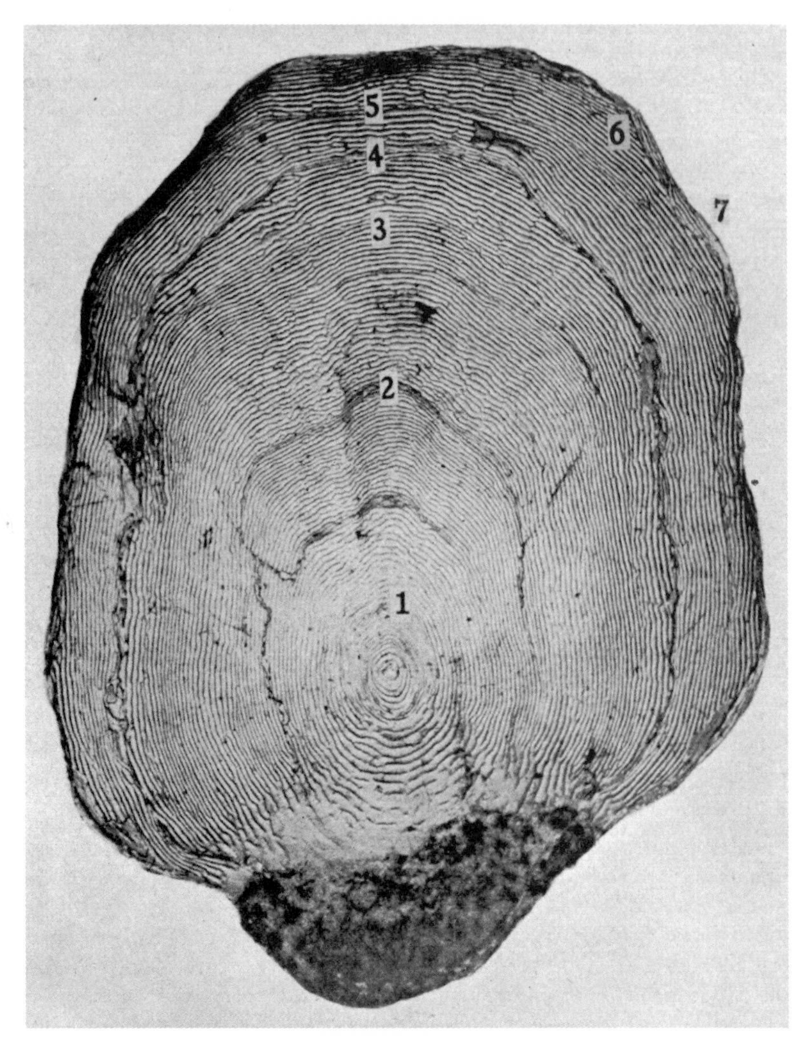

FIG. 6.—Scale from a 7 lb. female rainbow trout taken at spawning time, May 20, 1935, in Paul Creek, British Columbia, showing the age as indicated by winter rings (1-7). The ring at 4 is a typical example of a spawning mark. This fish probably did not spawn in its fifth (5) year but spawned for the second time in its sixth (6). The seventh (7) year is at the margin which is already showing signs of the absorption which is characteristic of the scales of spawning fish. This scale indicates that rainbow trout may skip a year or spawn for two successive years (photograph by courtesy of Dr. C. McC. Mottley of Cornell University).

fish but to get rid of an excess population so that a proper balance between food and growth may be reached. Periodic growth studies in any given water show in addition annual changes in the rate of growth resulting from previous plantings, and serve as a guide to later plantings.

Determination of the rate of growth by scales from wild trout that are to be selected for domestication in hatcheries would permit selection of fast-growing rather than slow-growing strains, the advantages of which are obvious.

Counts of the number of rows of scales on trout and salmon, as noted above, are commonly used as an aid in determining various species of salmonoids.*

The scales of trout are of course very minute and deeply bedded in the skin, but scale counts have long been used as specific characters. It is interesting to record here an experiment conducted by Mottley (1936) on the Kamloops trout of British Columbia. He, with others, noted that the steelhead of British Columbia averaged 130 rows of scales in the lateral line while the Kamloops trout of waters at moderate elevations in British Columbia averaged 145 rows, and the same species from waters at the higher elevations in the Selkirk Mountains averaged 150 rows. He says:

> The peculiar correlation between the number of scale-rows and altitudinal distribution led the writer to try an experiment to find out if the temperature at the time of early development might not be the cause of the differences observed.
>
> The eggs from a single female Kamloops trout, fertilized by the milt from a single male, were divided into two lots, one of which was raised at the ordinary hatchery temperature at Nelson, B.C., the other being kept for 5 weeks following the eyed-egg stage at a temperature about 9° F. higher. The fish were reared to a size of 3 inches, when they were killed and scale counts were made on a sample of 100 from each lot. Those raised at the higher temperature had an average of 5 rows less than those raised at the ordinary hatchery temperature. This experiment led to the conclusion that the number of scale-rows could be modified by changing the temperature at the time of early development.

He also discovered that other characters commonly used to designate various species, such as head and body proportions, could be modified by transferring mountain Kamloops trout to waters at lower elevations.

* The number above the lateral line is taken by counting in an oblique row starting at the center of the top of the fish in front of the dorsal fin down to the row of scales next above the lateral line; the number below the lateral line by starting the count with the scale just in front of one of the pelvic fins on the belly up to the first row below the lateral line; and the number in the lateral line by counting from the beginning of the lateral line just above the gill opening to the base of the tail-fin rays. Scales on the rays of the tail-fin are not counted (Fig. 3).

FIG. 7.—Upper, eastern brook trout, *Salvelinus fontinalis;* middle, steelhead or rainbow trout, *Salmo gairdnerii;* and lower, brown or Loch Leven trout, *Salmo trutta* (after *N. Y. State Conservation Dept. Biological Survey Reports,* Nos. IV, 1929; V, 1930; and VI, 1931).

His experiments tend to show that several characters formerly supposed to be stable are subject to considerable change when the normal environment of the fish is changed.

Anglers in the field have not time to count scales, fin rays and gill rakers. Instead they must depend upon general external appearance, size, and fighting ability when hooked, as means of identifying the trout they catch. For their use the color characters that best serve to distinguish the common kinds of trout are listed in the accompanying table. Although these seem simple and clean-cut, yet the recognition of many closely related varieties when creeled is not always easy. Promiscuous plantings by fish culturists of various species and races have permitted hybridization with the mixing of characters, and this adds greatly to the difficulty.

THE CHARRS

THE EASTERN BROOK TROUT

The eastern brook trout, *Salvelinus fontinalis*, is one of our most prized game fishes. Not only for its very beautiful coloration, gaminess, and edible qualities is this fish a favorite with anglers, but also because its home is in our most picturesque streams: those bubbling, swift-flowing, cold brooks that form the headwaters of our larger rivers. The beauty of its natural environment well matches its own beauty and grace of bodily form.

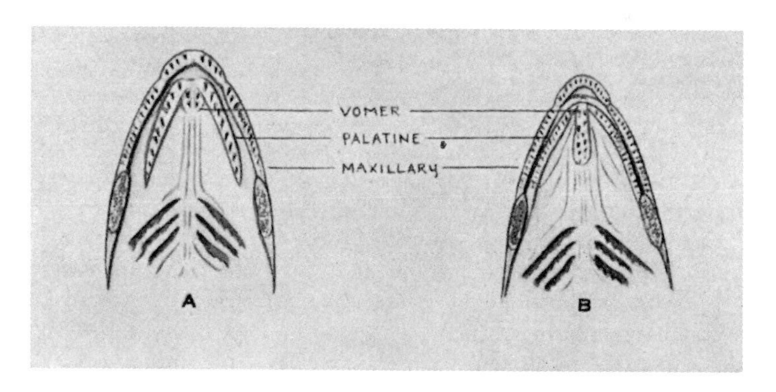

FIG. 8.—Diagram to show arrangement of teeth on bones in upper jaw and roof of mouth of *A*, a char (*Salvelinus*) and B, a trout of the genus *Salmo*. Note that in the char, or eastern brook trout, for example, the teeth on the vomer are restricted to the front end of this bone. In true trout such as a rainbow, the teeth extend well down the shaft of the vomer as well (modified after Dymond, 1932).

TABLE III

RECOGNITION CHARACTERS OF WIDELY DISTRIBUTED TROUT*
(Most important single recognition character in italics)

COMMON AND SCIENTIFIC NAMES	RECOGNITION CHARACTERS
Rainbow, or Steelhead: (*Salmo gairdnerii*)	*Red stripes on sides of body* and gill covers in spawning males; with *many black spots* on background of lighter color. Fish fresh from sea silvery with few spots. Lower fins light in color. Lacks red dash of color below lower jaw on each side.
Cutthroat or Black-spotted Trout: (*Salmo clarkii*)	*Red dash of color below lower jaw-bone on each side.*** Often heavily spotted with black on background of lighter color. Side of body without red spots, but red stripe on sides of spawning males is often evident.
Eastern Brook Trout: (*Salvelinus fontinalis*)	*Red-spotted, and with whitish spots on background of darker color;* lower fins edged in front with white stripe, bright red or orange behind this. Lower edge of belly bright red or orange in spawning males. Wavy olive worm-like lines on back.
Lake, or Mackinaw: (*Salvelinus namaycush*)	*Large whitish spots on background of darker color; no red spots;* fins uncolored; general color usually dark gray. Lives and spawns only in lakes.
Brown, or Loch Leven: (*Salmo trutta*)	*General color brownish yellow;* lower fins pale yellow to white; sides often with many large dark spots on background of lighter color; usually few red spots.

* Many commonly recognized forms of purely local distribution, such as golden trout of California and others, have been omitted from this table. The above listed forms probably cover over ninety-eight percent of the trout taken by anglers in America.

** To look for the "cut-throat" color on lower side of head, spread apart the lower junction of gills with head. The dash of color found here often cannot be seen unless this is done.

This fish may easily be recognized (Table 3) by bright red lower fins tipped with white on their anterior margins. Red spots stand out in clear contrast to dark areas on the sides while the dark olive upper surface is covered with a rather wavy, vermiculate marbling. The low sides and belly of males in breeding colors are often brilliant red or orange. The most brightly garbed specimens are found in cold, black, muck- or silt-bottomed ponds and streams.

Brook trout belong to the charr series, the members of which are characterized by the peculiar boat-shaped structure of the tooth-bearing bone (vomer) in the center of the roof of the mouth. This bone bears a small patch of teeth on its head or crest while the backward extension or shaft is depressed and lacks teeth. In lake trout the crest of the vomer is clearly raised and bears strong teeth, whence their former generic name "*Cristivomer*." With brown or Loch Leven, rainbow, steelhead, cutthroat trout, and Atlantic salmon, or other members of the genus *Salmo,* from one to several rows of teeth are found on the flat shaft of this bone, not being confined to the head or crest alone is in the chars (Fig. 8).

All charrs are fine-scaled forms, usually showing more than 200 diagonal rows in the lateral line. Scales are often accidentally rubbed off rainbows, cutthroat, and brown trout in handling, or when kept in leaves or grass in creels, though but seldom will the more deeply embedded scales of charrs be thus removed. Their skins are of softer and finer texture.

TABLE IV

THE BETTER KNOWN SPECIES OF CHARRS OCCURRING IN NORTH AMERICA

COMMON NAME	SCIENTIFIC NAME	DISTRIBUTION
Speckled trout or Eastern brook trout	*Salvelinus fontinalis*	General by introduction
Lake Sunapee trout	*S. aureolus*†	Lake Sunapee, N.H.
Rangeley Lake trout or blue-back trout	*S. oquassa*†	Rangeley Lakes of Maine and a few lakes of northern Canada
Lac de Marbre trout	*S. marstoni*†	Lac de Marbre, Quebec.
Dolly Varden trout (salmon trout of Alaska, western charr or bull trout)	*S. malma spectabilis*	Northern California to Alaska east to Alberta and Montana.*
Great Lakes trout.	*S. namaycush*	Northeastern U.S. west to Montana; Canada, and Alaska.

* Unpublished data from Dr. L. P. Schulz.

† Further studies might show these to be local varieties of *S. alpinus*.

Any person who has caught brook trout knows that they vary considerably in color, size, and shape, depending upon the waters from which they are taken. The most beautiful brook trout the writer ever saw came from a small spring-fed pond with a black-muck bottom near the headwaters of the Bouquet River in New York state. These had brilliant red bellies and fins while the upper portions of their bodies were very dark, the bright red spots standing out in beautiful contrast on their sides. Brook trout tend to be adapted in color to that of the stream or pond bottom over which they live. Most animals match their background; this aids in avoidance of enemies. Trout living over light yellow sand will often be extremely light in body color with but little contrast between spots, fins, and body.

Along the Atlantic Coast from Massachusetts northward occurs a race of sea-run brook trout which migrates up fresh water streams to spawn in the fall, and returns to salt water afterward. These trout are quite different in appearance from the typical fresh water brook trout of this region, being very light silver in body color after leaving the ocean. While in fresh water, the sea-run brook trout will not mate with stream forms of the same species. Specimens up to five and ten pounds are common, and the average weight of the sea-run trout is much above that of the stream trout.

Fig. 9.—A nice catch of eastern brook trout from Scott Lake, Willamette National Forest, Oregon (photograph by courtesy of Mr. Fred Ziesenhenne).

Eastern brook trout were native to this country and formed a staple food of the early settlers. Before introduction into western United States these fish occurred only on the eastern seaboard from northern Georgia to Labrador west to the Great Lakes region. Subsequently they were introduced into the western states.

Brook trout up to 17 pounds in weight have been recorded. These larger brook trout are known as "square-tails." Many large ones have been taken from the Nipigon River in Canada, and from the Rangeley Lakes in Maine. Brook trout of over three pounds are scarce nowadays, the average being far below this.

Water temperatures that exceed 75° F. may be fatal to brook trout. They thrive best in streams that show mid-summer maximum temperatures around 66° F. They live well in ponds and lakes in which the cool bottom waters contain sufficient oxygen. They apparently thrive equally well in hard and soft waters. The lower reaches of many streams, particularly those in the eastern states, have become suited only to brown or rainbow trout because of high summer temperatures, caused largely by the clearing away of shade next to the water courses. The upper, colder waters should be kept as brook trout waters in which the planting of brown trout should be avoided.

In eastern streams there are usually dams which offer impassable barriers to upstream movements of brown trout, and these often can be used as the up-stream limit for the planting of browns and the downstream limit for brook trout plantings. Temperatures, not dams, determine these divisions. Streams showing maximum temperatures of over 75° F. should not be considered brook trout waters.

As noted above, brook trout do particularly well in spring-fed, muck-bottomed ponds with abundant growths of lily pads, or pond weeds, such as are common in the Adirondack Mountains in New York state. Many such ponds unfortunately have been stocked indiscriminately with warm-water species such as the basses, perch, or pike. The usual result is that good fishing for trout has been completely destroyed. That trout and the large, predacious, warm-water species do not mix with beneficial results has been fully demonstrated.

Spawning. The life history of these trout runs as follows. In late summer brook trout migrate upstream. In late October or early November they seek gravel-bottomed areas in cold spring-fed tributaries in which to spawn. Those inhabiting lakes or ponds likewise at this time of year run up inflowing tributaries to spawn. Just what initiates their upstream movements toward the spawning areas is not well known, but it is probably the urge of the reproductive instincts, coupled with high late-summer temperatures which impel them to seek cooler waters.

Brook trout living in lakes or ponds without access to streams will often spawn on shallow, gravelly shores where spring water seeps up from below. Further, they will sometimes spawn in the deeper water of spring holes in either lakes or streams. One spawning area has been recorded in such a place in four feet of water.

The males arrive first at the spawning beds, followed shortly by the females. Here the females begin nest-building in gravel beds. They select gravel areas in both pools and riffles where there is upwelling water, and where the current is moderately swift. Selection of such areas assures the eggs a rich supply of pure water at even temperature. Nest building and egg covering are made a bit easier because the gravel is buoyed up slightly by the pressure of the rising water. The female prepares the nest, usually without help from the male. It is merely a circular depression in the gravel a foot or two in width and from two to eight inches deep. To make it she turns on her side and by vigorous up-and-down movements of head and tail the gravel is lifted and, with the aid of the current, is forced to one side and below the central pit in which the eggs will be laid.

The male during nest-building spends his time in fighting other smaller males, driving them off the nest in a vicious and aggressive manner. Many immature fish will dart into the nest at frequent intervals seeking eggs to eat, or, in the case of small ripe males, in hope of participating in the spawning act. Between fights, the male attempts to stimulate the female by gentle nudges or caresses, by swimming over or under her body, his fins rubbing lightly against her. Spawning sea-run steelhead males go through similar courtship activities. In addition male steelheads will be seen frequently to glide up against the side of the female vibrating their bodies rapidly as they do so.

Greeley (1932) says only male eastern brook and brown trout vibrate their bodies and that only one male brook or brown trout mates with one female. Hazzard (1932) says the male forces the female upon her side at the bottom of the nest. "A vigorous side-to-side vibration of both fish then occurred, during which it is supposed the eggs and milt were extruded, although sediment and motion of the water made it impossible to see them." Greeley (*loc. cit.*) does not report seeing eggs actually deposited.

Immediately the female begins to cover the eggs. This is done by digging above the eggs, gravel and pebbles being swept over them both by the current and by the digging action. She covers them thoroughly, filling the pit as high as surrounding bottom levels or higher.

The time required to dig the first pit and deposit the first eggs varies considerably, but usually it takes from several hours to half a day, once the fish are on the redds. All operations are continued both night and day.

Many eggs remain to be laid, and shortly after the first are covered, the female starts to dig another pit immediately above. Here she will lay more eggs, gradually working upstream from pit to pit until entirely spent.

Working from bottom to top of the redds has its advantages. In digging each new pit immediately above the point where eggs were last deposited, the lighter materials and gravel are swept downstream, covering eggs laid earlier with successive layers of materials which afford them additional protection against predators. The male does not assist in covering the eggs but goes merrily back to his fighting other males or driving off other fish that are attempting to eat the eggs.

One would naturally expect that the swift waters in which trout spawn would sweep all eggs away from the nests the moment they were laid. Nature has wisely provided for this emergency. The eggs of all trout, upon leaving the body of the female, are covered with a sticky secretion which hardens on contact with water. As the eggs fall to the bottom of the nest they immediately adhere to the gravel and stones on the bottom and thus are retained in the nest for a sufficient time for the female to cover them with gravel.

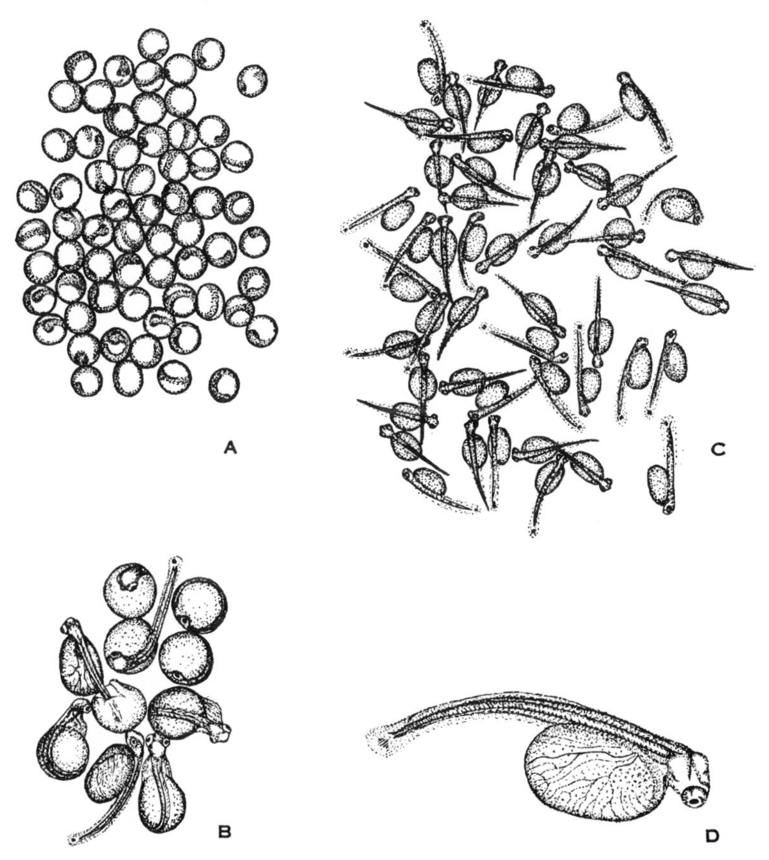

FIG. 10.—Early stages of eastern brook trout. *A,* eyed eggs before hatching showing developing embryos through the egg envelopes; *B,* eggs hatching, showing yolk-sac fry leaving envelopes; *C,* a group of yolk-sac fry; and, *D,* a single recently hatched fry showing rounded yolk sac attached to lower surface. This contains food that will nourish the fry until it is large enough to seek its own food. Note blood vessels extending around the yolk sac (*A,* enlarged approximately two times natural size; *B,* three times; and *D,* eight times).

When the eggs are all laid and well covered, the spent female leaves the nest, though the male may remain on guard for as long as two or three weeks afterward. Eventually the male also moves downstream seeking deep pools in which to winter.

With regard to the migrations of eastern brook trout Shetter (1936) presents some interesting data determined by tagging experiments* with this species in the North Branch of the Ausable River in Michigan. His recoveries of tagged fish in October and early November indicated that fifty to fifty-five per cent of breeding fish moved upstream to spawn; the average distance was less than a mile. Some twenty per cent spawned about where they were tagged, while about twenty-five per cent traveled less than one-half a mile downstream to spawn. Since the average size of the tagged fish was small and since apparently good spawning facilities were available close at hand, these data indicate less spawning movement than would probably be found in older fish of the same species living in larger streams. Shetter's work lends support to the belief that the bulk of eastern brook population migrates downstream to pass the colder winter months, returning to the same areas the following summer. He found but little movement of the fish during the summer months.

From the proportion of marked to unmarked fish caught it is of interest to note that Shetter (*loc. cit.*) calculated a total population of eastern brook trout to be 9,700 per mile of stream (near Lovells, Michigan) or about 700 per acre, of all sizes.

With regard to the percentage of survival of naturally spawned eggs, Hazzard (1932) reports an average of 79.8 per cent of eyed† eggs removed from twenty-one different eastern brook trout nests were alive and contained embryos. The number of eggs removed from each nest averaged 201. Hobbs (1937) in studies on natural reproduction of quinnat salmon, brown and rainbow trout in New Zealand, reports the efficiency of fertilization of the eggs of these species, deposited in natural redds, to be remarkably high. He states in his conclusions that "Material from redds of brown trout showed an efficiency of fertilization in excess of 99 per cent." When heavy losses did occur, he found them to be greater in the pre-eyed stage than in the later eyed or fry stages.

Among natural causes of heavy losses, Hobbs (*loc. cit.*) also says, "Heavy losses of fertilized ova are the outcome of adverse environmental conditions and not of inherent weakness." Among natural conditions causing losses, he cites such factors as (1) amounts of fine materials in the spawning beds during early development, (2) fungus (*Saprolegnia*) infections, (3) over-crowding of fish where only limited spawning areas

* Jaw tags of the strap or clip type bearing serial numbers were used in these experiments.

† Eyed eggs are those in which the eyes of the embryos can be seen through the egg envelope.

are available and late-spawning pairs disrupt the eggs laid by early-spawning pairs, (4) floods causing both silt deposition on eggs and disturbance to spawning beds, and (5) he suggests also the possibility that high water temperatures may be an important cause of losses. While, as Hobbs states, his results must be considered of a preliminary nature, this work represents a major contribution to knowledge of natural spawning.*

EGG PREDATORS

Much has been written regarding the destruction of trout eggs by trout, minnows, suckers, cottids or sculpins (also known as muddlers, bullheads, miller's thumb), fish-eating birds and animals. White (1930) reports finding 598 eastern brook trout eggs in the stomachs of thirty-two male trout of the same species examined. The largest number found in any single stomach was 97. In stomach examinations of 37 eastern brook trout taken in October and November during the spawning season, Needham (1930) found only nine trout eggs in one stomach of a seven inch male. Munroe (1923) has noted that mergansers and other birds will consume large numbers of the eggs of Pacific salmon when easily available. Greeley (1932) in a study of natural spawning of trout in relation to the egg predator problem concludes that:

> Attempts of trout and muddlers to take eggs from the pit were successfully prevented by female trout in the majority of observed instances. At most, a very slight percentage of the eggs deposited in the pit are taken in the interval between spawning and covering of the eggs. No attempts to dig out and feed upon eggs in the finished, covered redds were seen. By the time the female trout desert the eggs these are so well covered by gravel that disturbance by predators is unlikely.

Small trout attending spawning activities will often dart into nests as the eggs are dropped and try to secure a mouthful unless prevented, as they usually are by both the male and the female. Females particularly will rush viciously at such offending fish, and the eggs eaten at such times must be very few.

Gilbert and Rich (1927) have shown that late-spawning female Pacific salmon will in their nest-building activities dislodge many eggs laid in the same areas by early-spawning females. Greeley (1932) and White (1930) both report similar disturbance to trout redds by late spawning activities; and it seems probable that the bulk of eggs eaten come from such a source. Further, not all eggs fall safely to the bottom of the nests when deposited, some being swept away downstream. The latter are probably few, due to the extreme care with which female trout guard

* Later work has both borne out and enlarged upon the findings of Hobbs. Fine materials in or on the redds have the effects of cutting down the amount of oxygen-laden water that can flow past the egg, and of preventing easy egress from the nest by the young. (Phillips, 1965; Shumway, Warren and Doudoroff, 1964; Coble, 1961.) McNeil (1966) has reviewed the environmental effects upon salmon embryos.

their eggs. As Greeley (1932) points out, such eggs released by disturbances to the redds by late-spawning fish or by being swept away during mating will not hatch when adrift in the stream, and their presence in stomachs of other fish is an insufficient basis for condemning them as spawn destroyers. Far worse is the unmitigated, profligate waste of splendid trout killed by man for their spawn which is later sold for "tyee" bait.

The spawning period naturally varies with localities and with the strain of fish concerned. The most important factor in this regard seems to lie in the heredity of the fish. There are strains of trout that if kept separate from other fish in hatcheries will always spawn early, while other strains spawning late will follow the late trend from year to year. It seems probable that the same is true for various strains of wild brook trout. In most sections of this country spawning of eastern brook trout begins about the middle of October and is usually over by December first.

The number of eggs depends naturally upon the age of the fish. Most females in wild waters spawn for the first time at the end of their third year and produce from 100 to 300 eggs apiece (Table 5). Fish spawning for the third or fourth time may produce up to 2,000 eggs per female. In contrast with these figures, the progeny of a group of hatchery-reared brook trout in which selective breeding for high egg yields has been practiced for the last eleven years at the New Jersey State Hatchery at Hackettstown, New Jersey, produced at their first spawning an average of 1120 eggs per female, or about four times as many as in the wild state.* We do not know just how many eggs are produced on the average in wild fish, but actual counts of them from wild brook trout run from 80 in a fish slightly more than five inches long to 5,630 in a female twenty-two inches in length. The latter fish was taken in Lake Nipigon, Ontario and reported by Ricker (1932).

The time required for development in the egg varies directly with water temperature; the colder it is the longer it takes, while warmer water, within certain limits, speeds up development. At a water temperature between 50° F. and 52° F., approximately forty-four days are required for hatching. In water at 57° F. brook trout eggs will hatch in about thirty-three days. In extremely cold water below 40° F. trout eggs generally will be three months and more in hatching. Not all the eggs hatch at one time. A few hatch earlier and a few later than the bulk of the eggs in any given lot, but by far the majority hatch on the same date.

After hatching, the fry (Fig. 10) may remain in the gravel feeding upon the food stored in the yolk sac or it may rise out of the nest seeking the backwaters and shallower areas where it can seek its livelihood and find

* An average of about 1800 eggs per two-year-old female is listed for brook trout at the Benner Spring station in Pennsylvania by Buss and McCreary (1960).

protection from its enemies. After the yolk sac has been absorbed, the fry must all leave the nest and begin to find their own food. This consists of minute midge larvae, crustaceans, or other organisms. Those that survive the perils of their environment grow rapidly and by the following fall may be from two to four inches in length.

The young fish remain in the same waters in which they were born until from two to four inches in length. As they gain in size they naturally seek deeper waters in which to feed, and move downstream to find them. By the end of their second year many of them will be around six inches in length, and that fall a few of them may spawn for the first time. Each succeeding fall those that survive will migrate upstream to spawn, returning downstream to winter in large deep pools.

LAKE TROUT

Another char of interest to sportsmen is the lake trout, *Salvelinus namaycush,* otherwise known as the Mackinaw trout, longe or togue. Its natural range stretches from the larger, colder lakes of New England west to Minnesota and north to the Labrador peninsula in the east and into Alaska in the west. It has been established in mountain lakes in many western states. It is distinguished from the brook trout by greater development of teeth in the mouth and by its body spots. These are pale gray or whitish instead of red.

This is an excellent food fish and grows to large size. Specimens up to eighty pounds in weight have been recorded, but the usual size is from five to fifteen pounds. This trout is mainly a lake feeder and spawner, rarely entering fresh water streams. It is occasionally found in Canadian and Alaskan rivers, and also in a few very cold, small lakes, but reaches its maximum development in lakes of large size and great depth.

Dolly Varden trout, *Salvelinus malma spectabilis,* is the western representative of the char series. It occurs from a few localities in Northern California and Nevada northward (absent from the short coastal streams of Oregon and southern Washington) to Alaska, ranging inland to Alberta, Montana and Idaho. It is very voracious in its feeding habits and not highly regarded by fish-culturists. Indiscriminate stocking of lakes with this species in attempts to improve fishing has in many cases done more harm than good. In Alaska it is known as the salmon-trout, and it is supposed to be very destructive to the eggs and young of Pacific salmon.

RAINBOW TROUT

Rainbows, *Salmo gairdnerii,* love swift, turbulent water. These fish are essentially our mountain trout, and to take rainbows in fast, heavy water gives a never-to-be-forgotten thrill. Many anglers concede them first place in gaminess and fighting ability, probably because they often leap out of the water when hooked. From my own angling experience, I believe we have no better fighting trout than the rainbow. He is superb. His viciousness in taking the bait with a rush, his amazingly persistent leaps, his rushes, twists, and dogged determination to escape, make him a leader among fighting game fishes.

Rainbows are the most adaptable of the trout. They do well in warm or cold waters, and can stand maximum summer temperatures up to 83° F. if the oxygen content of the water remains high (Table 5). In hatcheries they lend themselves to intensive feeding under crowded conditions and are generally considered more disease-resistant than other species.

The migratory habits of rainbow trout have given rise to two types of fish. One is a sea-run type, and is usually known as the steelhead. The other is a less migratory type of fish. It remains as a resident in some of the larger rivers, even though it may have access to large bodies of quiet water to which it could migrate. Rivers possessing resident rainbows offer some of the finest fishing in America today. Such are the Pit River in California and the Ausable River in northern New York state. These are rough, wide, turbulent streams averaging more than one hundred feet in width, well stocked with rainbow trout which seem to be able to hold their own from year to year, even though the streams are intensively fished every season.

Steelheads generally remain in the ocean either two or three years, after which they return to spawn in the tributaries of coastal streams. When first returned to fresh water they are bright silvery in color on the sides and belly fading to darker above. Spotting is slight at this time, and as they slowly migrate upstream farther and farther from the ocean, and as the sex products are maturing, their light coloration gained in the sea is gradually replaced by the brilliant red stripe on the sides, particularly in the males, though the females usually darken considerably also. The rate of their migration upstream in the Klamath River as determined by competent observers is approximately 2½ to 3 miles per day.

They enter the streams in splendid condition after a long period of rich feeding in the ocean. They appear to feed to some extent as they move upstream, for how otherwise could they be taken so easily on spinners, bait, or flies? The stomachs of sea-run steelhead usually contain some stonefly or mayfly nymphs, caddice larvae, or other typical aquatic foods. In contrast, the Pacific salmon, on their upstream migrations, appear to take little or no food. The necessity for salmon to feed while in fresh water is, of course, less since all die after spawning. Steelheads, on the other hand, if they survive to spawn again must retain sufficient strength to make the return trip to the ocean.

The migratory tendency of rainbow makes them a poor selection for planting in waters where downstream migrations will mean their destruc-

Rainbows will spawn in the outlets of lakes if they are unable to ascend the inlets, or if inlets are lacking. It is not known definitely whether rainbow and brown trout will spawn on gravelly lake shores.* Rainbow have been seen over nests in shallow water in high Sierra lakes, but never in the act of spawning in them. On the other hand, in lakes where no spawning areas are available both rainbow and brown trout have been taken full of eggs which were apparently being reabsorbed. These appear to have been retained for lack of adequate spawning areas.

Costen, Pentelow, and Butcher (1936) in their *River Management* state that "spawn-bound" rainbow trout inhabiting certain land-locked lakes of Australia are said to have been killed by retention of eggs. It is also stated that scale readings disclosed the fact that not a single male or female fish had completed its fourth year in a land-locked water, all apparently being killed by retention of eggs in the body cavity. This is given as a possible cause of the disappearance of rainbow trout from British lakes after becoming well established. The fact that both brown and rainbow trout have been taken from land-locked California lakes in a spawn-bound condition while apparently otherwise healthy, would seem to show that not always are these species killed by retention of their eggs. Male trout, in any case, should not be injured by retention of milt. Ovaries taken from spawn-bound trout usually show many empty egg envelopes, which would indicate that reabsorption does take place. Eggs stripped from wild trout, spawned by hand, will often show empty egg envelopes or dead eggs retained from the previous spawnings.

Definite information as to whether rainbows can spawn successfully in lakes lacking the usual spawning places would be particularly helpful in the maintenance of fish populations.

While the spawning of rainbow or steelheads is somewhat similar to that of the eastern brook trout described above, a more detailed description of it may be of interest. Needham and Taft (1934) published observations on spawning of these fish, from which the following notes have been largely drawn.

In connection with some other experimental work on steelheads by the California Trout Investigations, the following observations were made during the spring of 1933. The work was done in Waddell Creek, about forty miles south of San Francisco. A pen was constructed of eight-inch mesh wire enclosing a portion of a pool and riffle such as is favored by the steelhead for spawning, the deeper part of the pool for shelter and the shallow end next to the riffle for the actual nest. A blind was constructed next to the pen for observations. The nests were started slightly above the lower fence and extended up about twelve feet to a point slightly upstream from the blind. The pen was roughly thirty-five feet in length and twenty feet wide. Anyone who has attempted to observe natural

* H. L. Kibby, in a study reported to the National Park Service, has presented circumstantial evidence for shore spawning of rainbow and brown trout in Crater Lake, Oregon, which has no inlet or outlet streams. Populations of trout have been present for many years even though planting has been discontinued. Kibby identified several areas where very young trout fry may have emerged from shoreline gravel.

spawning can appreciate the advantages of being able to bring about spawning of trout of known history within the space of a few hours and under such conditions as would make them easily observed.

The fish used in this experiment were obtained from the egg-taking station of the California Division of Fish and Game at Scott Creek, five miles from Waddell Creek. These fish were selected from among a lot of sea-run fish being held in a concrete tank. In both cases the females were selected by an experienced fish culturist as being too green to be stripped, but when placed in a natural environment both spawned within a few hours. The female described in the following was spawning for the first time and was 23.6 inches in length. Females of similar history and size whose eggs have been counted contained from 4,800 to 6,400 eggs.

Pre-spawning Activities. Two males and the large female noted above were placed in the spawning pen at 11:30 A.M. on April 6. The female began to dig her first nest at 2:30 P.M.

She started digging at a point about two feet above the wire screen at the lower end of the pen, where the velocity of the current over the redd was moderate. The water here was approximately three inches deep. Neither of the two males assisted in the process. The larger of the males, apparently being adversely affected by the trip over from Scott Creek, showed no interest in this procedure and remained hidden during the entire afternoon under the shelter of the alder at the upper end of the pen. The smaller male followed the female about in her nest-building.

In the actual work of digging the nest the female turned on her side and with powerful and rapid movements of the tail disturbed the bottom materials, which were then carried a short distance by the current. As this process was repeated the nest took form and finally resulted in a depression four or five inches in depth and about fifteen inches wide. After several vigorous digging operations, the female would drop back into the bottom of the nest and would seem to test with her anal fin the relative depth and width of the pit. It was evident that she was quite careful and particular in getting the nest just right to suit her needs.

That the digging of the female is able to break up and separate the bottom particles was shown to us very clearly at a natural redd just above the forks on Waddell Creek. At this point, a ford had been built for automobile passage across the stream and had been made by piling up rocks held in place by chicken wire along the downstream margin. At one side of this ford was a hard, gravel-like mixture of decomposing rock, forming a sort of hardpan bottom. We found one pair of steelhead spawning here March 27, and, remarkably enough, the female had been able to crumble this hardpan and had laid her eggs in it. We were able to dig them up later. In fact, the female of this pair had worn away the edge of this outcrop of hardpan until it was evenly broken off near the lip of the ford. One thing that may have attracted them to this place was the seepage down through the gravel in the bottom of the ford. At low water we noted that practically all of the water ran through the

Fig. 11.—Pair of steelhead trout over nest in Waddell Creek near Santa Cruz, California. The larger fish is a female. Note four small males facing nest.

chicken wire weir, none of it passing over the top. This being the case, any eggs deposited here would be assured of a good supply of water in which to hatch. White (1930), Greeley (1932), Kendall and Dence (1929), and Hazzard (1932) have pointed out that the brook trout, *S. fontinalis,* in both lakes and streams tend to select places where spring water bubbles up through the gravel, assuring the eggs a rich supply of pure water and even temperature. Rainbow trout, on the other hand, are known not to require such conditions, but they may select gravel beds at the lower ends of pools and above swift riffles, where considerable amounts of water must seep down through the gravel.

Activities of the Male. The males during the nest-building were often seen, both in the pen and under natural conditions, to try constantly to stimulate the female by swimming to her side and quivering slightly at the same instant. Also, particularly with nests where many small males were in attendance, a great deal of fighting and driving away of the smaller fish occurred. In several instances we saw males viciously chasing smaller males, even going to the extent of driving them out of the pool into riffles both above and below it. In the accompanying figure four males will be seen ranged along the sides and lower portions of the nest. There was a total of six males accompanying this pair. Two of these, from six to nine inches long, are not shown in Figure 11, p. 39.

Both the attendant males and the participating male maintain a position at one side and to the rear of the female. The smaller males are kept at various distances, depending upon the pugnacity of the larger male.

The male in returning to the nest from an attack on smaller fish, will often be seen to rub his nose both over and under the tail of the female in an attempt at stimulation. Perhaps the most characteristic behavior aside from defending the nest from other males is the sliding up against the sides of the female and quivering at the same time.

Spawning Act. The first spawning act took place in the pen at 3:55 P.M., four hours and twenty-five minutes after the fish were placed there. The act took place about six feet from the holes in our blind so we were able to observe the details with great clarity.

The female dropped back in the center of the pit with her vent and anal fin well down in the deepest part. The male instantly moved into position parallel to her. Their vents were opposite and, since he was considerably shorter, his head came only about to her pectorals. Both fish opened their mouths wide, and the female particularly was seen to arch her body, raising her head so that the tip of her snout was out of water. Eggs and milt were exuded with a quivering motion by both fish at exactly the same instant. The snout of the female, where it protruded from the water, was seen to cause ripples on the surface from the quivering motion as the eggs were deposited. The white cloud of milt partially obscured the eggs from our view, but we could clearly see the stream of bright pink eggs dropping into the bottom of the nest. They appeared to stay in a very compact group and none was observed floating from the nest. The milt settled in a more or less compact way about the eggs though some of it was carried away by the current. The whole process did not require much more than two seconds. The male during this process was on the left side of the female as she faced upstream. The female remained in a vertical position. The male inclined slightly toward her and appeared to be in definite contact.

Even though the current was moderately swift, not a single egg was seen to be swept out of the pit of the nest by the current. Since the pit of the nest was about four inches below the gravel of the sides, we were unable to see the eggs after they had fallen to the bottom. In the short interval between the time she deposited the eggs in the pit and just before she started to cover them up, we were even unable to see the eggs by standing up and looking over the top of the blind. They must have rolled into the crevices between the gravel immediately upon lodging in the bottom. Predators which might desire to secure such eggs would have little opportunity, for the eggs settled out of sight and were covered by the female in the space of a few seconds.

Post-spawning Behavior. Within a few seconds after the mating act, the female turned on her side and began covering the eggs. This she accomplished by digging, not directly over the point where the eggs had been dropped into the pit of the nest, but slightly to each side and forward of the nest, the current sweeping the displaced materials into the pit over the eggs. This gravel was moved into the pit within a minute. As soon as the eggs were well covered she began digging another pit about two and one-half feet above the point where she had previously deposited eggs. The male was not interested in these proceedings and did not assist her at any time.

One hour and forty minutes later the second pit was completed and she spawned again. This time, however, the male was on her right side obstructing our view from the blind and we did not see the eggs actually emitted, though we did see milt from the male. The procedure followed was in all respects the same as we observed at the first spawning. The act lasted about two seconds as before. She immediately covered the eggs and shortly began digging at a third pit above the point where eggs were last deposited.

Observation was discontinued at that time but was resumed the next morning. The female had left the nest and retired to the pool. She made no effort to continue spawning during the morning. In the early afternoon she was taken from the pen and killed for examination. Only seven eggs remained. Examination of her coelomic cavity showed no blood to be present: it is usually found in females stripped by hand. Apparently she had continued her spawning after dark and completed it during the night.

When we examined and measured the completed redd on the morning of April 7, this area was found to be approximately twelve feet in length and five feet wide. The depth of the water averaged about five inches over the whole area.

From the separately raised piles of gravel we believe that six or seven nest pits were dug to complete the spawning. These were in a straight line following the current upstream. As has already been stated, a female of this size would lay from 4,800 to 6,400 eggs. If six pits were utilized this would mean an average of from 800 to 1,000 eggs for each separate spawning.

An examination of some twenty natural spawning redds in Waddell Creek showed that the fish invariably selected the lower ends of pools where the water was shallow but relatively swift and where good gravel beds composed of medium and small sized stones were available. Examination of Figure 11 shows the nest of the pair pictured to be just above the point where the water breaks over the lip of the pool into a swift riffle.

With regard to the immature males invariably found with adult pairs, seining of these small specimens usually showed them to be ripe, and it seems evident that these smaller trout are there to participate in the spawning activities rather than to secure eggs to eat after deposition by the female.

The attention of those who are interested in making observations of this sort should be called to the ease with which wild fish can be made to spawn under natural conditions in confined areas after they have been held in tanks until nearly ripe. Fish so held will spawn in small observation pens of the type described above. With the aid of a blind, detailed observations can be made.

NOTE: Briggs (1953) has made additional studies of the spawning of steelhead as well as coho and chinook.

GOLDEN TROUT

The golden trout, *Salmo agua-bonita,* was described from its native home in the headwaters of the Kern River, California, at elevations around 10,000 feet. The specific scientific name, *agua-bonita,* or "pretty water," is quite appropriate, for these fish live in some of the most beautiful waters of the Sierra Nevada Mountains. Three separate species of golden trout have been described. However distinct these may be today, all probably arose through ages of isolation, impassable falls preventing upstream migrations and mixing with other stocks. Dr. David Starr Jordan (1907) said of these fish:

> In isolated streams with a bottom of red granite at the headwaters of the Kern are three species called "golden trout," all small and all brilliantly colored, each of the species being independently derived from *Salmo gilberti* [Kern River trout], the special traits fixed through isolation—these rank with the most beautiful of all the many forms of trout, in which group their coloration is quite unique.

The beauty of these fish cannot be praised too highly. My premier angling experience was the thrill of catching my first golden. A more striking combination of colors cannot be imagined: deep vermilion on the belly fading to light gold on the sides, with a bright rosy stripe on the sides crossed at intervals by beautifully contrasting dark parallel parr marks which persist to maturity. The cheeks are of the brightest gold, while black spots cover the upper sides and dusky olive upper surface. The lower fins are orange tipped with white; the dark olive dorsal fin carries a single bright red spot on its upper anterior surface. Truly here was that "living flash of light" I had seen on the first rise.

Golden trout of large size are seldom taken. Those caught by anglers usually run from six to ten inches, though specimens up to sixteen inches are taken occasionally. In California a bag limit of twenty and a size limit of five inches is imposed. In streams where both rainbow and golden have been planted it is often possible to catch pure examples of either species, and hybrids which will show some of the characteristics of each. True goldens are unmistakable. They will always be called goldens no matter who catches them or where they are caught.

Golden trout are limited to high mountain areas in central California. They are well adapted to the rigors of long hard winters, short growing summer seasons and poor food conditions of lakes lying in granitic glaciated rocks. The young are not generally available for planting outside California.*

CUTTHROAT TROUT

The cutthroat or black-spotted trout, *Salmo clarkii,* can easily be distinguished from rainbows by the presence of a red streak below the lower jaw on each side, by greater spotting (Fig. 12), and by the presence of teeth on the hyoid bone at the base of the tongue. Like rainbows, they spawn in the spring.

In many streams today they are found in the same waters with rainbows, and as noted above, hatcherymen have frequently crossed the species in spawning operations where both species are trapped on their spawning migrations. While fertile offspring result, eggs produced from such hybrids are of poor quality, showing high mortality.*

As pointed out by Dr. David Starr Jordan, the cutthroats of the great interior basins of Utah, Nevada, and other inter-mountain states were probably derived ages ago by migrations of cutthroats from the upper Snake and Columbia River basins. Here again subsequent isolation has produced a number of forms which may or may not be good species. Besides the coast and Yellowstone or Montana cutthroats listed earlier, a host of additional cutthroats have been described as distinct species. Among these are the Rio Grande cutthroat, *Salmo spilurus;* the Piute trout, *Salmo seleniris,* recently described by Snyder (1934) from a high

* Unpublished work by Dr. H. S. Davis, U. S. Bureau of Fisheries.

* Robert J. Behnke and other trout systematists tend toward the view that *Salmo gilae* and other trout of the Southwest and Mexico may form a complex related to the golden trout.

mountain tributary of the Carson River in California; Lake Tahoe cutthroat, *Salmo henshawi;* Colorado River cutthroat, *Salmo pleuriticus;* Utah cutthroat, *Salmo utah;* Greenback trout, *Salmo stomias,* and others.

The coast cutthroat, *Salmo clarkii clarkii,* a sea-run form, occurs in coastal streams of northern California, north to Alaska. It ascends but a short distance up fresh water to spawn, usually lacking the tendency of salmon or steelheads to migrate long distances upstream. Lake-inhabiting

FIG. 12.—Cutthroat or black-spotted trout taken in a high Sierra lake near Bishop, California.

cutthroats seek small tributary streams of clear, fast water for spawning, behaving like lake-run rainbows in this respect.

It is a curious and important fact that in some waters where fish culturists have attempted to establish non-native trout by continued heavy annual plantings, the native species will continue to be caught year after year in greater numbers by anglers than the introduced ones, even though the native forms are not restocked. When this occurs it is obvious that naturally spawned offspring of the natives are maintaining the fishing. Only their greater adaptability to the waters in question could make this possible. This is true of native trout in a number of streams in western United States and should demonstrate fairly conclusively that the planting of non-native fish should not be done except where stream conditions have become so changed as to warrant the use of exotic species.

BROWN OR LOCH LEVEN TROUT

The brown trout, *Salmo trutta,* while lacking the beautiful coloration of many other salmonoids, nevertheless is a favorite with many anglers. It is generally conceded to be a bit wiser and harder to take on a line. This trout was introduced from Germany where it was native and has become one of the mainstays of anglers in this country. It is a hardier fish than the native eastern brook trout and better adapted to withstand modern conditions in our larger streams (Fig. 7).

These fish do well in a variety of waters. Apparently they reach their maximum development in the lower reaches of good-sized streams. In the east, in Catskill streams such as the Esopus, Willowemoc, Neversink, and Beaverkill, fine brown trout fishing has long been available: in spite of extremely heavy fishing, these fish have been able to survive. In California these fish have likewise prospered in the lower reaches of Sierran streams, such as the Merced, American, and Feather rivers. While they seem to hold their own in many turbulent fast-water streams, general observations show that they do best in waters that run at a somewhat slower pace through meadowlike sections.

The introduction of brown trout into lakes at high elevations where low water temperatures prevail the year around has done more harm than good. Placed in such waters they feed on other more adaptable species such as rainbow or eastern brook trout, and when large they offer but scant sport to fly fishermen. A small population of large two to eight pound predacious brown trout in a lake makes restocking with the young of other species difficult; most of those planted come to a prompt end in the stomachs of the larger fish. A study of "condition factors"* of rainbows and brown or Loch Leven trout has given additional proof of the poor adaptability of the brown trout to cold water. In high, cold-water Sierran lakes in California, United States Bureau of Fisheries workers found the condition factors of rainbows to average over 14% higher than brown or Loch Leven from the same lakes or from others of like character.

Concerning condition factors of large artificially reared trout intended for stocking, Hewitt (1934) says:

> I have discovered—that if trout are fat when liberated and have a condition of 55 or more . . . that they have enough reserve fat to carry them through the fishing season without getting below normal and that they are likely to reach the following spring so that they can recover a good part of their weight and may go through the second spawning without damage. I regard this observation of great value to the art of stocking.

* The condition factor of a fish is a measure of its plumpness in relation to its length. It is determined by taking the weight in pounds multiplied by 100,000 and divided by the cube of the standard length in inches. A condition number of 42 is considered about normal; higher figures represent fatter fish and lower figures, thinner fish.

There is no fish so smart as a large brown trout, or so difficult to catch. While a few may occasionally be taken either by bait or by trolling with spinners or spoons, most of the larger ones are night feeders.

Few brown trout over five pounds in weight are taken from streams nowadays. One taken on bait from the Merced River in Yosemite National Park several years ago weighed over twelve pounds. One was taken from Arrowhead Lake in Southern California the summer of 1933 that weighed sixteen pounds, nine ounces.

Brown trout will survive water temperatures up to 81° F. There are a few records that have shown these fish to survive even higher temperatures. They seem to do best in water that does not exceed 80° F. Hewitt in his *Telling on the Trout* (1930) speaks of finding these trout buried in gravel beds with only their dorsal fins showing, apparently in an effort to avoid uncomfortable high water temperatures.

Brown trout have a life cycle similar to brook trout in that they migrate to their breeding areas in late summer and spawn at about the same time in late October and early November. They also select the smaller spring-fed tributaries, but will spawn in comparatively heavy water from six inches to two feet in depth. Those that spawn in deeper, wider streams do not have to migrate close to the very sources of the headwater streams as brook trout do. They are able to find suitable spawning grounds much farther downstream. Many large brown trout from one to four pounds in weight have been seen moving up comparatively small tributaries of the east branch of the Ausable River near the town of Jay, New York. These tributaries, while small, are about twice the size of the streams in which brook trout usually spawn.

The length of the incubation period in brown trout is about the same as for brook trout. In water at 57° F., from thirty to thirty-three days is required from the date of fertilization. In water of the same temperature, the incubation period of rainbow eggs is much shorter, requiring only from twenty to twenty-two days. Golden trout eggs require about the same length of time as rainbow eggs, which gives added evidence of their close relationship to rainbows.

Eggs of true Loch Leven trout, *Salmo trutta levensis,* were first brought to the United States from the Howieton fishery of Sir J. Ramsay Gibson Maitland of Sterling, Scotland, in 1884. It is extremely doubtful whether there is such a thing as a pure strain of these trout in this country today. Fish culturists, not being able to distinguish these fish from brown trout, have crossed the two, producing hybrids with characters of both species. Further, these fish have undoubtedly interbred naturally to produce hybrids in streams where both species were planted years ago. Haphazard intermixing of these species has resulted in loss of purity of either strain so it is just about as safe to call them "brown trout"

FIG. 13.—At top: Lake Trout, *Cristivomer namaycush;* middle: Dolly Varden, *Salvelinus malma spectabilis;* and lower: Montana Grayling, *Thymallus montanus* (photographs by courtesy of J. Everett Hancey).

as it is to call them "Loch Levens." The former term is generally used in eastern United States while the latter is the name commonly used by anglers on the Pacific Coast.

Those older anglers who used to fish for eastern brook trout in the heyday of its abundance look upon brown trout with considerable disfavor. Browns offer far less to the eye, but, as most anglers know, in skill required to creel them they demand the best. For keen discrimination of what is, and what is not food, and for general all-round ability to avoid anything artificial, the educated brown trout of heavily fished streams is a challenge to the best of fishermen.

THE GRAYLING

Grayling, *Thymallus arcticus,* can always be recognized by the extremely large, high, sail-like dorsal fin. Other characteristics which aid in distinguishing these fish are a small mouth, concentration of black spots on sides of the front part of the body, lack of teeth on tongue, large scales, and orange or reddish markings on the large dorsal fin.

These fish belong to the *Thymallidae,** or grayling family, and are very closely related to the salmon as well as to the smelt and whitefishes that they superficially resemble. Three species of grayling have been described: one in the headwaters of the Missouri River in Montana, the Montana grayling; one in Michigan, the Michigan grayling; and one from the Arctic regions of the north, the Arctic grayling.

Montana grayling were introduced into a lake at the headwaters of the Merced River in Yosemite National Park and one year later one good catch was made. However, two years later an examination of the lake and of its outlet (no inlet was present) failed to locate a single mature fish. Many grayling fry from the Yosemite Hatchery that had been planted earlier in the season were seen in the outlet stream.

Grayling are spring-spawners. They thrive well in hatcheries, particularly if the water remains cold over their incubation period.

These fish take flies readily, indeed too readily when considered from the standpoint of their conservation. They put up a splendid battle when hooked on light tackle. The usual size taken runs from nine to twelve inches, and individuals as heavy as four pounds have been recorded. For eating purposes, their flesh is considered superior to that of trout. These are essentially cold-water fish and are widely distributed in Alaska, Canada, and northern Europe.

* Now considered to be part of Salmonidae.

II

Stream Conditions, Physical and Chemical

TEMPERATURE

TEMPERATURE is probably the most important single factor governing the distribution of all species of trout. It exerts profound effects upon fish and their foods alike. In general, high temperatures will within the limits of tolerance promote rapid development and growth, while low temperatures retard growth and inhibit development. In the hatchery, in spring water at 52° F. the year round, it is possible to grow eastern brook trout to an average size of six inches in a year's time. In shallow raceways supplied with spring water at 63° F. at Hot Creek near Bishop, California, rainbow trout have grown over an inch a month. Artificial food was used and the experiment started with fish five inches long.

These growth rates are exceptional. Trout in hatcheries supplied with spring water between 50° F. and 60° F. the year around usually greatly exceed wild trout in growth. This is due both to better growing temperatures, adequate food, and to protection from enemies. Wild trout living in colder waters or in waters that fluctuate considerably in temperature from season to season grow much more slowly. Temperature coupled with available food supply are the major conditions that determine the rate of growth.

Small lakes and streams, sheltered but little from the sun's rays, usually show greater seasonal and daily fluctuations in temperature than large ones. In cultivated farm lands the portions of streams that are sheltered from the sun by patches of trees are often the means of cooling water to a limit tolerable by trout. More often, cold springs or spring-fed tributaries are the sole means of maintaining sufficiently cool water in the lower reaches of trout streams during the warmer months of the year.

It is usually the upper portions of streams that are coldest and hence furnish most of the trout fishing, though notable exceptions occur. In some streams that drain large lakes where in summer the water has been warmed close to the limits of trout tolerance, the water near the lake outlet is too warm for good trout production. After the water has been cooled either by shade or by spring-fed tributaries, or by both, at some distance from the lake the temperature may become quite suitable. Temperatures either "make or break" trout waters.

In the lower portions of large streams draining wide areas where temperatures range close to or above the tolerance of trout, bass and other warm-water species are often taken along with trout. In such areas their ranges overlap. Good early season trout fishing may sometimes be had, but as the water temperatures become higher in summer the trout vanish.

Fig. 14.—Darwin Canyon Lakes, Sierra National Forest, California. Elevation over 11,000 ft. In bare granite but well exposed to the sun. Golden trout native to high mountain waters in California often produce much excellent sport fishing in such waters.

They seek cooler water either upstream, if no barriers to upward migration exist, or if in a lake, in the cooler, deeper waters. When the water becomes excessively warm brown trout cease feeding entirely and rest on the bottom.

Temperatures suitable for trout are highly important. In Table 5, Chapter I, the limiting high temperatures for brook, brown, and rainbow trout are recorded as 75° F., 81° F., and 83° F. respectively. These figures await verification by more complete experimental work. Eastern brook trout have been taken in Martis Creek, a tributary of the Truckee River in California, where the temperature recorded was 77° F. and similar findings have been reported elsewhere. It is undoubtedly true that the temperature tolerance of trout is dependent upon accompanying factors such as amounts of oxygen and other gases in solution, chemical nature of the water, presence or absence of pollutants, condition of the fish, etc.

The ideal summer temperature for eastern brook trout has been shown to be around 66° F. Brown trout reach their best development in warmer streams showing maximum daily summer temperatures between 70° F. and 80° F. Rainbow trout, being the most adaptable of the three, apparently do equally well in cold and warm waters. In their native streams of

Fig. 15.—Floating ice in unnamed lake, Sierra National Forest, California, July 14, 1934. Elevation over 10,000 ft. A few high western lakes such as the one shown here, fed by glaciers and snow the year round, are too cold to permit good growth of trout, and fish available for planting are better utilized in warmer waters.

the far west good rainbow fishing is to be had in both, though their best development is reached in the larger, swift, "white-water" streams showing maximum summer temperatures of from 75° F. to 80° F. This statement applies to sea-run steelhead as well as to the less migratory stream form of rainbow.

Maximum summer temperatures usually occur only for brief periods of one or two days each season. Such maxima are usually reached in the late afternoon following several days of an extremely hot spell with warm nights in addition. However, as soon as the setting sun's rays are intercepted, the natural evaporation of water causes the temperature to drop rather rapidly. This is fortunate for the trout.

Waters can be too cold for good trout production. Temperatures extremely low during most of the year retard growth, giving rise to mature but stunted, emaciated fish of little sport value. Some extremely cold, glacier-fed streams and lakes at high elevations in states of the Rocky Mountain and Pacific coast regions have been shown to produce fish of this kind. Stocking of such water may be considered a waste of fish in so far as the resultant sport fishing is concerned. Hazzard (1933) cites cold water as the cause of poor fishing in some lakes in Glacier National Park. He says:

> A rather careful record of plantings in Glacier National Park since 1912 has been kept by the Bureau and the National Park Service. Comparison of this with data secured by the Survey of 1932 reveals that some streams and lakes have been stocked with little or no success and, furthermore, that these waters are, without exception, low in temperature, rarely, if ever, attaining or exceeding 55° F. even during the height of the summer. On the other hand, the productive waters exhibited summer temperatures ranging from 54° F. to 70° F. during the months of July, August and September. The lakes and streams in this park having the warmest waters (all well below the upper limits of tolerance) proved to be the most productive of trout. It was a conclusion of the Survey that the poor stream fishing found here is due primarily to this factor. The lakes afford much better results though many are high and, in some instances, glacier fed. However, the great majority of these are situated so that they receive considerable sunlight and in addition have a large percentage of shallow water which is quickly warmed.

It should be stated here that stocking beyond the limits of the food supply, particularly in lakes, will likewise produce stunted, big-headed trout. Only careful analyses of temperatures, food supplies, and growth rates of trout inhabiting such "problem lakes" will reveal whether low temperatures or overstocking is the real cause or a contributory cause of poor fishing. Intensive angling carries one distinct benefit in overstocked waters. There trout are usually hungry and easy to catch, with the result that the population level may be reduced and made more nearly consistent with the food supply. However, in all too few waters today is an over-abundance of trout the problem.

Needless to say, we are more interested in maximum water temperatures than in daily or monthly means, for it is the higher temperatures near the upper limits of tolerance by trout that largely determine their distribution. It is these that guide us in selecting the species for planting. Maximum water temperatures should be taken on the hottest days of the year in the late afternoons, when skies are clear and the weather is settled.

Everyone knows that maximum air temperatures found in inland regions vary greatly with elevation. We escape hot spells on the plains by spending a few weeks in the mountains. At high altitudes lower maximum air temperatures and fewer extended, uncomfortably warm periods occur. Cooler air temperatures make for cooler water and account for the fact that most mountain streams are trout streams. In the hot, arid, desert regions of the Rocky Mountain and eastern portions of the Pacific coast states trout waters are such largely because most of them flow at altitudes in excess of 3,000 feet.

Some workers have held that in deep wide pools thermal stratification of water occurs. That such stratification takes place in deep lakes, and in shallower ponds sheltered from the effects of wind circulation is well known, as are also some of the biological consequences. In extremely wide or deep pools stratification of the water is doubtless possible but concrete evidence is lacking. In a study made in the San Joaquin River in California at the head of a pool some four hundred feet long by sixty feet in width, the following results were obtained for both temperatures and amounts of oxygen present at various depths:

TABLE VI

POOL TEMPERATURES, JUNE 21, 1934, SAN JOAQUIN RIVER AT SAN JOAQUIN BRIDGE*

DEPTH IN FEET	FAHRENHEIT TEMPERATURE	OXYGEN IN PARTS PER MILLION
Surface	64°	8.9
17	63°	8.4
34	63°	8.4

* (After Needham and Hanson, 1934)

Here a difference of 1° F. is shown between top and bottom water. The pool was only thirty-four feet deep. The oxygen difference was likewise small, being 0.5 parts per million between top and bottom waters.

Trout seek the bottom of the deeper pools in the lower sections of streams in winter, perhaps because the water is then warmer on the bottom.

Surface waters of trout lakes often become too warm for trout in the summer time, but if the lower layers remain cold and if sufficient oxygen is present in deeper water, the trout will survive without harm. As an illustration of this, a small natural, three acre brook trout pond in the Adirondacks in New York state that I once fished showed a surface temperature of 78° F. in late afternoon. This temperature offered a gloomy outlook so far as fishing was concerned, but I decided to try to catch some fish anyhow. Much to my amazement the first cast raised a nice nine-inch fish, and before long ten were bagged in quick succession. The trout were rising through the warm upper layer of water to take the flies cast over them. I was curious, naturally, to know the bottom temperature, and using a water bottle I took a sample of the bottom water. The depth was only about four feet and the water temperature was around 60° F. Cool water seeping up through bottom silt was the probable explanation. Since the pond was well protected by trees, wind circulation of water was prevented and only the upper foot or so of water became too warm for brook trout to live in, and it did not prevent their rising through it to secure food.

Winter conditions and their actual effect on stream life are poorly understood at present. In non-spring-fed streams of rapid flow, ice usually forms on the sides and bottom first. The current is slowest at the bottom, and this condition, coupled with freezing temperatures, permits ice to form in smooth, streamlined cakes over and among the bottom stones and gravel. This is called "anchor ice." After these cakes have become large, they will tear loose from the stream bed because of their buoyancy and, carrying with them adherent gravel and stones, will be swept off downstream. The abrasive action of both the ice and embedded particles destroys large numbers of aquatic bottom organisms. In the larger streams that fall below 32° F. in the winter there is less aquatic food than in the smaller, spring-fed tributaries.

Snow is much less harmful than ice, though when abundant in floating clumps will occlude the surfaces of pools, slow the rate of flow, and assist in ice formation. Snow is sometimes a benefit, as snow bridges will often form over small head-water brooks in winter, affording an insulation against low air temperatures. Nursery and spawning streams are thus protected against cold as well as against predatory mammals and birds.

Observations made while taking winter stream foods samples in the Feather River near Chester, California, January 25, 1933, following a heavy winter snow storm, show the marked effects of a heavy snowfall on this stream. A fall series of food samples had been taken at the same point in the Feather River in the previous November. Clear definition of pool and riffle was now lacking where earlier each was quite apparent. The banks were covered five feet deep with snow and large masses of it were seen floating downstream. Pools that could be recognized as such were covered with clumps of floating snow. The water level was at least a foot and a half higher than in the fall. The water temperature was 33° F. and tiny slivers of ice crystals carried in suspension clogged the 30-mesh screen sieves that were used to take the food samples. Ice on the stream margins out of the current plus floating rafts of snow left only a narrow stretch of open water in midstream. No anchor-ice on the bottom was noted but the stones were exceedingly slippery. This was due to rich growths of diatoms coating them. The aquatic insects taken were quite torpid and slow-moving, making but slight effort to escape. They were found in good abundance at the sides of the stream in gravel areas that in the previous fall had been dry because of low water. Apparently they had spread to new areas as the water level had risen.

Many observers have noted that adult trout usually seek the warmer spring-holes and deep pools in which to spend the winter. In such places there is warmer water and better protection from enemies. As also noted by Hewitt and others, if such spring-holes can be supplied, trout will often use them in preference to migrating downstream. Young trout living in the smaller spring-fed nursery streams or tributaries usually remain where they are or move upstream seeking warmer spring waters in which to winter.

One of the worst effects of lumbering, road-building and allied activities is the removal of shade, exposing the water to the sun and thus raising temperatures to dangerous limits, or making streams entirely unfit for trout. Many formerly excellent brook trout waters have been spoiled in this way.

TRANSPARENCY

Pure water, as everyone knows, is tasteless, odorless, and transparent. The last characteristic is of great biological consequence. The light of the sun engenders growth of green plants in water; upon these the animals are either indirectly or directly dependent for food. Perhaps a major reason why shallow riffles produce the bulk of food in streams is because they are the better lighted areas. Unshaded riffles in streams are richer in foods than riffles under dense forest cover.

Minerals in solution, microscopic organisms, plant and animal remains, dissolved food stuffs, silt, and other materials, both inorganic and organic, impede light penetration into water. Suspended materials such as mud, silt, and microscopic animals and plants cause turbidity of water. Dissolved materials, unless greatly concentrated, do not affect light penetration as much as suspended materials. Either may give the water color. Bog waters or waters draining heavily forested regions and containing much rotting submerged plant remains are usually dark brown in color and often acid in reaction, owing to the tannic acid leached from plant remains.

Stream waters, as contrasted with lake waters, carry far more materials in suspension. This is directly related to rate and volume of flow. Heavy run-off from rain, melting snow, or ice often causes excessive erosion of the stream bed. At such times the transparency of the water will be practically lost due to soil washed in from the land. The large amounts of silt discharged in streams by mining operations often prevent all light penetration. In addition, silt, when heavy, will smother bottom foods, fill pools, and completely ruin the fishing in trout streams.

On the other hand lack of transparency may be due to excessive amounts of organic matter such as algae and other plancton organisms carried in suspension. The waters of the Klamath River in northern

California furnish a good illustration of this. In midsummer, water in the main stream is often of a dark green color that is caused by large amounts of microscopic algae floating downstream. The upper Klamath flows through weed-bordered Klamath Lake and various power dams, where it accumulates the algae. Such materials furnish food to aquatic organisms and make for greater richness in stream foods.

GASES IN SOLUTION

Equally important in relation to fish life are the gases in solution. Oxygen (O_2) dissolved in water and absorbed by the gills of fishes, and carbon dioxide (CO_2) used by aquatic plants in photosynthesis, are both absolutely essential to aquatic life. They play opposite roles in the organic cycle. Carbon dioxide is used during sunlight in the manufacture of starch by green plants and oxygen is given off in the process. The oxygen in water is used in both plant and animal respiration and in decomposition of organic matter. On bright sunny days streams of bubbles of oxygen can often be seen rising from aquatic plant beds and chemical analyses will show extremely high oxygen content at such times. After dark, however, conditions are reversed. The large amounts of oxygen stored in the daytime are consumed both by plants and animals so that in early morning the lowest amounts of oxygen are usually present.

The sources of oxygen and carbon dioxide in water are varied. The atmosphere of course contains a mixture of these and other gases; but diffusion from the atmosphere into quiet water is very slow. Hence most of these gases are renewed from the water itself by the regular metabolic activities of the plants and animals living in it. Oxygen is obtained by the natural aerating effect of exposure to air in falls, cascades, and riffles of swift streams. Carbon dioxide may also be supplied in small

Fahrenheit Temperature	Oxygen in Parts per Million
32°	14.62
41°	12.80
50°	11.33
59°	10.15
68°	9.17
77°	8.38
86°	7.63

amounts from the atmosphere, but the largest amounts in water are produced by the decomposition of organic matter and the respiration of aquatic plants and animals.

Cold water can hold more oxygen than warm water. The amount held in solution is directly dependent upon the water temperature. Listed below* are the amounts that can be held in solution at varying temperatures when exposed to air containing 20.9% oxygen and under sea-level atmospheric pressure of 760 mm. Water under the same pressure can hold almost twice as much oxygen in solution at 32° F. as it can at 86° F. These figures do not represent by any means the amount of oxygen that would actually be found in water at any of the temperatures listed, but merely show the maximum solubility of this gas under the conditions described.

Varying atmospheric pressure will also change the solubility of oxygen in water. At high elevations where lowered pressures exist less of this gas will be found at any given temperature than at sea level. An increase in pressure and decrease in temperature together will further increase amounts of oxygen in water, while increase in temperature and decrease in pressure will reduce it.

The major factors then, in determining the amounts of oxygen found in water at any given time are: (1) temperature, (2) pressure, (3) abundance of aquatic plants, (4) amounts of oxygen-consuming materials and organisms present, and (5) amount of natural aeration from contact with atmospheric air.

The deeper layers of lake or pond waters often become depleted of their oxygen supply, which causes trout to seek the better-aerated upper layers.

Oxygen analyses of lake and pond waters have given satisfactory explanation of lack of success in stocking some ponds with trout. Where the deeper waters are cold enough but lack sufficient oxygen for trout, stocking is predestined to failure. The only recourse where such conditions exist is to stock with warm-water species such as bass, perch, or sunfish.

Embody (1927) states that brook trout waters should contain over 3 cc. of oxygen per liter (4.29 parts per million). He also says that brown trout require about the same oxygen and carbon dioxide conditions as brook trout, while rainbows will tolerate temperatures as high as 83° F. if the water is nearly saturated with oxygen (5.5 cc. per liter or 7.8 parts per million). Various workers have noted that trout can stand extremely low oxygen for brief periods without asphyxiation. In so far as brook, brown, and rainbow trout are concerned, and without knowing the exact oxygen requirements in relation to temperature, 4 parts per million of oxygen should be a minimum safe limit for clean, natural trout waters.†

In general and within certain limits, higher temperatures speed up metabolic rates, and this causes increased demand for oxygen. Great bodily activity, such as is demanded in upstream migrations, spawning efforts, or capture of prey, likewise produces increased demand for

* From *Standard Methods of Water Analysis,* published by American Public Health Association, 370 Seventh Ave., New York City.

† Asphyxiation would be prevented by a 4 ppm minimum, but higher levels are probably necessary for growth and optimum activity (Doudoroff and Shumway, 1967).

oxygen. The quiescent state that brown and brook trout appear to assume with the advent of dangerously high temperatures naturally reduces bodily demand for oxygen to a low level. A display of activity at such times might quite easily cause severe respiratory difficulties because of the lowered total amounts that are available in solution in warmer waters. At any given temperature within the range of tolerance, the exact amounts of oxygen required to prevent asphyxiation are not known. Only general limits can be assigned at present.

The oxygen requirements of brown trout are roughly indicated by the following experiment. Twenty-five fingerlings averaging one and one-half inches in length were confined in an open top battery jar in 1200 cc. of water. Oxygen and carbon dioxide analyses were made at varying time intervals to determine decrease of oxygen and increase of carbon dioxide in solution. The respiratory rate was determined by counting the number of pulsations per minute of the lower jaw.

TABLE VII

EFFECTS OF LOW OXYGEN ON BROWN TROUT FINGERLINGS*

HOUR	OXYGEN IN PARTS PER MILLION	CARBON DIOXIDE IN PARTS PER MILLION	FAHRENHEIT TEMPERATURE	RESPIRATORY RATE	CONDITION AND ACTIVITY OF FISH
11:30 A.M.	6.7	10.0	54.0°	—	Good.
1:30 P.M.	4.8	14.0	60.2°	140	Somewhat restless.
3:30 P.M.	2.94	18.0	64.0°	165	Fish in obvious distress, quite restless.
4:05 P.M.	2.7	20.0	64.0°	170	Bad, first fish died at 3:45 P.M.
4:30 P.M.	2.6	21.0	64.0°	170	Distress acute, fish coming to surface.
5:00 P.M.	2.43	21.5	64.0°	170	Many dying, upturned.

* Experiment carried on at New Jersey State Hatchery in 1932. Only one fish was allowed to die; when about dead the others were revived by removal to fresh, cold water.

In Table 7 above are the results obtained. It is to be noted that no deaths occurred until the oxygen supply had dropped below 3.0 ppm. of oxygen. The first fish died when the oxygen was approximately 2.8 ppm. Distress became acute and many fish were almost dead when the oxygen supply had dropped to 2.6 ppm. The temperature ranged between 54° F. (min.) and 64° F. (max.) over the course of the experiment.

OXYGEN SUPPLY OF STREAMS

In so far as natural unpolluted trout streams are concerned, the available oxygen seldom falls below the minimum required by trout. Most trout waters run well below 70° F. over most of the year and the increased solubility of oxygen in cold water tends to keep this gas well above danger limits. Water in streams of rapid flow and steep gradient where constant mixing with the air is possible seldom show oxygen depletion. Oxygen analyses in good trout streams usually show from 4.5 to 9.5 parts per million to be present. Only under conditions of little current, excessive temperatures, and the presence of large amounts of oxygen-consuming natural or artificial pollutants, will this gas drop to dangerous limits. This is most likely to happen in poorly aerated side pools of flood-created channels.

One often hears of winter-killing of trout in lakes—instances where, after the ice breaks up on lakes in the spring, all or most of the fishes have been found dead. Heavy losses of both trout and warm-water fishes have been known to take place. The explanation seems to lie in depletion of the oxygen. This is coupled with great increase in carbon dioxide content of the water, due to animal respiration and the presence of large amounts of decaying organic matter, which reduces the oxygen supply below the minimum required. Ice and snow prevent the penetration of light, which would permit growth of aquatic plants and consequent renewal of oxygen. Shallow-water ponds rich in organic detritus are most often affected where the total volume of water is small compared with the total volume of oxygen-consuming materials. Decomposition, as is well known, uses oxygen and gives off carbon dioxide. Other gases are also involved, and when the ice breaks off such ponds in the spring, a bad odor may be noticeable at a considerable distance. Once in a shallow pond near Rochester, New York, tons of dead carp, bass, and pickerel were killed by asphyxiation. Possibly oxygen depletion alone was the cause, but more likely than not, both the low amounts of this gas and excessively high carbon dioxide were jointly involved. In addition, poisonous methane is produced by decomposition in the absence of oxygen, and also hydrogen sulphide, with an odor like that of rotten eggs. The actual role each of these gases plays yet remains to be demonstrated.*

In the winter many western high mountain lakes lacking inlet streams may become covered with very thick ice which in turn may be covered by many feet of snow. Under such conditions lack of light probably causes an almost complete cessation of oxygen renewal by plants. Possibly the reason trout in such lakes are not killed is that oxygen-consuming materials are scarce, and even though light is excluded, the demand for oxygen is at no time in excess of the available supply remaining in the water. Lowered water temperatures in the winter reduce both metabolic rates of the fish and rates of decomposition of bottom materials, thus reducing the oxygen demand. Oxygen renewal takes place rapidly

* Various schemes for breaking up winter ice cover and aerating lakes have been tried. Some success has been achieved by releasing compressed air through a perforated hose or pipe laid in the bottom of the lake (Rasmussen, 1960). Summer kill has been prevented by similar means, although compressed air released from a cluster of small apertures so that they rise through a large vertical pipe appears to circulate the water more efficiently (Johnson, 1966).

in the spring once the surface layers of ice and snow are thawed sufficiently to permit light penetration.

CARBON DIOXIDE

The true effect of carbon dioxide on trout and associated animals is little understood at present. Its reciprocal relationship with oxygen and its importance in the primary food cycle are well known, but the conditions that cause this gas to become harmful and the manner in which injury takes place needs much further study.

Creaser (1930) has said with regard to brook trout:

> The carbon dioxide tension has little influence on the general distribution of brook trout. A range from 0.21 to 1.62 (mm.) has been recorded in brook trout streams, while non-brook trout streams of the same region had a range from 0.28 to 1.99.

High carbon dioxide is not usually harmful unless accompanied by low oxygen supply. When oxygen is abundant the carbon dioxide seems to have but little effect. Underground waters and some spring waters are known to be high in this gas. Simple aerating devices will remove a major portion of the carbon dioxide in such waters if they are needed to supply hatcheries or rearing ponds.*

Davidson (1933) cites an interesting instance in an Alaskan stream where hundreds of pink salmon, trout, and other stream fish were killed, apparently by a sudden increase in the carbon dioxide content of the water. Freezing temperatures in the evening reduced the flow of water from melting snow and ice in the upper reaches of the stream, but the seepage of ground water continued; and this ground water, highly charged with the gas, apparently was the cause of the death of the fish when dilution with large amounts of run-off water ceased. He found high carbon dioxide (pH† 5.6) where the fish were dying. Just below this point and below a falls it was lower (pH 6.1). Aeration of water passing over the falls apparently released large amounts of the gas.

Powers (1934) also points out that sudden high increase in the carbon dioxide content of water will sometimes kill fresh water fishes. The difficulty in determining the reasons for sudden losses of fish either in natural waters or in hatcheries and rearing ponds is that one must be on the job to make chemical analyses of the water when such occurrences take

* Thorough chemical analyses should be made of all spring water supplies to be used in fish rearing operations. It is necessary to find out before expensive construction work is begun whether or not the water to be used is suitable.

† On the pH scale neutrality is 7.0. Values below 7.0 indicate acidity of the water. Conversely, values higher than 7.0 indicate alkalinity. For methods used in chemical analyses of water see "Standard Methods of Water Analysis," published by American Public Health Association, 370 Seventh Ave., New York City.

place. Analyses of water made later, when losses have ceased and conditions have changed, mean little or nothing.

Embody (1936) says in regard to carbon dioxide content of hatchery waters:

In experiments conducted in the Ithaca station . . . it was found impossible to develop eggs beyond the appearance of the neural ridge when the carbon dioxide was greater than 22 ppm. with an oxygen concentration of 4.5 ppm. However, when the CO_2 was lowered to 15 ppm. and the O_2 increased to 5.5 ppm. the eggs continued development to hatching.

Fig. 16.—Canyon Falls on the Big Quilcene River, Olympic National Forest, Washington. This falls is a barrier to fish migration upstream but a scenic asset to the Rainbow Forest Camp nearby (photograph by courtesy of U. S. Forest Service).

Embody also states in the same article that waters containing over 15 ppm. CO_2 must be looked upon with suspicion when the water is to be used continuously for hatchery purposes.

All investigations carried on to date have shown that trout can withstand wide variations in pH range without apparent harm. In natural unpolluted waters apparently this is of little importance in affecting their distribution. Creaser (1930) says in this regard:

We may conclude from the existing data that the range of voluntary toleration of hydrogen-ion concentration by brook trout is greater than the maximum and minimum found in practically all natural waters. This range of toleration by brook trout varies at least from 4.1 to 9.5, and furthermore the hydrogen-ion concentration throughout this range does not seem to shift the voluntary toleration limits either of temperature or of dissolved oxygen content.

Creaser also states that there is no indication that either acid or alkaline waters are more favorable or more generally preferred by brook trout.

Extremely acid seepages from coal mines have been known to kill trout inhabiting some streams thus polluted. Old beaver dams on trout streams have likewise been said to cause stronger acidity than normal, because of the large amounts of rotting vegetation in the water. This has reduced the trout population, and has made the flesh of those remaining unpalatable.

One of the most important factors governing the acidity and alkalinity of streams is the character of the terrain drained. If limestone areas are drained the waters will be rich in calcium and will show high alkalinity. Similarly waters draining forested lands or swamp or marsh lands containing much humic acid from rotting plant debris usually show low pH values, indicating high acidity.

Considerable daily fluctuations in pH values have been observed by various workers in waters containing abundant growths of aquatic plant beds. Carbon dioxide is consumed by plants during daylight, thus reducing the acidity of water, while at night this gas may accumulate in considerable quantities and cause the water to become more acid.

Carbon dioxide combines with lime to form calcium carbonate and with magnesia to form magnesium carbonate. Marl is formed this way in the shells or about the bodies of various aquatic snails, clams, and lime-encrusting plants. The remains of these accumulate as marl on the bottoms of both streams and lakes. The white deposits of marl commonly seen around lakes or ponds are sometimes many feet deep. In water free from CO_2 the simple carbonates are almost insoluble, but when this gas is present it combines again to form soluble bicarbonates. These are utilized over and over again by aquatic life.

Natural waters showing strongly alkaline (pH) values and those rich in carbonates, bicarbonates, and various allied salts, are well known to support greater amounts of trout foods than acid waters. The coastal streams of California are rich in food; the pH value of those tested show ranges from 7.2 to 8.6. On the other hand, lakes in the Sierra and Mono-Inyo National forests at high elevations in the high Sierra of California show pH values from 7.1 on the alkaline side of the scale to 5.8 on the acid side. The average for the surface waters of twenty-three lakes above 5,000 feet was pH 6.8, indicating a condition of slight acidity. Water in the lakes studied is very pure, so pure in fact as to lack of common salts that make for greater richness of food organisms. Granitic rock areas offer scanty soluble food materials.

OTHER GASES

Excess nitrogen* in water has been shown by Marsh and Gorham (1904) to be the cause of gas disease in trout, goldfish, bullheads, and various other species of fish. Common symptoms of this disease are the formation of gas bubbles in the fins, in the gill filaments, under the skin, in internal organs, and especially behind the eyes, which consequently protrude. As a result of the latter symptom, fish culturists usually refer to the gas disease as "pop-eye" disease. It is usually curable by removal of the fish to water of ordinary gas content. It was formerly contended that excess oxygen in water was by itself enough to cause the gas bubble disease. However, work by Wiebe (1932) and others has shown this to be untrue. In Wiebe's experiments trout and other fish were held in water containing excessive amounts of dissolved oxygen.

Free nitrogen has been shown to occur in water from springs, lakes, and deep wells. It is quite inactive and its presence in water is probably due to contact with air, or to nitrogen-producing bacteria. Most waters do not contain excesses of this gas. If tests show excessive amounts, it can easily be removed for hatchery or rearing pond uses by simple aeration of the water by means of falls or breakers, to break it up and release the excess. For fish cultural uses supersaturated water is thus made harmless. Spring water lacking sufficient oxygen for fish life can likewise be improved by aerating devices to increase the supply. Spring waters which are supersaturated with nitrogen or deficient in oxygen where the water emerges from the ground are often made suitable for fish life by flowing in contact with the air for some distance. Subdividing the water mechanically by aerating devices merely hastens the natural purifying processes.

Trout in "spring holes"—pools where the water wells up from below—will often show typical pop-eye disease. These fish are in the worst possible place, as they are right in the water as it leaves the ground before it has had any chance to lose the excess nitrogen by contact with air. In the same water but some distance downstream below its source trout may be in fine condition with absolutely no signs of pop-eye. Before any water supplies are utilized for fish cultural purposes, the average of a series of tests for nitrogen should be used to determine the amount of nitrogen present and consequently the amount of aeration necessary to purify it for safe usage.†

* Ordinary air usually contains 79 parts of nitrogen to 21 parts of oxygen, along with other minor constituents. One liter of water at 68° F. is known to absorb around 18 parts per million of nitrogen at a pressure of 760 mm.

† During the summer of 1968, excess nitrogen in the Columbia River below the Dalles and McNary dams caused distress and mortality among chinook salmon. Supersaturations of up to 150% were noted by U. S. Bureau of Commercial Fisheries investigators.

Hydrogen sulphide gas is quite toxic to trout when in excess of their normal tolerance. Belding (1929) states that 0.86 ppm. is lethal to eastern brook trout. Most natural waters probably contain amounts of this gas well below the limits of tolerance of fish. However, in a series of trout rearing ponds into which large amounts of artificial food are thrown daily, the decomposition set up from waste of the fish and from uneaten food may at times produce dangerous amounts of this gas. In fact, on warm, rainy spring evenings when the air is damp it is often possible to smell this gas rising from the surface of trout ponds.* Dr. H. S. Davis of the United States Bureau of Fisheries reports a stream in Vermont that produces excellent trout fishing, and the odor of hydrogen sulphide can be detected ten or fifteen feet distant from its banks. He also reports that trout taken from this stream are exceedingly highly colored. Belding (1929) states that respiratory movements of fish may serve as an indicator in determining the presence of both hydrogen sulphide and other toxic agents and that this gas produces a variation from the normal sufficiently characteristic to be diagnostic.

In thirty-three determinations for hydrogen sulphide made of water from trout rearing ponds where considerable losses were thought to have been caused by excess hydrogen sulphide present, the maximum amount found was 0.34 ppm. and the least 0.017 ppm. The average of all samples tested was 0.13 ppm. It was possible to detect the presence of the gas by smell in most of the samples analyzed. Water high in hydrogen sulphide is supposed to contain low amounts of oxygen. In these cases, however, oxygen tests made at the same time varied between 5.01 and 6.0 ppm., showing ample amounts present. The water temperature varied between 41.0° F. and 50.0° F. The gas was present in slightly greater quantities in the water of lower ponds after it had flowed through a series of ponds carrying the accumulated wastes from each. Losses of trout were likewise greater in the lower series of ponds. It was not possible definitely to determine that excess hydrogen sulphide was the cause of the losses. They were small each day but high in total. Undoubtedly this gas was at least a contributing cause.

Methane, otherwise known as "marsh gas," is produced by decomposition of bottom materials when the oxygen supply is extremely low or entirely lacking. This gas is not produced in swift, cold water trout streams; but in headwater trout streams that flow slowly through upland bogs or marshes with large amounts of decomposing plant remains and muck or silt bottoms, considerable amounts of it may be produced during the summer months of the year. Methane is inflammable, and if an oar be pushed into soft muck bottoms, the bubbles released may easily be ignited with a match. Spontaneous combustion of this gas in marshes and swamps has been commonly called "will-o-the-wisp." The work of Allgeier, Peterson, Juday, and Birge (1932) on the decomposi-

* Unpublished.

tion of bottom deposits from Lake Mendota, Wisconsin, under laboratory conditions showed that methane formed 65% to 85% of the gases produced. Practically nothing is known at present regarding the real effects of this gas on trout or other animals in either lakes or streams.

POLLUTION

Pollution has rightly been termed our "national shame." Near and in most large cities streams are largely used as open sewers or drainage ditches to remove the waste products of urban populations and of manufacturing establishments. In less densely populated areas wastes from creameries, canneries, mines, lumber and paper mills have wrought ruin in many waters that prior to pollution furnished much splendid fishing. Instead of sparkling waters inviting sport we have the deadening appearance of foul water. Such streams offered in the past splendid opportunities for developing beautiful recreational areas for the use and pleasure of the people close to their homes. Instead, as if going on the theory that streams were put there for use as catch-alls for man's wastes, we see them lined with sewer outlets, garage wastes, garbage dumps, and other eye-sores. And in most cities expensive artificial parks have had to be built elsewhere. To cite a good example of the despoiling of a stream of great natural beauty, Farrell (1930) says regarding a certain village in northern New York state through which the Salmon River flows:

> This is a village with a population of approximately 9,000, which is by nature very beautiful, having a chasm 150 feet deep crossed by the main street. Instead of beautifying this feature, the town has emptied the waste from creameries, sewers, laundries, dye factories, garages and mills into the stream by means of forty sewers over a distance of 2½ miles, or about one sewer every 100 yards.

Hundreds of other villages on streams, ponds, rivers, or lakes could be cited where the "open sewer policy" of stream management has been allowed full sway. A few of the smaller towns and cities have taken advantage of streams within their limits to develop shady parks along their banks, keeping the water clean for fishing, swimming, and boating. But in the main man's economic interests have been followed with no thought of the end result. We are beginning to measure the evil not only in terms of pollution and lost miles of fishing water, but in terms of the aesthetic value of clean waters.

BIOLOGY OF POLLUTION

Any stream or lake is constantly "purifying" itself. Wastes of plants and animals are oxidized and destroyed in the normal organic cycle, usually without serious depletion of the oxygen supply. The effect of dumping large amounts of sewage into a stream is greatly to increase the oxygen demand. If the supply is brought below the lethal limit for fish they will be killed or driven out. But it is well known that small amounts of organic wastes such as sewage and wastes from creameries, distilleries, canneries, and wineries may greatly enrich a stream by furnishing additional food to the normal populations. Small amounts of milk wastes from creameries have been noted to increase greatly the growth

FIG. 17.—Big Quilcene River, Olympic National Forest, Washington. Typical shade and cover in an unburned area. Note figure of man standing at right of water's edge (photograph by courtesy of U. S. Forest Service).

of bottom-dwelling midge larvae. But such instances of man-made pollution actually benefiting the food supply are rare.

Other pollutants that are poisonous to aquatic life are wastes from mines, gas works, metal working factories, dye works, artificial silk factories, chemical plants and paper mills. Ellis (1935) says regarding these:

> Two statements can be made here covering these toxic pollutants; namely, all cumulative wastes, that is those not readily oxidizable or removable by the stream, as gas factory wastes, should be entirely excluded. This is particularly true of wastes carrying metallic ions, including copper, arsenic, lead, zinc, and even iron, since these metals are often temporarily removed from stream waters by precipitation, only to be redissolved in quantity at some other time. Deposits of wastes carrying heavy metals constitute therefore potentially acute pollution hazards at all times, especially since many metallic salts are active protoplasmic poisons. Second, no substance should be admitted to a stream until it has been shown that the material in question will be not only non-toxic under the conditions and in the dilutions as operative

in the stream to receive this effluent, but that the substance will not produce unfavorable cumulative effects.

As noted by Ellis, some toxic wastes may not be immediately lethal but their cumulative effects may be most deadly. Small changes in the chemical balance of waters may exert profound changes in the effects of these poisons and release large amounts of toxic substances long after they have been dumped into water.*

Fig. 18.—Little Quilcene River in Snow Creek burn, Olympic National Forest, Washington. Shade completely removed and stream choked with half-burned debris (photograph by courtesy of U. S. Forest Service).

A third class of pollutants which cause excessive harm in American trout streams includes such wastes as oil, sawdust, waste pulp from paper mills, coal dust, washings from mines of various sorts, mining and erosion silt.† These wastes are particularly harmful for two reasons: they cause actual injury to the gills and other soft parts of aquatic animals by abrasive action, and they smother the bottom-dwelling animals and

* Related to this cumulative toxicity is the ability of persistent pesticides such as DDT and its derivatives to accumulate in fatty tissues of organisms high in the aquatic food chain. In one of the most publicized incidences, fish-eating birds accumulated lethal amounts of chlorinated hydrocarbons following use of insecticides in Clear Lake, California (Hunt and Bischoff, 1960). The discovery of DDT and derivatives at concentrations up to 90 ppm in fatty portions of coho salmon from Lake Michigan has caused doubts about the continued use of this chemical in the Great Lakes area.

† At least two additional classes of pollutants that should be recognized here are radioactive materials, and heated effluents that can raise the stream temperature beyond the tolerance of aquatic organisms.

plants. Likewise, increased turbidity caused by suspended particles prevents light penetration, and hence hinders the growth of aquatic plants. Waste pulp fibers not only smother out all bottom foods and reduce oxygen supply, but in many instances cause greyish mats of extremely evil-appearing fungus to grow. Mining wastes in many western trout waters completely rob streams of their aquatic food supplies by their combined abrasive and smothering action. Sawdust dumped into streams has the same effects and in addition probably contributes to higher than normal acidities of stream waters.

Outflow from unsealed, abandoned coal mines has been the cause of very considerable pollution in the eastern coal regions. Air combining with sulphur compounds in mine waters forms sulphuric acid, and that does the damage. All that is necessary to control such pollution is to seal the mine entrances to prevent air contact before the water leaves the mine. The object is to keep the air out, not to keep the water in. Much good work was accomplished with relief funds in sealing abandoned mines in the east in 1934 and 1935.

The consequences of oil pollution to both fish and game make an evil story. Ducks and other aquatic birds have been killed by the thousands as the direct result of their alighting in oil-covered water. Their feathers become coated with a slimy black mess that waterlogs the downy under-feathers, thus preventing flight. As many observers have pointed out, the results are losses to sportsmen of untold millions of game birds. With fish the effects are only indirect, but none the less serious for that. Oil forms a film on the surface of water, preventing free exchange of gases. The free emergence of aquatic insects from water is prevented. The oil also forms a slimy coating over submerged bottom areas, smothering out all forms of life. Fish remaining in such areas will starve to death.

Below pollution outlets most streams and lakes show well-defined zones of decomposition and oxidation of the polluting substances. Three zones have been described which indicate rather well the varying stages of pollution and recovery of streams. They are: (1) zone of recent pollution, (2) septic zone, and (3) zone of recovery.

The zone of recent pollution is that area lying closest to the polluting effluent. Here fairly normal stream populations may be found before oxidation of the pollutant has well begun. Organic materials such as sewage and milk wastes usually do not kill aquatic animals immediately on contact with the water, as do some toxic poisons. Naturally considerable mixing of the water with organic wastes is necessary before oxidation begins.

The septic zone is the term given to those foul-water areas where oxidation is at its height and where the oxygen supply may be low or absent. Hydrogen sulphide, methane, and other decomposition gases will often be found present. Only the most hardy aquatic animals will be found, and those are usually the direct air breathers. Strange as it may seem, there are a few aquatic animals that seem to prefer badly polluted conditions. Among these are the sludge worms, *Tubifex*; rattailed maggots (larvae of Syrphus-flies), *Eristalis,* a few air-breathing snails, and a few species of midges. These are good biological indicators of pollution and have long been used as such in pollution studies. Other forms, less tolerant to polluting substances and often found in the zones of recent pollution and recovery, are likewise used as indices to determine the area and general limits of these zones. Farrell (1930) says concerning the use of bottom fauna as indices to the study of polluted conditions:

> In a study of stream pollution a determination of the bottom fauna often gives a more exact index of the extent of pollution than does a chemical analysis, which may have been taken during a period of either high or low outflow of polluting substances. The plants and animals living on the bottom are present both during a high and low water level and during high and low concentrations of the various pollutions. These bottom inhabitants give a more accurate picture of the unfavorable conditions which exist all year round than any other analysis. In this year's survey the bottom fauna was a more reliable index of pollution because all the streams are thoroughly aerated by ripples, falls and overflow of dams and few low oxygen values were found, while the bottom fauna in these same areas showed the presence of polluting influences.

The zone of recovery is, as the word implies, that area wherein the water recovers a proportion of its oxygen supply and wherein the natural purifying processes are being completed. Some fishes, many snails, and other tolerant forms will often inhabit this zone. The greater the distance from the source of the pollution after the septic zone is passed, the cleaner the water will gradually become, until complete recovery is made —always assuming a new source of pollution is not encountered.

In determining the area or length of any given pollution zone, the most important factors are: (1) volume and type of polluting substance in relation to volume of stream, (2) rate of flow of the water, and (3) temperature of the water. Warm, wide, quiet waters recover much more slowly than cold, swift, well-aerated streams. Also the time required for any stream or lake to recover from the effects of temporary pollution depends upon the same conditions. Various workers have pointed out that anywhere from a few weeks to years may be required.

Ellis (1935) of the United States Bureau of Fisheries, in his recent excellent paper entitled "Water Purity Standards for Fresh Water Fishes," quoted in the foregoing discussion, points out that standards for fishes and other aquatic organisms are not identical with those for drinking purposes or for industrial uses. He says:

> The statement which is so often quoted, that water leaving a particular manufacturing establishment or flowing in a given stream, is "good enough to drink," and therefore by inference favorable for fish life, is without scientific background, and must be refuted.

He points out clearly that the tolerance of fishes to pollutants and their cumulative effects varies with the species, their age, and with the degree of pollution. No one standard can be set up that will cover all ranges and degrees of pollution.

A common method of testing the effect of pollution on fishes is to place fishes which normally inhabit clean water in a cage and suspend them in polluted areas, noting the effects on them after given periods of time. This method is faulty because the fish are subject to those conditions and concentrations of pollution which exist only at the time such tests are made. This is why, as Farrell (1930) states, bottom-dwelling forms give better indices of true conditions: they are exposed to all ranges and degrees of concentration, and all types of pollution. For purposes of enforcement of anti-pollution laws, the types of bottom organisms present or the clean-water forms absent offer the best indicators of the extent and nature of the damage done in polluted areas.*

One of the most important phases in the management of trout waters should be the cleaning-up of existing cases of pollution and the prevention of further contamination. It is obvious that all substances to be dumped into water should be classified as to their toxic action on fish and on their food organisms; that all should be rendered inert or harmless prior to dumping by proper recoverage or treatment, and that all toxins should be entirely excluded.

Our worst polluted streams are found in the larger, lower reaches of interstate rivers along which lie the industrial centers of the nation. These are largely non-trout waters that produced in the past warm-water game fishes such as bass, pike, perch, muskelunge, and other species. Trout waters show somewhat less pollution on the whole than those waters closer to population centers. Nevertheless there are many hundreds of miles of trout streams contaminated with filth and unfit for either fish, bird, or mammal. Loss of these has increased greatly the intensity of fishing on open unpolluted streams and lakes. If those thrown out of productivity by pollution were cleaned up the greater spread of anglers would reduce the intensity of angling considerably on many now "over-whipped" waters.

One argument commonly advanced against clean-up campaigns is that the value of the angling concerned is far less than that of the industries doing the polluting. The fact that these industries are valuable does not give them *a priori* rights to use streams as open sewers. The problem carries back to the very roots of our economic system. Industry is no

* The study of the pollutional aspects of aquatic biology has been greatly advanced. See Doudoroff et al. (1951), Patrick and Hohn (1956), Hynes (1956).

Research into nutrient balance and primary productivity, and the relation of these to enrichment of waters by organic materials, leading to eutrophication of many still waters, is receiving major emphasis. Most states have commissions or boards charged with maintaining water quality through investigation and regulations. The Federal Water Pollution Control Administration with its regional water laboratories is helping to set and maintain standards.

more to blame than municipalities, and the real obstacles are the apathy of the public, and the cost of rendering harmless industrial or domestic wastes before they are turned loose into water to be purified by nature. Pecuniary profit to a few at the expense of the outdoor enjoyment of hundreds of thousands of people upon whom the livelihood of industry depends, would seem shortsighted. Clean-up of pollution will not stop the profits. It is more likely to increase them.

Modern methods of sewage treatment can prevent pollution from domestic wastes. But sewage treatment plants cost money and today, according to the *Report on Water Pollution* (1935) by the National Resources Committee, which says:

> Sewerage systems are available to over half the population of the United States, or in other words to about 68 million persons. The great majority of the *urban* population is served by such systems. The sewage from approximately 28,400,000 persons, or about two-fifths of the urban population, receives treatment; about half of it receives both primary and secondary treatment. This indicates how large a proportion of the urban population disposes of sewage without treatment prior to discharge. Probably not all of it needs treatment, but a considerable part of it does.

With regard to the effect of pollution on wild life, the report goes on to say that pollution inimical to fish, waterfowl and other wild life involves losses of large but indeterminate proportions. In most states no comprehensive survey has been made of such matters. Despite the great interest of sportsmen's organizations, insufficient action has been taken to abate these abuses, or even to appraise the nature and extent of the effect of pollution on fish and bird life.

Sportsmen and conservationists generally should do everything possible to focus public attention upon the disgraceful condition of our waters so that definite action may be started toward its abatement. Some progress has been made; some cities with their attached industries have so befouled their drainage basins that the obvious danger to public health forced them to clean up. It seems strange that we should spend millions to create parks, and at the same time allow areas that should have been made into parks in the first place, to become abominations to the eye and nose.

> The landscape belongs to all. Its condition affects the public weal. It is good to dwell in a place where the environment breeds contentment; where peace and plenty and satisfaction grow out of the right use of nature's resources; where wise measures are taken to preserve the bounteous gifts of nature and to leave them unimpaired for the use and benefit of coming generations.
>
> Much of the scenic beauty of every land lies in its shore lines; and it should be a part of public policy to keep unimpaired as far as possible the

attractiveness of all public waters. Streams differ far less from one another in their own intrinsic characters than in the way they have been used by the hand of man. They differ less by topography and latitude; far more by the cleanness of their waters, by the trees that crown their headlands, and by the flower-decked water-meadows that fill their bays and shoals. The famous distant lakes and streams that attract so many people far from home every summer are not more beautiful or restful than many homeland waters once were, or might again be, were but a little public care exercised to keep their waters clean and the beauty of their shores and bordering vegetation unspoiled. (J. G. Needham and J. T. Lloyd, 1930.)

III

Trout Stream Animals

PREDATORS

Around fish hatcheries or rearing ponds kingfishers, herons, water ouzels, and other birds cause very considerable losses, and control measures are often needed. But stomach examinations of fish-eating birds by workers of the Division of Wildlife Research of the U. S. Bureau of Biological Survey have shown that along the average open trout stream or lake, most of their food consists of non-game fishes that are easier to catch than are bass or trout. Cottam and Uhler (1936) say:

> The name "fish-eating" birds as commonly understood, implies a menace to legitimate sport or an encroachment upon the food supply of mankind. This conception, while occasionally true, particularly at fish hatcheries and to a lesser extent on small streams where plantings are made or where these birds may be unduly abundant, is often ridiculously extreme. The belief that these birds are an important factor in limiting the supply of necessary human food is essentially false. The results of most comprehensive investigations of their food show that except under unusual circumstances the bulk of their food consists of fishes not prized by anglers and of little, if any, commercial value. Their diet has often been found to include large numbers of fishes whose destructive tendencies as spawn-eaters are well known to all fish culturists. Availability is usually the principal limiting factor—the more common and easily captured species being those most frequently consumed. Consequently the sluggish surface feeders, such as menhaden, gizzard shad, killifish, or minnows, are most frequently the victims.

There has been much destructive and misguided conservation work done in indiscriminate campaigns to destroy so-called fish predators. Why anyone would want to kill the dainty dipping water ouzel, a none too familiar sight along western mountain streams, is hard to understand. This bird, a beautiful songster, usually solitary in habits, has been shown to feed almost exclusively on aquatic insects, eating only rarely trout eggs or small fry and then usually in rearing ponds or hatcheries.

The chattering, impudent kingfisher has been accused of many nefarious sins, but stomach examinations of hundreds of these birds have shown the greatest part of their diet to be coarse, non-game varieties of fishes. What angler who enjoys the beauty of the streamside and all that goes with it would like to see these birds completely destroyed? Man may lay the blame for the lack of game fish today, as he usually does, on fish-eating birds, or anything but himself, but he and his activities are mainly responsible.

Leonard and Shetter (1936), in studies of the depredations of mergansers in Michigan, report that of 100 stomachs examined, fifty-six contained trout and thirty-three had eaten trout exclusively. In mergansers killed only on trout waters, over sixty per cent contained trout. They point out that occasional concentrations of these birds on trout waters for brief periods in winter may be a potent factor in reducing trout populations.

Control of fish-eating birds at fish hatcheries or rearing ponds is essential. Concentrations of young trout in ponds or troughs offer opportunities for easy feeding that many birds are quick to seize if they are not prevented. Great blue herons have caused serious losses in rearing ponds in eastern California. In one pond that herons seemed to prefer more than others, a survival rate of only six per cent was obtained from the 10,995 rainbow trout planted in the pond some nine months previously. The herons were not entirely responsible as there was considerable cannibalism by large fish eating the smaller, weaker ones.

Concentrations of recently, improperly planted fry or fingerlings offer ideal opportunities for fish-eating birds to destroy large numbers. Young trout that have been "schooled up" in ponds or troughs, if dumped into streams without careful distribution into places affording good protection, will tend to remain in schools for some time after planting. Under such conditions is it any wonder that fish-eating birds may take advantage of the opportunity afforded to get an easy meal or two? Proper distribution in planting is the remedy for this.

Various measures have been used to control fish-eating birds at hatcheries or rearing ponds. Hewitt (1935) recommends rearing trout in wire-covered tanks completely screened from vermin. Cottam and Uhler (1936) recommend various devices for frightening birds away, such as pieces of shiny tin hung over the edge of ponds so that they are swung about by breezes, casting reflections in all directions. Scarecrows, pieces of cloth or tin suspended on cord or wire over the water, various noise-making devices, oscillating electric lights for night protection, gongs, clappers, and other devices have proved useful at times in preventing depredations. But if these are kept in continual use, birds usually become familiar with and unafraid of such devices.

The great value to man of many supposed game-fish destroyers has been shown by their consumption of insects, mice and other harmful animals. What is needed is fair consideration and balancing of interests between anglers, bird-lovers, farmers, or others whose sporting, aesthetic, or economic interests are directly concerned in any control measures adopted. If we are to let the facts determine the severity of the sentence to be imposed, the evidence from stomach examinations of most fish-eating birds commonly accused of excessive destruction to both food and game fishes along open waters (and not around fish-cultural establishments) is in their favor. There is no doubt that around rearing ponds and hatcheries severe control measures will at times have to be taken to prevent serious and continuous losses of fish.

PARASITES

Wild trout are particularly clean with respect to parasites and diseases. It further may be said that so far as known, none of these can be transmitted to man if infected fish are properly cooked before being eaten.

Protection of both wild and hatchery trout from infections of all kinds is an important part of fishery management. In hatcheries trout are often crowded together in troughs and ponds and various maladies afflict them under conditions that are often unsanitary. Diseased wild trout are rarely seen by anglers. The commonest infestations are by tapeworms, roundworms, and flukes. In Pacific coast streams sea-run steelhead trout on their spawning migrations have been seen with typical furunculosis or "boil" disease, though apparently but few fish were affected. Warm-water fish such as bass, perch, pike, and carp harbor more parasites than do cold-water species such as trout. Both at times will show severe external or internal infestations. A case in point is the tapeworm, *Diphyllobothrium cordiceps,* that occurs in the cutthroat trout of Yellowstone Lake. It is unfortunate that while a few fish may be infested, anglers will throw entire catches away on the theory that if one is infested, all are in like condition; thus many pest-free trout are wasted.

NOTE: Advances in aquatic entomology have resulted in rearrangement of many of the genera listed in the original text. Most of the names used by Dr. Needham are preserved here with some supposed equivalents given in footnotes.

Much good work is going on in this field, but an account of it must be left to the pen of some of the capable investigators who are doing it, for we are here concerned with conditions in the open streams.

STREAM INSECTS

The catching of fish at certain times is next to impossible, but it is always possible to catch stream insects. In the heat of midday, or after the streamside lunch, or before the afternoon "rises" have begun, is a good time to spend a few moments getting acquainted with the animals that supply trout with most of their food. Their beautiful coloration, stream-lined forms, agility, and ingeniousness as architects in shelter construction are well worth observation both for pleasure and profit. The profit will be in a new understanding of trout stream fauna as an independent and self-sustaining society.

Over eighty-five per cent of trout stream organisms belong to five main groups of insects: caddisflies, mayflies, stoneflies, two-winged flies, and alderflies (the last including dobsons, fish-flies, and hellgramites). This has been determined by quantitative counts of stream bottom organisms. Because of their importance in trout stream biology, these five groups will be considered first. An angler gathering stream insects for examination will, in all likelihood, pick up members of all these groups.

Some of them may not appear to be abundant forms in streams. Most of them are small and hard to see. Larger forms such as minnows, crayfish, and water bugs, may seem much more common. But these little forms make up in numbers for what they lack in size. Examination of trout stomachs will give proof of this. The stream bed may appear deserted, the surface may be a blank as far as rising fish or insects are concerned; however, just stir up the bottom a bit, preferably in a riffle, holding a fine-meshed net downstream to catch the "rile," and most of what your net contains will be mixture of these very abundant insect larvae. They lie hidden in their shelters, buried in the gravel, under stones or in the bottom trash, and all that is needed to show them up is a little disturbance of the stream bed. The simplest way to observe them, however, is to pick stones out of the water by hand and look at the under side. The sprawlers clinging to the surface may easily be washed off into a shallow pan or dish for more detailed study. A small hand-lens is a useful aid for magnifying the smaller ones.

Of course every observant fisherman knows that the young of most aquatic insects are very different from adults. There are two different methods of growth or development from egg to adult. The immature underwater forms of mayflies, stoneflies, dragonflies and damselflies are best termed *nymphs*. Except for lack of wings, nymphs closely resemble adults. Nymphs merely shed their skins upon leaving the water, directly assuming the adult form. The empty nymphal skins can often be seen by the hundreds on stones, sticks, or grasses above the water's edge where they were shed. Development with nymphs is direct. The stages passed through are *egg* to *nymph* to *adult*. Growth is gradual to the

---

FIG. 19.—Cases of caddisfly larvae.

A, *Platyphylax*
B, *Arctoecia*
C, Cross-section of case of *Arctoecia*
D, *Helicopsyche*
E, *Brachycentrus*
F, *Goera*
G, *Notidobia*
H, Perforated disc-like plug from narrow, posterior end of *Notidobia* case
I, *Limnephilus*
J, *Psilotreta*
K, *Molanna*
L, *Triaenodes*
M, *Leptocerus*
N, *Stenophylax*
O, *Glossosoma*
P, Pupal cocoon of *Rhyacophila* in stone shelter
Q, *Chilostigma*

Only *I* and *L* are characteristic of ponds and lakes.

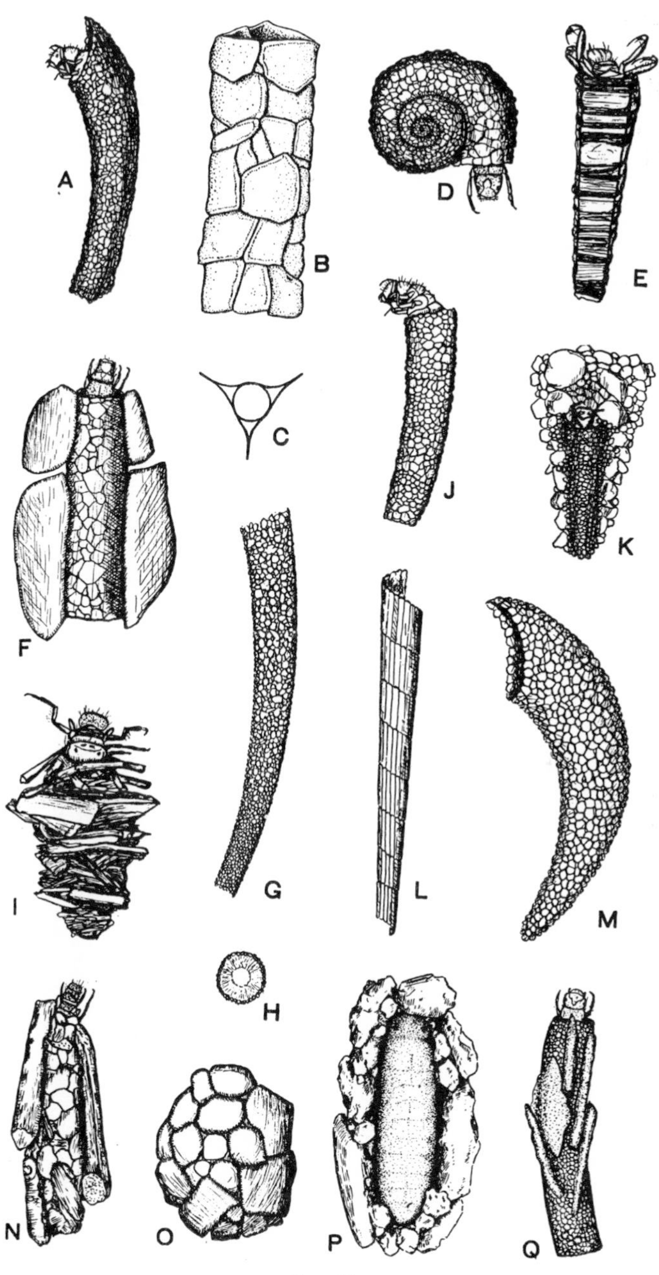

Fig. 19

TABLE VIII

RECOGNITION CHARACTERS OF THE FIVE MAJOR GROUPS OF TROUT STREAM INSECT LARVAE AND NYMPHS.
Most Distinctive Character Italicized in Each Group

COMMON NAME	Caddicefly larvae	Mayfly nymphs	Stonefly nymphs	True-fly larvae	Hellgramites, dobson, alder, or fish-fly larvae
ORDER	Trichoptera	Ephemeroptera	Plecoptera	Diptera	Neuroptera
FORM	Cylindric, elongate. Body arcuate in side view.	Flattened in swift water forms, elongate, variable.	Flattened, elongate.	Quite worm-like, slender "maggots."	Long, slender, flattened.
TAILS	Lacking, having instead 1 pair of fleshy prolegs—each armed with movable hook or claw.	3-long (rarely 2) many jointed.	*2-long* many jointed.	Lacking or short and fleshy.	1 median tail long and tapering, or else with a pair of double hooked prolegs.
GILLS	In tufts, variable or wanting. Always on abdomen* when present.	4 to 7 *pairs on back of abdomen.*	In minute tufts at bases of legs or lacking.	Minute cluster on posterior end as a rule.	Tufts at bases of lateral filaments or lacking.
LEGS	3 pairs, long, and dark in color.	3 pairs, moderate in length.	3 pairs, moderate length.	*Legs lacking.*	3 pairs.
HABITAT	In riffles mostly.	In riffles; few burrow in soft stream or lake bottoms.	In riffles mostly.	All waters.	In riffles and pools, often in gravel beds and silt.
OTHER PECULIARITIES	*Living in cases of sand grains, wood, etc., or in fixed shelters on stones.*	Very delicate, fragile, small forms as a rule.	*Often brilliant black and yellow color pattern on back and head.*	Head small, apparently lacking in many larvae.	*1 pair of long lateral filaments on each segment of abdomen.*

* Hind-body, the body of an insect being in three main divisions; head, thorax, and abdomen.

adult form and takes place by a series of molts of the outer skin from time to time. In the final molt, the wings unfold from the nymphal pads on the back as the adult emerges.

The underwater stages of caddisflies, true-flies (*i.e.,* two-winged flies such as midges, black flies and punkies) and alderflies and dobsons are best termed *larvae* (sing., *larva*). They differ more from their adults, and they develop indirectly, through *four* distinct stages: *egg, larva, pupa,* and *adult.* The pupal stage is the added feature: it is a resting stage, a period for the making-over of the larva into the very different adult, and it is spent in seclusion in some sort of shelter.

The most obvious difference between nymphs and larvae is that in nymphs the wings develop on the outside in small wingpads on the back while in larvae they develop inside, out of sight, and do not become visible until the pupal stage is reached. In the following pages the term nymphs will be restricted to the young of insects such as mayflies and stoneflies having direct development, and the term larvae to the young of caddiceflies, etc., having indirect development, with the added pupal stage.

Key to Five Major Groups of Insect Larvae and Nymphs Found in Trout Streams*

1—Larvae not worm-like, with wings developing externally and plainly visible as small flat pads on the back of the thorax 2
—Larvae worm-like with wings developing inside body and invisible from the outside 3

2—Gills mainly under thorax in white clusters; tails two; feet 2-clawed .... Stonefly nymphs (Plecoptera)
—Gills in two rows on upper sides of abdomen; feet 1-clawed .... Mayfly nymphs (Ephemeroptera)

3—Larvae quite worm-like, entirely lacking legs on the thorax .... Truefly larvae (Diptera)
—Larvae with three pairs of legs on thorax 4

4—Abdominal segments each with a pair of long lateral filaments .... Hellgramites or Dobsonflies, Alderflies, Fishflies (Neuroptera)
—Long lateral filaments lacking on abdomen. Larvae generally living in portable cases made of sand grains, bark, wood or leaves, etc., or in silken bags .... Caddisflies (Trichoptera)

* In using, start with number 1 at left top. Read both characters. See which one applies to the insect in hand and go to number given. Thus if the larva is "worm-like with wings developing inside body and invisible . . . 3," go to 3 on left below and continue in same manner.

For more complete keys and abundant illustrations of aquatic insects and other animals see *A Guide to the Study of Fresh-water Biology,* by J. G. and P. R. Needham (Comstock Publishing Co, Inc.).

For literature references, more complete keys and abundant illustrations of aquatic insects, other animals, and algae, see *A Guide to The Study of Fresh-Water Biology,* by J. G. and P. R. Needham (Holden-Day, Inc.).

In order to identify an insect nymph or larva, the first thing to find out is what group it belongs to: whether it is a mayfly nymph, or caddisfly larva, etc. The accompanying table of recognition characters (Table 8) may be used for this purpose. By taking one character at a time and fitting the description to the insect (largely a process of elimination) it is easy to place the animal in the correct group. A key to these groups is also given (p. 79). This is used in the same manner as the table but is somewhat more convenient, as the marginal numbers lead one directly to the correct group.

Caddisflies (*Trichoptera*)*

Shad-flies, grannoms, sedge-flies, caperers
and cinnamons of anglers

Caddisflies abound in trout streams. Their larvae and pupae live submerged, usually in cases that they carry about over the stream bed or in shelters fixed to the stones. The larger larvae living in stick cases have long been used by anglers for bait by merely fastening the case with the larvae in it on the hook and fishing it close to the bottom. Trout are well acquainted with these; they form a very large part of trout diet, as will be shown later. Trout eat them, cases and all. The cases rapidly disintegrate in the stomachs and apparently pass through the gut without any harmful effects on the fish. The debris thus obtained probably serves as roughage. Many stomachs examined have been literally jammed with pebbles, sticks, leaves, etc., from the cases of the larvae and pupae which had been eaten.

Adult caddisflies are quite moth-like in appearance. In length they are usually from half an inch to two inches long. They are dull in color, generally brown or black. Their mouthparts are undeveloped, as they take no food after the larval stage. Their objectives now are to mate and lay eggs. The four wings in resting insects are laid roof-like over the body, sloping down at the sides (See Fig. 20, *D*). Both body and wings are clothed with fine silken hairs which give to the wings a dull, semi-opaque appearance. The feelers are quite long and slender, often several times as long as the body. The best recognition characters for the adults are the manner in which the wings are held when at rest and their clothing of hairs. (Fig. p. 81)

Largely nocturnal in habit, adult caddisflies are seldom active in daylight hours. Large swarms can often be seen along streams at night or in late summer evenings. They are attracted to lights and may be collected easily under street or camp lights, or other sources of illumination near the waterside.

The females lay their eggs either in the water or upon objects above

* From *trichos*—hair; *pteron*—wing; hairy-winged forms.

the water where the hatching young can easily make their way into it. In a few species the females descend below the surface and glue them to various objects. The eggs are laid in clumps of strings covered by masses of gelatin. The gelatin surrounding the eggs swells to many times its original size after coming in contact with the water (See Fig. 20, *A*).

The eggs hatch into tiny larvae which soon set about the business of home-making. Some will make portable cases of bits of leaves, grass, stems, bark, pieces of wood, etc. Others will make shelters on the stones in front of which they will spin tiny nets to catch food floating down-stream in the current. The materials selected for case- or shelter-building

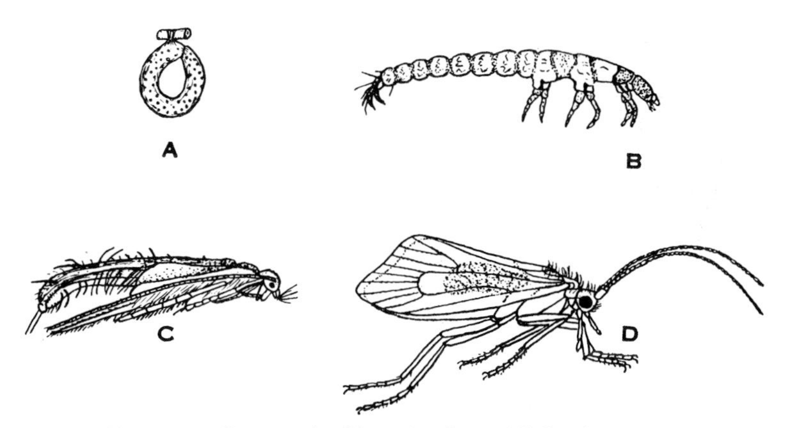

FIG. 20.—Diagram to illustrate the life cycle of a caddisfly. *A*, eggs laid in water attached to sunken twig; *B*, larva; *C*, pupa; and *D*, adult after it has left the water.

are generally the same for all the individuals of each species, and it is possible to recognize many merely by their architectural patterns. The materials used in case-making are cemented together by a fluid secreted in the salivary glands of the larva. This substance hardens on contact with water and holds each particle firmly glued in place on the case. When a case becomes too small for a lusty young larva, he may crawl out and build a new case or he may enlarge the old one. Portable cases are held on their bodies by the drag-hooks on the tip of the abdomen. The case is generally slightly longer than the body, providing ample room to retire completely inside when disturbed.

The gills, when present, are developed on the sides and underneath the abdomen either singly or in clusters. Water is kept circulating over the gills by constant weaving movements of the abdomen which the larva will keep up even after removed from the case.

Caddisfly larvae are largely herbivorous and feed on plant materials; a few are carnivorous, feeding on other stream animals; and some are cannibalistic, eating their own kind. What is eaten by aquatic larvae depends on conditions in streams. Life is strenuous here. Like trout, they are opportunists, and eat what is at hand or go hungry. They secure enough food as larvae since they store up in their bodies sufficient reserve to carry them through the pupal and adult stages, during which they do not feed.

They pupate in their cases after carefully sealing the ends up against intruders. Most caddiceworms do not seal them tightly, but leave tiny holes through which water may pass for aeration of the pupal gills. Then great changes take place. The larval parts are completely changed and those of the very different-appearing adult are molded into their final form. This takes time, and the pupal period may last several weeks or months. When the time is ripe the pupa cuts the end out of the case with its huge mandibles, and then works its way out of the case, swims rapidly to the surface and sheds the pupal skin. Instantly the wings unfold and the adult insect flies to the leafy margins on the stream bank where it will rest and hide until mating time.

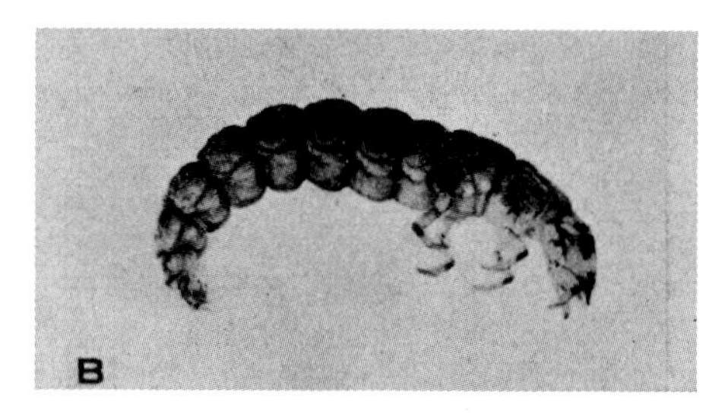

FIG. 21.—Two common net-spinning caddisfly larvae. *A, Hydropsyche,* showing characteristic gills underneath abdomen, and *B,* the "green" larva, *Rhyacophila;* so-called because of its deep green color when alive.

The story just told is one with the happy ending. Many are abruptly ended. Trout seize many pupae that never reach the surface. Emergence times are hard times for aquatic insects. They are utterly unprotected after leaving the bottom and entirely at the mercy of any fish which happens to be near. Furthermore, as they attempt to swim to the surface in swift water, they may be swept downstream into a pool full of rising trout (See Fig. 54). Only the great reproductive capacity of the survivors maintains their abundance in trout waters. (Fig. p. 144)

Few of those that hatch from eggs ever reach adulthood. This is probably true for all aquatic insects that must rise to the surface, shed their skins and take flight.

Caddisflies of trout streams are too numerous in kinds to be described at length here. Only the larvae of the more common forms are discussed

Fig. 22.—Diagram showing position of caddisfly larva, *Hydropsyche,* in bed of stream. Note net constructed in front of pebble shelter for straining food from the water (modified from J. G. Needham's *Elementary Lessons on Insects*).

and their cases figured. The names used are those given them by entomologists. Common names will be used when possible along with the scientific names. Animals acquire common names only after they become fairly well-known to people at large, and such small, inconspicuous forms as these larvae have not yet reached that stage of familiarity.

The Net-spinners

Hydropsyche (Fig. 21, *A*). This is the commonest caddisfly of trout waters; it occurs by thousands in most trout streams in the riffles and in large lakes along the shore-line in the wave-zone. Their nets (Fig. 22) are funnel-shaped and look much like miniature fyke-nets fastened to the rocks and stones in swift water, opening upstream. At the rear end of the net the larva builds a shelter of small pebbles cemented closely together. The larva feeds on minute plants and animals that are swept into the meshes of the net by the water. When disturbed or when resting the larva retreats under the pebbly shelter at the rear of the net. The nets are quite easily found, some being as much as three-fourths of an inch across their outer margins. They are fastened to the tops of stones, flat ledges, or the brinks of falls where the water is swiftest, by means of the salivary cement which has been mentioned above. The full-grown larvae construct cases of fine sand or gravel in which the pupal stage is passed. The larvae range in size up to an inch in length. In Figure 21, *A*, are shown the fringed tufts of gills below the abdomen, a good recognition character for this larva. (Fig. p. 82)

Trout are fond of these larvae and may often be seen sweeping the rocks in sidewise motions, their jaws scraping these larvae into their mouths.

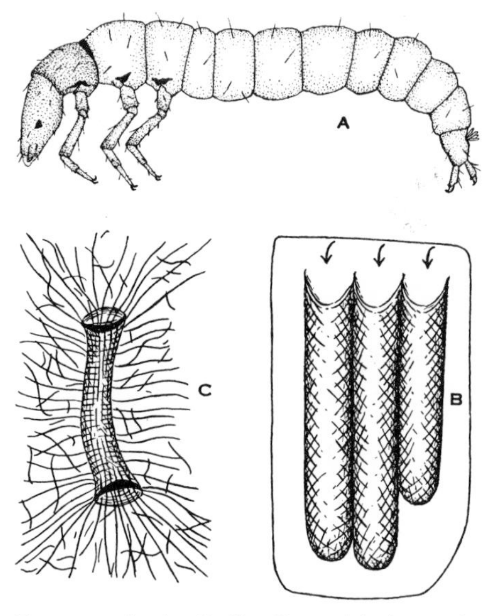

FIG. 23.—*A*, the "yellow," net-spinning caddisfly larva, *Chimarra;* so-called because of its bright yellow color when alive. *B*, slender, fingerlike nets of same. Arrows indicate direction of water flow. *C*, net of *Polycentropus*.

Chimarra. One recognition character for these larvae when alive is their bright yellow or orange body color. This immediately catches the eye when they wiggle out of their webbed retreats on the lower surface of a stone removed from the water. Preserved specimens usually fade quickly and become white. These larvae spin delicate nets of fine silk quite different in appearance from those just described for *Hydropsyche.* They are long, slender and somewhat finger-like in outline, an inch to an inch and a half in length (Fig. 23, *B*). The larvae seem to be quite gregarious; there are often five or six together in a single row. So abundant do they become that oftentimes the under-surfaces of the bottom stones will be covered by their flocculent, silky nets in untidy masses. The larger open end of each net faces the current while the rear end has but a small aperture to permit escape of the larva in case of necessity. The force of the current keeps the nets expanded and entangles in the meshes food particles which the larvae eat. The larvae do not build a shelter of pebbles at the base of the net like *Hydropsyche.* Gills are lacking. These larvae are from one-quarter to three-quarters of an inch long.

Polycentropus. In slow-flowing streams on the under sides of stones larvae of this genus construct long, tubular silken nets which often are found together in great numbers. (Fig. 23, *C*). Along the sides of the net are numerous strands of silk that serve partly to entangle food and partly to obscure the net. The upstream ends of the nets are securely fastened to stones while the posterior floats free in the current. The larvae feed on mayfly nymphs, midge larvae, and other animals that become entangled in the net.

Rhyacophila (Fig. 21, *B*). This caddisworm is very abundant in swift-water streams with stony bottoms and may always be recognized by the bright green color of the body. In preserved specimens the color fades, changing to brown. These larvae do not spin nets, but range rather freely over the bottom in search of food. Just before pupation they construct a shelter of stones about their bodies. Within this shelter they spin a brown parchment-like cocoon in which the pupal stage is passed. This cocoon is transparent and the quiescent pupa can be seen on the inside (Fig. 19, *P*). These larvae and pupae are quite characteristic of trout waters and may easily be found by lifting a few stones from swift water. They feed on small larvae of various kinds, and occasionally they take filamentous algae. The adults are most abundant in May and June.

The Case-makers

Glossosoma (Fig. 19, *O*). The cases of these larvae are made of small pebbles and sand grains securely cemented together. The larvae can move them freely over stones, but before pupation each larva fastens the case immovably in place on the surface of a stone. They are typical residents of trout waters and their cases may be seen plastered by the hundreds over the surfaces of stones in riffles. Trout often eat them, case and all, as is evidenced by stomach examinations. Larvae, pupae, and adults may be found over the entire summer. (Fig. p. 77)

Molanna (Fig. 19, *K*). These larvae are often found in great abundance in slow or quiet waters, where their flat cases of sand grains blend perfectly with sandy bottoms, making it almost impossible to see them. The hood of the case is over the head of the larva and conceals it from view from above. These occur in great abundance in such streams as the Nissequogue River on Long Island, a sandy-bottomed, slow-moving stream. They are entirely absent in turbulent or swift water.

Triaenodes (Fig. 19, *L*). This is another inhabitant of quiet or slowly moving waters, and is common among aquatic plants in dilations of creeks or in ponds. The case is from three-quarters to one inch in length, made of tiny bits of leaves fitted together side to side and end to end spirally with wonderful accuracy. Instead of crawling about over the bottom, the larvae swim with ease, using their long fringed legs as paddles and carrying case and all from place to place. In June the flat, spirally coiled egg masses may be seen in great numbers on the under sides of floating sticks or leaves. There are about two hundred eggs in each mass. This larva, being an inhabitant of weed beds, is not abundant in most trout waters.

FIG. 24.—Final molt of a mayfly. The empty skin of the subimago appears below (from Dr. A. H. Morgan's *Field Book of Ponds and Streams*).

Leptocerus (Fig. 19, *M*). These cornucopia-like cases made of sand grains are often found in great numbers on the sides and surfaces of submerged stones in riffles. The larvae move the cases freely from place to place.

Psilotreta (Fig. 19, *J*). These larvae are usually quite abundant in riffles in trout waters. The cases are made of tiny pebbles or large grains of sand neatly cemented together to form a slightly curved tube. In early life the larvae move freely over the bottom. However, just before pupation in early spring they come together in large numbers on the sides of stones, where their cases may be found fastened one on top of another, with the head ends projecting toward the surface of the water. Such congregations offer a good recognition character for these larvae, for but few other caddiceworms exhibit such strongly gregarious instincts. Before pupation each larva cements a flat pebble over the ends of the case to keep out enemies. Then it spins a watertight cocoon in which the pupal stage is passed. (Fig. p. 77)

Brachycentrus (Fig. 19, *E*). This larva is characteristic of head-water trout streams and of some colder, wider streams. The case is made of minute twigs or wood fragments cut to the correct length and placed crosswise. It tapers to the rear and is square in cross-section. While the larva is young it feeds at the sides of streams; as it becomes older it moves to mid-channel where it feeds in swift water on mayfly nymphs, midge larvae, etc. The case is from one-half to three-quarters of an inch long. The adults emerge in late May or early June. (Fig. p. 77)

*Notidobia** (Fig. 19, *G*). Larvae of this caddisfly are particularly abundant in the small coastal streams of central California. They are seldom found in swiftly running water, but congregate in large numbers in quiet back-waters or side pools out of the main current. During the rainy season when such areas are swept by floods, large numbers are washed downstream to lagoons next to the ocean where they are dropped by slack water. These larvae can easily be recognized by the shape and character of their cases, which are always cornucopia-shaped and are made of very fine grains of sand held in a matrix of silk. They are often over an inch in length, widest at the head end, narrowing gradually to the rear. The narrow, posterior end of the case is partially closed by a disk-like silk plug with a narrow, round central opening that permits passage of water through the case (Fig. 19, *H*). These larvae are scavengers at times. Large numbers can often be seen eating the decaying bodies of dead salmon or trout. Like some other caddicefly larvae, they congregate together during pupation periods, when large numbers of the cases can be seen crowded together in protected crevices on rocks, logs, or sticks. The larvae when removed from the case are green or yellow in appearance. The head bears a black, inverted V-shaped mark.

Goera (Fig. 19, *F*). This common trout stream larva ingeniously fastens large pebbles on the sides of its sand-grain case for ballast to avoid being swept away by the current. This larva is often found associated with *Psilotreta* and *Glossosoma* in the riffles. At pupation the larva fastens a pebble over each end of the case. Adults emerge in late April and early May. The larvae are common on current-swept rocks from July until April. (Fig. p. 77)

Helicopsyche (Fig. 19, *D*). The dwellings of these larvae closely resemble spiral snail shells and were originally described as snails. These are found in swift water where the larvae roam at will until time of pupation, when the cases are cemented tightly to stones with the openings closed by a lid of silk. Trout scrape the larvae from the stones, eating case and all. (Fig. p. 77)

Chilostigma† (Fig. 19, *Q*). The case is made of sand grains, usually with a few plant fragments mixed in. It is cylindrical and slightly curved in shape. These larvae are usually found in cold water brooks, where the cases will often be seen congregated in large numbers fastened to sticks or stones, much like *Psilotreta* described above. (Fig. p. 77)

* = *Sericostoma?*

† = *Frenesie* or *Psychoglypha?*

*Platyphylax** (Fig. 19, *A*). This is a spring water inhabitant; it is usually found in water that never freezes in the winter. The case is round, tapering to the rear. There is a hood over the head end of the case that hides all but the legs of the larva from view. Sand grains (or bits of bark when over muck bottom) are the building materials. The adults are most abundant in the spring or early summer. (Fig. p. 77)

FIG. 25.—Adult mayfly freshly emerged from the nymphal skin and resting on the surface of the water (from Dr. A. H. Morgan's *Field Book of Ponds and Streams*).

Arctoecia,† "the leaf-case caddisworm" (Fig. 19,, *B*). This larva is not uncommon in the quieter back water of most eastern trout waters. The case is triangular in cross-section, from an inch to an inch and one-half in length, made of bits of dead leaves fastened together with silk. Adults are common in late June. (Fig. p. 77)

Limnephilus (Fig. 19, *I*). Cases of these larvae may be constructed of various materials. Sometimes tiny discarded snail shells will be used; at times seeds, bark, leaves, or sand may be used. These are common in slow and quiet waters. One common *Limnephilus* in ponds uses grass stems to form a sort of cross stick case very irregular in outline. Trout eat case and all. (Fig. p. 77)

* = *Hesperophylax*

† Now in *Limnephilus*

*Stenophylax** (Fig. 19, *N*). Larvae carrying these large stick cases can often be seen lumbering over the bottoms of streams searching for food in either summer or winter. They are very common in most headwater trout streams and in some large rivers. The length of the case is from an inch to two inches. The adults emerge in early summer, and are large brown insects. They are eagerly taken by trout. (Fig. p. 77)

MAYFLIES (*Ephemeroptera*)*

(Duns, drakes, lake-flies and mayflies of anglers)

The members of this group of insects are well-known to anglers, for many wet and dryflies are patterned after both nymphs and adults. For beauty of form and delicacy of construction of body parts, these fragile insects are unsurpassed. They are abundant alike in lakes, streams, ponds, or quiet spring pools, and almost every type of fresh water situation has some representatives present.

At certain seasons, usually in late spring or early summer, large numbers of the adults will leave the water at the same time in immense swarms. Street lights by the water's edge will attract them and huge piles of the dead ones may often be seen beneath them. In some cities the dead flies when crushed by passing autos will make the pavement dangerously slippery, causing accidents and delaying traffic.

Mayfly nymphs are the most abundant and typical of trout stream insects. They are commonest in the riffles, though a few of the burrowing nymphs can often be found in pools. In form of body, there are roughly two groups. Some are flattened and depressed with flaring body margins for deflecting the current. These live on the stones in the swiftest waters. The others are fish-like in form, cylindric in body outline, and cling to plant stems or swim about actively by swift synchronous movements of tails and gills.

The best recognition character for the nymphs of all mayflies is the presence of four to seven pairs of gills on the back of the abdomen. No other aquatic insect has gills in this position. They always have two or three slender tails and but one claw on each foot.

In contrast with the caddisworms, the nymphs of mayflies never build cases or shelters over their bodies; are often much smaller and more fragile and hence more inconspicuous. In size the nymphs range up to an inch and a half in length.

These nymphs are entirely herbivorous, feeding on microscopic plants in the water. Thus they are one of the principal agencies in streams for turning plant materials into the animal food upon which trout are dependent. In no way are they competitors with trout.

Mayfly nymphs live from several weeks to a year or more in the

* From *ephemeros,* lasting but a day.

* = *Pycnopsyche?*

water before emerging from the water as adults. Some species will produce several generations in a summer.

Out of the nymph stage emerge the fully winged, so-called "subimagos." These molt their outer skins after a short time while resting on marginal trees or banks, and become fully adult (Fig. 24). Many mayflies will "leave the water, molt twice, mate, lay their eggs, and die in the course of an evening or early morning." (Comstock, 1925.) On warm evenings in May and June large numbers may leave the water at the same time, giving rise to the "hatches" of anglers. Subsequently these may be seen in the twilight in their mating flights, dancing in large swarms, up and down over the water in rhythmic movements. During the flights females will deposit their eggs in the water. Many are eaten by fish, which gorge themselves on them. At such times trout are fickle in accepting artificials, even though an exact replica of the hatching insect may be offered them. (Fig. p. 86)

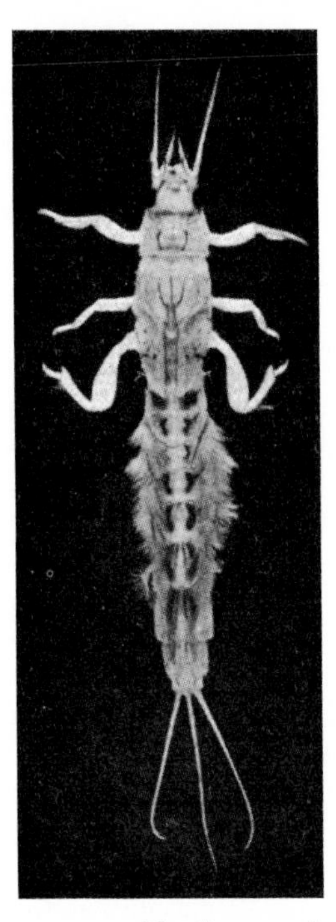

FIG. 26.—Mayfly nymph, *Ephemera;* burrows in silted stream beds. Note tufts of gills at sides of abdomen (three times natural size).

Adult mayflies are pale grey, brown, yellow, or reddish in color, possessing either two or three tail filaments much longer than those of the nymphs. The wings are always held upright over the body when at rest, never folded over the abdomen (Fig. 25, p. 88).

The forelegs are usually held straight out in front of the body; along with tails at the rear, they serve as outriggers for balancing in flight. A resting mayfly uses only the two hind pairs of legs for support. The many-veined wings are fan-shaped, the front pair being much larger than the hind pair. In a few small species, such as the little white *Caenis,* the hind wings may be entirely absent. The mouth parts are under-developed, no food being taken in the adult stage.

The eggs are always laid in water, being either washed off the tip of the abdomen or spread by females that descend below the water and lay them in irregular, greyish patches on the under sides of stones.

The following nymphs are quite general in their distribution in the trout waters of the United States and Canada.

Hexagenia and Ephemera (Fig. 26). These nymphs are burrowers. They are the largest mayflies present in trout streams. In quiet or semi-quiet stretches of water, they will be found buried in soft bottoms of fine silt or sand. They may also be found in great numbers in muddy lake bottoms or in the silt of upland bog streams. Their huge, brown jaws protruding in front of their heads, and long, bushy, grey-brown filamentous gills in two rows down the back, offer distinct characters by which to recognize them. Their enormous tusk-like jaws are used, along with their spade-like legs, to help them burrow through the bottom silt. They are repelled by light and in the daytime lie safely hidden in the bottom silt or mud. (Fig. p. 90)

In size *Hexagenia* is larger than *Ephemera* and may be recognized by a rounded, shelf-like prominence on the front of the head. In *Ephemera* this is divided by a deep notch into two parallel spines.

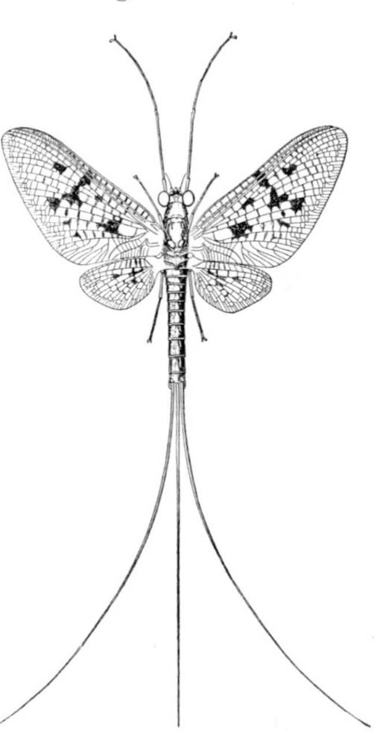

FIG. 27.—Adult mayfly, *Ephemera,* whose nymph is a burrower in silted stream beds (about two times natural size; after drawing by C. H. Kennedy).

The large, adult flies (Fig. 27) emerge in enormous numbers from late spring until about the middle of August. Swarms come out of the water at twilight to a resting place on shore. The next day they enter upon their nuptial flights, lay eggs, and die in a very short time. At such times they furnish food to fishes in superabundance. These mayflies are most common in the larger waters of eastern United States.

Baetis. This is one of the commonest of trout stream mayfly nymphs and is eaten in large quantities by trout. The body is fish-like in form, small in size (one-quarter to three-quarters of an inch in length), with two rows of simple, oval plate-like gills down each side of the abdomen. This nymph is very similar to *Ameletus* shown in Figure 28, *C*, p. 92.

These nymphs face the current when at rest and can often be seen darting swiftly about from stone to stone on the bottom. Their color is often a decided green, though grey-green or grey forms are common. Out of the water they flop about with fish-like movements in a manner unlike most other nymphs. Three tails are present, the outer two being longer than the middle one. In Figure 52, p. 139, are shown some that were found in the stomach of a brown trout.

Stenonema (Fig. 29). In the riffles this "redtail" nymph is common. Its flattened head and body are well adapted for deflection of the current and for maintaining its position on stones in the most turbulent waters. The tails are long and often quite red in color. The gill plates are flat, and those of the last pair are modified into tapering filaments. The adult may be found emerging throughout the summer months.

Rhithrogena (Fig. 30, *A*). In the streams of Utah, California, and other western states this beautiful "redgill" nymph is common. The gill plates are bright red in color, and form an overlapping even margin around the sides of the body. The tips of the first pair extend inward toward each other below the thorax. The whole form of the body and

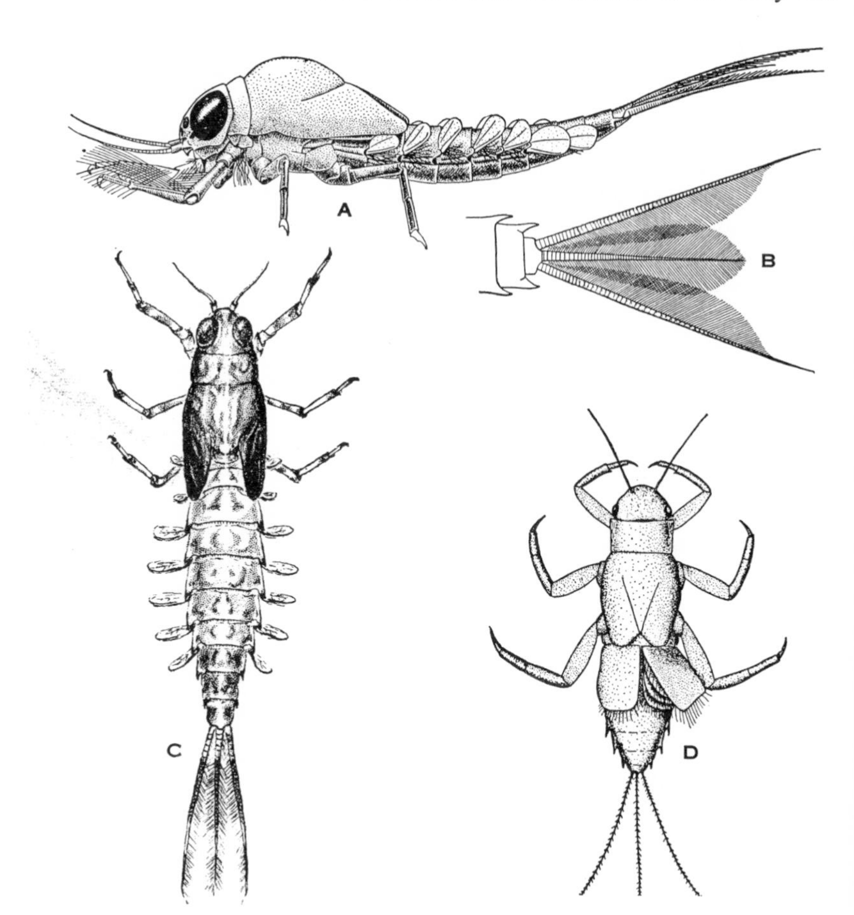

FIG. 28.—Three common mayfly nymphs found in trout waters. *A*, the "howdy," *Isonychia*. Note food-gathering fringes of hair on forelegs; *B*, tails of same from above; *C*, *Ameletus* (similar to *Baetis*), and *D*, the "square-gill," *Caenis* (*C* and *D* after drawings by Dr. A. H. Morgan).

gills is so flattened as to offer an almost perfect disc for deflection of the current, much as in the "redtail" described above but far more perfect. Swarms of male adults are often seen dancing over the water at nightfall in late June or early July. (Fig. p. 94)

Iron, the "two-tailed" nymph (Fig. 31). These are exceedingly beautiful, flattened forms that live in the swiftest water, in association with the "redgill" and the "redtail." When lifted from the water on stones, they move about uneasily, in short, jerky movements as they shift about in the thin film of water adhering to the stone. Their color is usually greenish mottled with darker areas. (Fig. p. 95)

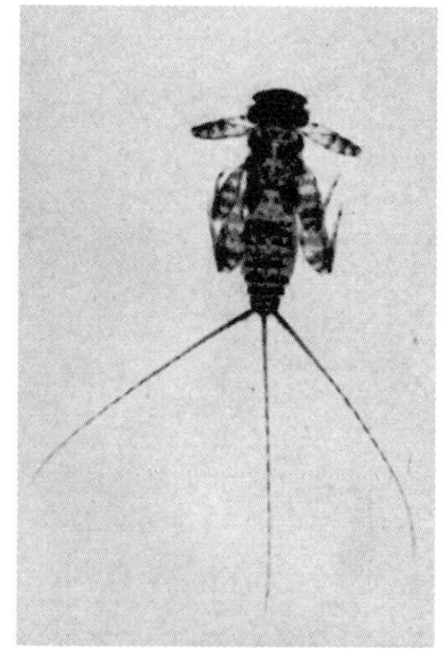

Fig. 29.—The "redtail" mayfly nymph, *Stenonema,* from stones in rapid water (three times natural size).

The flattened nymphs of *Stenonema, Rhithrogena,* and *Iron* illustrate perfect adaptation to swift water. Their depressed, disc-like bodies easily turn it aside. They are able to move freely about, browsing over the stones. They are pretty little nymphs and their fitness for rugged life in riffles is attested by their abundance.

Ephemerella (Fig. 30, *C*). These stout-bodied, humped-up "prickle-back" nymphs are common in trout waters from coast to coast. The long, slender tails are usually marked in alternating light and dark areas. Usually these nymphs have a double row of tubercles or spines on the back of the abdomen, from which feature the common name is derived. They are often found in large numbers in trout stomachs, as are also the adults. The nymphs occur among stones in swift water, on roots of plants trailing in the water, among decaying leaves and in fact may be found almost any place in flowing water. (Fig. p. 94)

Paraleptophlebia, the "forkgilled" nymph. The gills of this nymph are split fork-like into two branches. (Fig. 32.) The nymphs are short, usually less than half an inch, and their bodies are quite slender, rounded, and brown or brownish-green in color. They prefer the quieter side-waters and shallows, where they live among the stones and gravel in more or less sheltered areas. A *Paraleptophlebia* found in streams of the Rockies in western United States has been termed the "tusker" as it has large, yellowish, pincher-like jaw tusks that project prominently out in front of the head. (Fig. p. 96)

Isonychia, the "howdy" nymph (Fig. 28, *A*). This large, agile, and beautifully stream-lined nymph can be recognized by the fringes of hairs on the inside of the forelegs. These serve as strainers for food particles brought by the current upon which it feeds. They thus function similarly to the nets of the *Hydropsyche.* With the forelegs held out in front facing the current, an attitude of greeting is assumed, whence the term "howdy." In the Ausable River and other streams of northeastern United States these nymphs are one of the major foods of trout, often as many

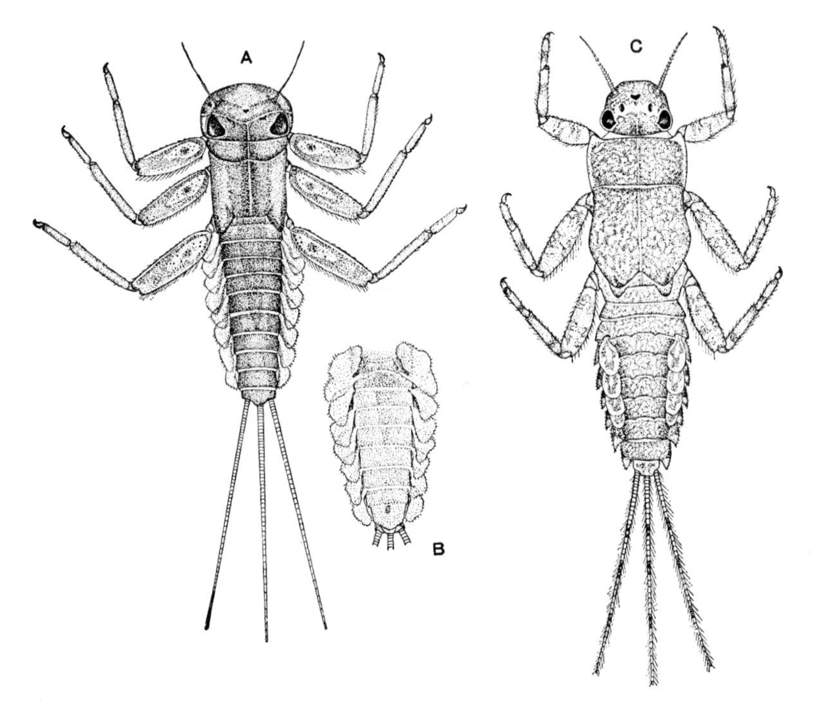

Fig. 30.—Two common trout stream mayfly nymphs of the United States. *A,* the "redgill," *Rhithrogena,* and *B,* underside of abdomen of same showing sucking disc formed by the gills. *C,* the "prickleback" *Ephemerella.*

as two hundred being found in a single stomach. The nymphs are expert swimmers and may be seen darting about among the stones in swift water. (Fig. p. 92)

Caenis, the "square-gill" nymph (Fig. 28, *D*). In silted pool bottoms or in the soft mud of quiet water, these very small slow-moving nymphs may be collected. Instead of having the gills on each segment of the abdomen wide apart, they are crowded close together under a quadrangular flap which fits down over them for protection from silt. In *Caenis* this flap is square, while in a closely allied form, *Tricorythodes,* it is triangular in shape. *Caenis* is common in slow water, *Tricorythodes,* in shallow streams. Adults of the latter may often be seen by the millions along streams in daytime, tiny white flies looking much like snowflakes, the females dipping into the water surface releasing eggs.

STONEFLIES (*Plecoptera*)*

(Stoneflies, yellow sallys, willow flies, creepers, rock rollers, of anglers.)

Some of the most beautiful and striking nymphs found in trout waters belong to this group of aquatic insects. Among the larger nymphs, *Perla*† and *Acroneuria* are brilliantly decorated with contrasting black and yellow areas on the top of the head and body. *Pteronarcys,* the "big curler," on the other hand, is a dull brown lacking distinctive body color pattern. Smaller nymphs, such as *Perlodes,*** are generally less than three-quarters of an inch in length and usually pale yellow or brown in color.

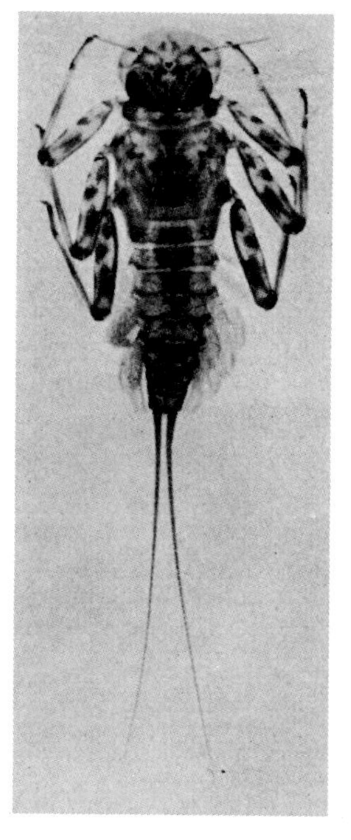

FIG. 31.—The "two-tailed" mayfly nymph, *Iron.* Note flattened form of body for living in swift water (six times natural size).

Stonefly nymphs may be recognized by their two tails, which are long and stiff, by the tufts of filamentous gills usually present at the bases of the legs below the thorax, and by the feet, which have two claws. In some of the smaller nymphs gills are lacking. In contrast with mayfly nymphs these are stout, hardy forms, not so fragile and slender. Stonefly nymphs love swift waters where they dwell among the stones. Some forage about in search of small mayfly nymphs, midge larvae, etc.; others eat small plants or decaying vegetation.

Adult stoneflies are lumbering, awkward four-winged fellows that are quite unattractive in appearance, usually being dull grey, yellow-green or brown in color. In size they range from half an inch to over two inches in length. The tails are generally shorter than in the nymph. The wings are many-veined and when at rest the forewings are folded over the hind ones. Both pairs lie lengthwise upon the abdomen. They are weak fliers. They fly but short distances, resting frequently on streamside vegetation.

The eggs are deposited in the water by the females, usually in masses. These hatch into the nymphs, which pass from less than a year to over two years below water, according to species. When fully developed the

* From *plecos,* folded, and *pteron,* wing.

† *Perla* is no longer recognized as a North American genus. Our species formerly placed in the genus are now in such genera as *Phasgonophora* and *Isogenus.*

** North American species formerly in *Perlodes* are now placed in *Arcynopteryx.*

nymphs crawl up out of the water on stones or logs where they shed their nymphal skins. Cast skins can often be found by the hundreds on stones and sticks along streams. (See Fig. 33, p. 97)

Stonefly nymphs form a major part of trout diet in some streams, notably those of mountainous regions. In the low-land streams of level country they are often scarce.

Pteronarcys, the "big curler" nymph (Fig. 34, *A*). This is the largest stonefly nymph found in streams. It is often over two inches in length. Being a vegetable feeder, it is most often found in leaf drifts on the upstream sides of logs and stones where debris becomes lodged by the current. When removed from the water it immediately curls up much like a millipede. It can be recognized by this behavior. (Fig. p. 98)

FIG. 32.—A single gill filament of the "forkgilled" nymph, *Paraleptophlebia* (magnified about eighteen times).

Tufts of filamentous gills occur below the legs and below the first two segments of the abdomen. This is a common form in clear, unpolluted hill streams throughout the United States.

Perla (Fig. 34, *B*) and *Acroneuria.* These black and yellow nymphs, the most striking in color of all stream insects, are usually common in most trout waters. In size they range up to more than an inch in length. They are carnivorous, and therefore compete with trout fry for food. *Perla* may be distinguished from *Acroneuria* by the presence of a distinct ridge extending from eye to eye along the posterior, top margin of the head. In *Acroneuria* this ridge is generally missing. (Fig. p. 98)

Peltoperla (Fig. 35, *B*). This cockroach-like form is common among leaves and debris in the smaller cold headwater streams and tributary brooks. It is easily recognized by the enlarged thorax, which is a dull red-brown in color, and by its short tails. (Fig. p. 99)

Taeniopteryx, the "snow-bank" nymph (Fig. 35, *A*). In early spring, when the snow is still on the ground, the small, black adults of this stonefly will be found crawling on the drifts along streams. The nymph may be recognized by the wing pads on back of the thorax; these are extremely divergent, spreading far out over the side margins of the body. (Fig. p. 99)

TRUE-FLIES (*Diptera*)*

True-flies or two-winged flies may always be recognized by the presence of only one pair of wings. Mayflies, caddiceflies, stoneflies, etc., as noted above, have two pairs. This group includes most of the well-known biting streamside pests such as the punkies, midges, blackflies, mosquitoes, deer-flies, and horseflies. Larvae of some of these forms live in water and furnish considerable amounts of food to trout, compensating somewhat for their bad behavior as adults.

* From *dis,* two, and *pteron,* wing.

Aquatic fly larvae are among the commonest of stream organisms. They occur in all types of situations and are very diverse in form and size. The larvae are legless, worm-like creatures, white, yellow, red, or green in color, and range in size from midge larvae, which are usually less than half an inch in length, to the large cranefly larvae which are often over two inches.

The life cycle of aquatic true-flies is similar to that of the caddiceflies in that the first three stages (egg, larva, and pupa) are generally passed under water, but the larvae of some will migrate to moist places out of water along the banks of streams to pupate.

Fig. 33.—Stonefly nymph in stream bed and a cast nymphal skin on large stone above water from which the adult has issued (modified from J. G. Needham's *Elementary Lessons on Insects*).

The food habits vary with the larva concerned. Midge larvae are mainly herbivorous. Some cranefly larvae are predacious, feeding on mayfly nymphs, midge larvae, etc.; and some are scavengers. Horsefly larvae are carnivorous. Blackfly larvae strain minute algae and diatoms from the water by means of fan-shaped organs on the head, and net-winged midge larvae scrape similar food from flat rocks in swift water where they live.

In the following pages, only trout stream larvae that are both abundant and easy to collect are figured and discussed. These are the ones that anglers are most likely to pick up.

Chironomus, the midge larva (Fig. 36). If it were not for the superabundance of these minute, seldom observed larvae, it is safe to say that fewer fresh-water fishes would ever attain maturity. They are extremely important in the diet of young fishes. This is equally true in pond or stream, for midge larvae occur abundantly in both. (Fig. p. 100)

Of pond midge larvae, the common "blood-worm" is the most conspicuous form. Its color is a deep red; hence, its common name. This is one of the few insect larvae possessing red blood. It is the largest of midge larvae, often over an inch in length. Examination with a hand lens will reveal a small, dark brown head, and a long, slender red body. Near the rear end of the body two pairs of finger-like blood gills can be seen on each side. Just back of the head and on the tip-end can be seen two downward projecting, stump-like legs that are used in crawling from place to place. The looping movements are much like those of a measuring worm.

While this larva is more commonly found in ponds, it will also often be found in silt bottoms in slow-flowing water. These larvae all construct tiny flocculent tubes made of bits of silt cemented together. In these they live among the bottom trash.

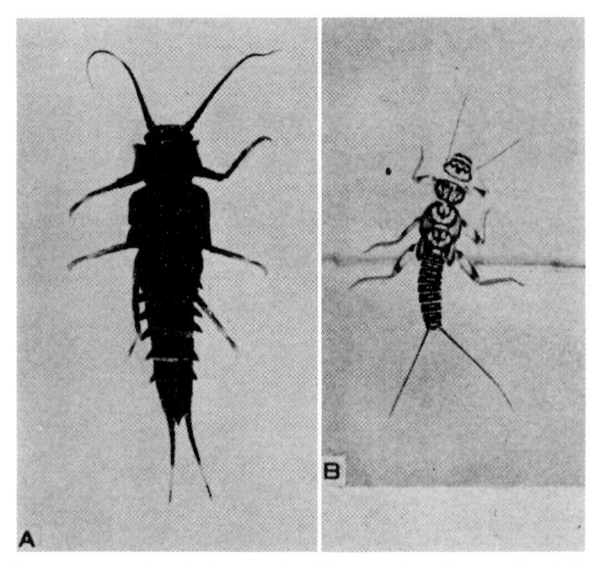

FIG. 34.—Two common trout stream stonefly nymphs. *A*, nymph of the "curler," *Pteronarcys*; *B*, the "black and yellow," *Perla*. Adults of the "curler" are commonly called "salmon-flies" by western fishermen (natural size; photograph of *Perla* made from a living nymph by Dr. Myron Gordon).

Stream midges make their tubes on the under sides of stones and in bottom crevices. Here they feed on algae and on decaying organic matter brought into the tubes by undulating movements of the abdomen. They pick out food particles carried to them by the current.

Pupation occurs below water and the adult midge (Fig. 36) emerges in a few days to several weeks. The eggs are laid in the water by the females in tiny gelatinous clumps, a single one of which may contain as many as 2500 eggs. (Fig. p. 100)

A vicious near-relative of the common midge is the "punkie," also known as "midget," "gnat," or "no-see-um" (*Palpomyia*). (Fig. 37, *B*.) This pest of sportsmen and vacationists in the northeastern mountain regions of the United States, when abundant, will drive people from the woods to shelter by its attacks. Each bite is like the jab of a pin, and exceedingly painful. (Fig. p. 101)

The punkie larva lives amid trash in the slack waters of mountain streams where it is associated with other fly larvae, mayfly nymphs, and caddice larvae. It is exceedingly small, needle-shaped, and less than one quarter of an inch in length, and it has no appendages at all.

Simulium, the blackfly larva (Fig. 37, *C*). Another serious pest of anglers is the blackfly, the larvae and pupae of which are common on the

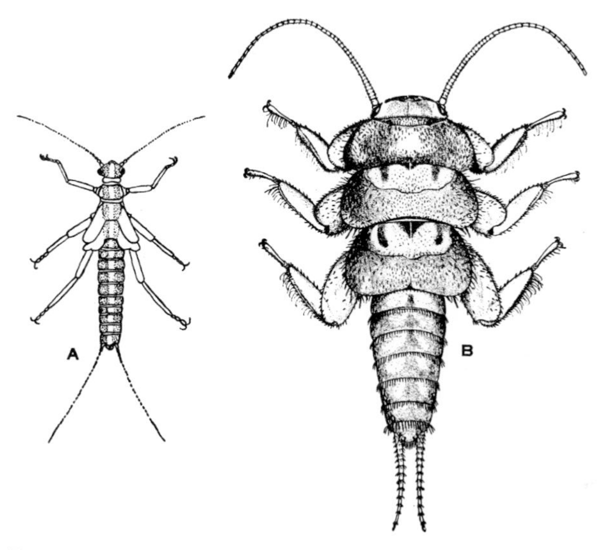

FIG. 35.—Two stonefly nymphs inhabiting trout waters. *A*, the "snow-bank" nymph, *Taeniopteryx* (from Claassen, 1931); and *B*, the "roach" nymph, *Peltoperla* (greatly enlarged).

upper surfaces of stones, logs, sticks, or grass stems in the swiftest water. These are about one-quarter to one-half inch in length, a dull grey-brown or drab color, and can instantly be recognized by the pair of feeding fans on the head which project out like miniature combs. At the swollen posterior end is a sucking disc by means of which this larva securely fastens itself to stones. It hangs swaying in the water, head-end downstream, feeding fans extended to strain out food brought to it by the current. Here also when grown it spins a dirty-greyish brown cocoon in which it pupates, the blood-thirsty adult emerging a short time thereafter. (Fig. p. 101)

Blepharocera, the "net-winged" midge larva (Fig. 37, *A*). This is another common larva associated with *Simulium* on the surfaces of stones in the swiftest waters. It is usually about one-quarter of an inch in length, dark above and light below, and on the underside is found a row of round, powerful, sucking discs by means of which it creeps safely about in swift water. Between the suckers the body is deeply notched. By this form of body it is at once distinguished from all other aquatic larvae. The larva forms a small, jet-black pupa on the surfaces of stones. These can often be seen as dense black patches dotting the rocks in shallow but very swift water. (Fig. p. 101)

Cranefly Larvae and Related Forms

These larvae occur in a great variety of forms and in many different types of situations. The adults are large, long-legged flies that dance over

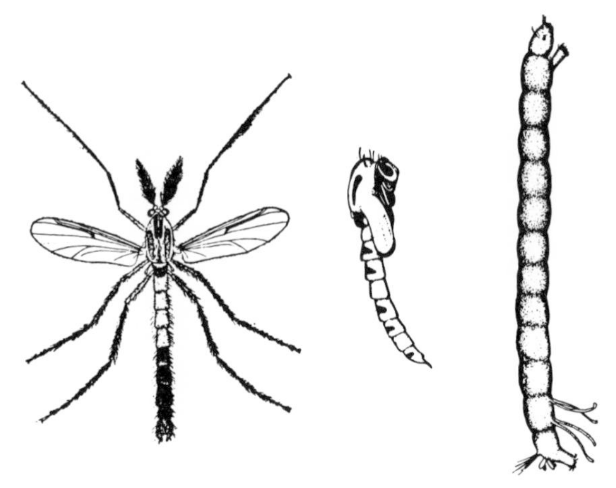

Fig. 36.—Midge, *Chironomus.* Left to right, adult, pupa, and larva. Larval midges bright red in color are called "blood-worms." Common in most clean waters. Midge larvae and pupae are the most important single item in food of trout under three inches in length (six times natural size).

streams at twilight. These spider-like flies have been termed "spinners" by anglers, and many artificial flies are patterned after them.

The larvae are legless "maggots," often of large size, sometimes reaching over two inches in length. The following five cranefly larvae are the commonest in trout waters and appear frequently in trout stomachs.

Tipula (Fig. 38). This is the largest of aquatic cranefly larvae and may be found up to three inches long. It lives in leaf drifts and root mats at the sides of streams out of the main current or in submerged back waters where it feeds on rotting leaves, plant stems, diatoms, etc. Its color is a pale, greyish brown or drab, darker at the anterior end. The skin is thin and internal organs are visible through it. At the posterior end are six lobes which border a respiratory disc inside which are two openings through which air is taken in when the disc is raised slightly out of the water. Pupation occurs in moist mud out of water and adults emerge from June to September. (Fig. p. 102)

Antocha (Fig. 37, *E, F*). This inch-long larva lives in a silken tube in crevices on the downstream side of stones in the fastest waters of trout

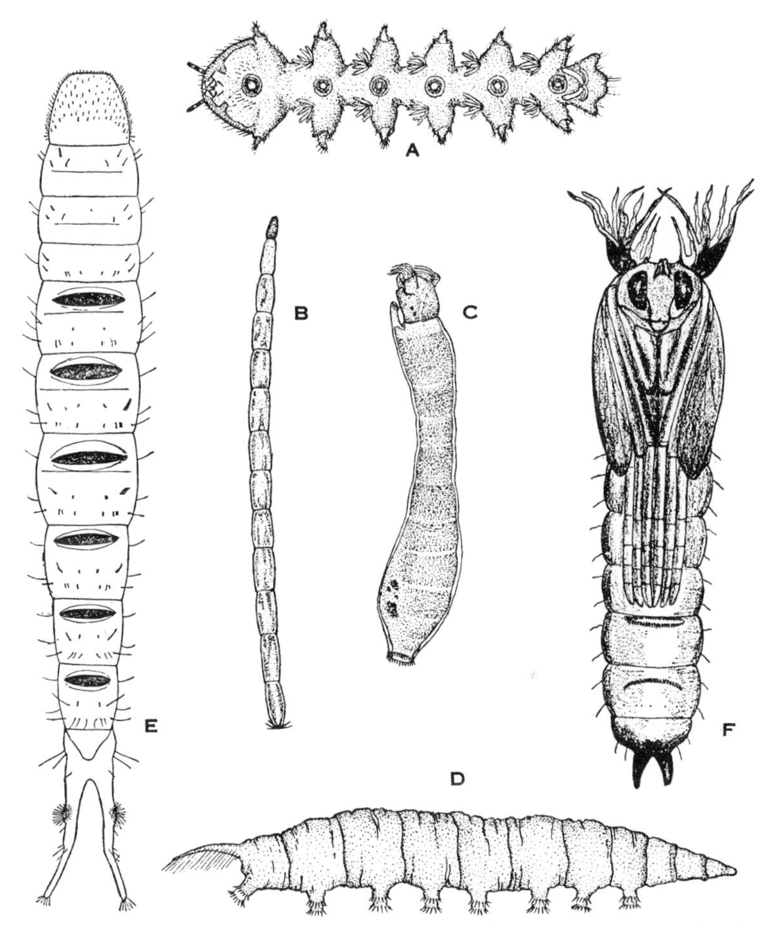

FIG. 37.—Miscellaneous aquatic true-fly larvae (Diptera). *A*, net-winged midge larva, *Blepharocera; B*, punkie larva, *Palpomyia; C*, black-fly larva, *Simulium; D*, snipe-fly larva, *Atherix; E* and *F*, larva and pupa, respectively, of the cranefly, *Antocha* (all greatly enlarged).

streams. It possesses gills, four of which, tube-like in form, may be found at the rear end. The body form is slender, tapering behind into two elongated lobes tipped with hairs. The pupa is formed in the silken larval tube and possesses conspicuous breathing horns which superficially suggest antlers. Adults are found throughout the summer.

Eriocera, the "push-ring" larva (Fig. 39). This cranefly larva, when alive, can instantly be recognized by the great expansion of a ring at the rear of the body. This is used in pushing its way among bottom gravel and sand. It can be contracted or expanded at will. These larvae pass the winter in streams, migrating in late spring to the shore line where they pupate in moist gravel. (Fig. p. 103)

Fig. 38.—Cranefly larva, *Tipula,* common in leaf drifts in most trout streams. Adults of this form are called "spinners" by anglers (natural size; photograph of living specimen by Dr. Myron Gordon).

Atherix, the snipe fly (Fig. 37, *D*). The larva of this fly frequents the gravel and stones of flowing water where it creeps about by means of leg-like protuberances on the underside. The head is very small and the posterior end is tipped by two fringed tails. (Fig. p. 101)

Chrysops, the deer fly (Fig. 40). This blood-sucking pest of man and animals is also produced in the water. The larva lives in quiet or slowly moving water, burrowing in sand and gravel beds where it feeds on associated small animals. It can easily be recognized by the spindle-like form of body and by the tubercles girdling each segment. It is eaten occasionally by trout. (Fig. p. 105)

Hilara, dance-flies, are minute, dusky flies that are often seen by the hundreds skimming close over the water in countless circles in the sunlight.

Alderflies (*Neuroptera*)*

(Hellgramites, fish-flies, dobsons, and alder flies of anglers)

This order of insects is represented in water by three conspicuous forms, the largest and best-known of which is the hellgramite or dobson larva, which is widely collected and used for bait by anglers. The life cycle is similar to that of caddiceflies in that there are egg, larval, pupal, and adult stages. Only the larval stage is passed in the water. The eggs are laid on stones and timbers projecting above the water. Upon hatching the young larvae fall into the water and begin their aquatic existence. The common hellgramite passes three years in the water as a larva, after which it seeks the bank and pupates under a stone. Others spend only a year in water, but like the hellgramite, pupate in the stream banks.

Corydalus, the "hellgrammite" (Fig. 41, *B*). The adult is the "dobsonfly." This giant insect lives as a larva among stones and gravel in the swiftest current where it feeds on stonefly and mayfly nymphs, caddiceworms, etc. It can instantly be recognized by its long, paired lateral

* From *neuron,* a nerve, and *pteron,* wing. Some authors place the forms mentioned here into Megaloptera.

appendages at the bases of which, on each side, are tufts of white filamentous gills. No other aquatic insect has gills in this position. The lower, warmer parts of trout waters contain these larvae in greater abundance than the smaller, colder headwater streams. In size, specimens up to four inches in length are common. The adults have a wing spread of from four to five inches. The male adult possesses enormous elongate, tusk-like jaws which project far out in front of the head. The female adult resembles the male except that the jaws are much shorter. In flight they are awkward and lumbering fellows, taking off slowly and resting frequently. The eggs are laid in conspicuous white patches on the sides of stones, ends upward, and covered with a protective whitish incrustation. (Fig. p. 109)

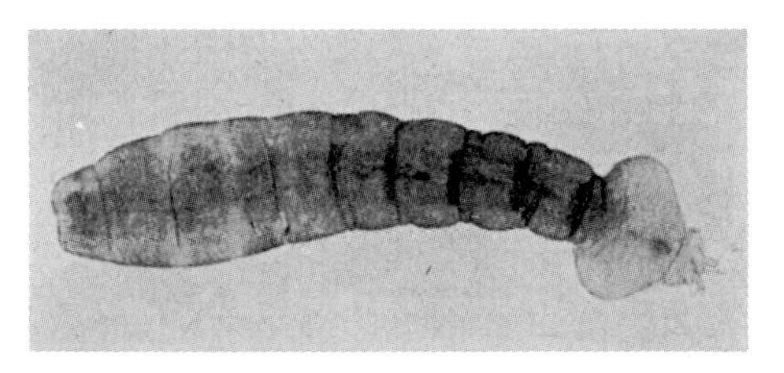

Fig. 39.—The "push-ring" cranefly larva, *Eriocera*. Easily recognized alive by its ability to expand the posterior end of the body into a pushing ring (enlarged slightly over two times).

Chauliodes, the fish-fly (Fig. 41, *C*). The larval fish-fly superficially resembles the hellgramite, but is smaller and lacks gills at the bases of the lateral appendages. These larvae may be found in both swift and slow waters. They are carnivorous. The adults are smaller than the dobson-flies, and have brownish wings with white blotches. The larvae make good trout bait on occasion and are often collected as hellgramites which they closely resemble. (Fig. p. 109)

Sialis, the alderfly (Fig. 41, *A*). The larva of this fly can usually be found in silty bottoms. It can easily be distinguished from the two larvae above by the presence of a long slender tail filament on the tip of the abdomen. In *Corydalus* and *Chauliodes* this is lacking and these forms have instead a pair of prolegs, each of which is armed with a pair of hooks. *Sialis* also has long lateral filaments but lacks the prolegs. Further, *Sialis* is the smallest of the three; it is usually less than an inch in length. The larvae of *Sialis* pupate in moist earth. The adults are humped-backed, four-winged flies, blackish in color, of uncertain flight. They are often seen clambering about on alders at the edges of streams. English anglers termed them "alderflies" from observation of this habit.

Other Insects

There remain a number of groups of insects of less importance that should be mentioned in passing because they may be found in all trout streams. Some of them are occasionally and locally of importance, either as food for trout or as enemies of fry.

The beetles of swift water are limited for the most part to the riffle beetles or Elmids and the water pennies, Psephenidae, which have most interesting larvae (Fig. 42). These are shaped much like a penny, rounded and flat in form, with the head and legs safely hidden underneath the flaring edges of a protective shell. These larvae live on the surface of stones; their dull brown color harmonizes perfectly with the background, making them almost undiscoverable. The flattened disc-like back turns aside the roughest water with ease. When a stone is removed from the water these beetles will betray their presence by starting at once to crawl about. Turned over on the back, three pairs of legs and five pairs of white branching gills are seen (Fig. 42, *B*). Pupation takes place underneath stones above water on stream banks (Fig. p. 110).

The Elmids (Fig. 43) are blackish, inconspicuous little sprawlers, less than a quarter of an inch in length; they live either in moss patches and crevices of sunken logs or hidden among the stones and gravel where the current is swift. Larvae and adults are found together. The larvae may be exceedingly abundant in riffles. Instead of being broad and flat like the water penny, they are long and slender and live in crevices among stones and gravel. They are less than half an inch long. A living larva placed in a pan of water will be seen to fold and unfold the fan-like anal gills at the tip of its abdomen in rhythmic movements. (Fig. p. 114)

In addition to the riffle beetles of swift waters there are three common types that inhabit the quieter stretches among weeds: diving beetles that hang beneath the surface, whirligig beetles that gyrate on the surface, and crawling Haliplid beetles that hide amid the coarser algae.

Three kinds of true bugs (*Hemiptera*) are worthy of mention here because of their abundance and because they form a typical part of the fauna of trout waters. All true bugs may be recognized as such by their mouth parts. Instead of the usual jaws and lips, these have jointed, sucking beaks. No other aquatic insects possess this type of mouth parts. The beak is used to suck the juices from their prey and also for defense.

Water striders or water skaters are the first of these bugs. Darting about on the placid surfaces of pools or at the edges of riffles, these conspicuous spider-like forms are common. In unceasing, restless movements they search for food floating on the surface film. Their feet, fringed with water-repellent hairs, easily support them on the surface film. The large water strider, *Gerris* (Fig. 44, *B*), is the common trout stream "skater." Pairs mating will often be seen swimming about together. The wings are usually lacking in the adults. As food, these are taken only occasionally by trout when other foods are scarce.

Water boatmen (Fig. 44, *A*) often occur by the hundreds in weed beds of slow or quiet water. Their blunt heads, flattened bodies, and long, hair-fringed hind legs extending oar-like out at the sides offer easy means of recognition. Air is secured at the water surface and spread over the undersides in a silvery sheet, as may be seen when they are under water.

They feed on plants and debris of various kinds found on the bottom. To remain below water they must anchor a claw to some support to prevent bobbing back to the surface, for they are lighter than water.

Backswimmers (Fig. 44, *C*), are the third group of water bugs. As the name implies, these bugs swim on their backs. Correspondingly, their body coloration is the reverse of that usually found in animals. Instead of having dark above and lighter colors below, their dorsal sides are light and ventral sides are dark. The hind legs are long and fringed for swimming. The fore legs are fitted with strong, prehensile claws for catching and holding their prey, which consists of small scuds, water fleas, etc. When obtaining air at the surface they hang head downward, with just the tip of the abdomen breaking through the surface film. Care should be exercised in handling these forms, for they can inflict painful stings with their puncturing beaks. They are common in quiet ponds or streams, but they are unimportant as a trout food. (Fig. p. 116)

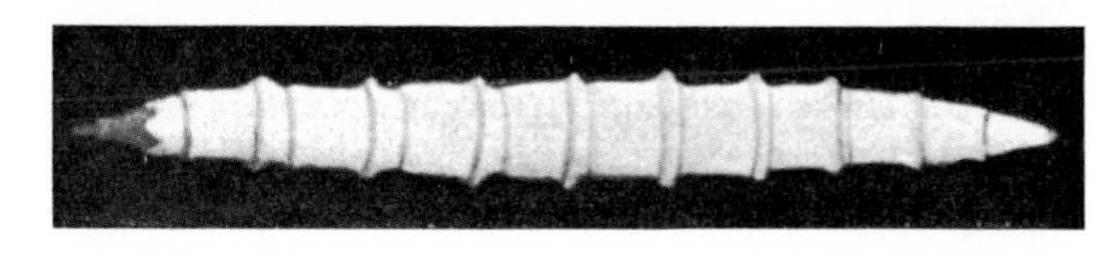

FIG. 40.—Larva of the deerfly, *Chrysops*. Easily recognized by spindle-like form and tubercles girdling each segment (about four times natural size).

Dragonflies and damselflies (*Odonata*) are important carnivorous insects. Adult dragonflies are commonly known as "mosquito hawks," "snake-feeders" and "darning needles" and are those large, expert, swift fliers that are seen darting over streams and ponds in midsummer. Damselflies are more slender and more daintily colored. They flit about over the water, resting frequently on low vegetation.

Both dragonfly and damselfly nymphs can be recognized as such by the peculiar form of the lower lip. This organ has been molded into a long, prehensile "meat-hook," armed with sharp spines for securing and holding the prey. In no other aquatic insect is this appendage so modified.

Some trout streams contain large numbers of dragonfly nymphs, and when abundant, they are eaten in considerable quantities by trout. Damselflies rarely become sufficiently abundant to constitute an important part of trout diet. Both kinds of nymphs are meat-eaters and so are competitors with trout for foods.

Dragonfly nymphs eat voraciously young trout or bass and other fishes. For this reason it is debatable whether or not they do more harm than good in game fish waters. Most fish culturists claim that they are responsible for enormous losses of young hatchery-reared fish and will do everything possible to control them. It should be stated, in their favor, that adult dragonflies are efficient destroyers of adult mosquitoes, punkies and other flies which they catch and eat on the wing.

Most dragonfly and damselfly nymphs are inhabitants of warm-water ponds or lakes. The three nymphs described below are those most typical of trout streams.

A big hairy nymph, *Cordulegaster* (Fig. 45, *B*), is a usual inhabitant of cold tributary brooks. It lives in silt or mud beds in settling basins or among the trash in back water eddies. These nymphs have mats of fine hairs over their bodies in which filaments of algae will grow and fine particles of silt will be deposited, making them very difficult to see either in or out of the water. Their movements are quite sluggish. (Fig. p. 118)

A smaller type of burrowing dragonfly nymph, *Lanthus* (Fig. 45, *A*), in eastern waters and replaced by *Octogomphus* in the streams of the Pacific slope, is found in spring brooks in sand beds in which they burrow on the downstream side of rocks. They are short-bodied chaps having the abdomen bluntly rounded; the abdomen is pointed in *Cordulegaster.* The tips of their feelers (antennae) are greatly expanded and cover the front lower part of the head. When sifted from the sand they feign death, and unless observed carefully are apt to be thrown away as trash.

Argia, a damselfly nymph (Fig. 45, *C*), can be found clinging to water plants or to roots in slack-water areas, or to stones in the riffles. Its thickset body and abdomen tipped with three broad, short, gill plates offer easy means for recognition. (Fig. p. 118)

CRUSTACEANS

Crayfish, shrimps, scuds, and sow-bugs

The crustaceans of fresh water are few compared to the many kinds found in salt water. Their salt water relatives are various crabs, lobsters, and other forms. The larger ones in fresh water that are important as trout foods are the crayfish, scuds, and sow-bugs. A multitude of smaller forms such as water fleas, copepods, and ostracods occur in fresh water ponds and lakes, where they form a large part of the free-swimming population of the open waters. Here the discussion will be limited to the more important stream forms.

Superficially crustaceans somewhat resemble insects by the possession of numerous jointed appendages, but always they have a larger number of them. Unlike insects, the head is broadly jointed to the thorax so that a definite neck region is lacking. Most crustaceans breathe by means of gills. Their bodies are covered by a hard, tough, external shell which is secreted by a layer of cells just under the body surface. Lime in the water is absorbed and utilized in its formation. In growth, this shell is molted from time to time in the same way that insects molt their skins.

The common crayfish, *Cambarus,* is often found in the quiet waters of streams or under stones in the slower riffles. It seems to prefer, and is usually more abundant in, hard or lime-stone waters. With its big red pincher-like forelegs poised ready for action it crawls about seeking small fishes or other things on which to feed. The eggs and young are carried beneath the abdomen, where they are stuck to the short swimmerets. The gills are at the sides, above the bases of the legs and beneath an overhanging flap of the shell.

Crayfish are common all over the United States. They are eaten more by trout over twelve inches in length than by smaller fish. Large trout capture them mostly at night while foraging in the riffles and back waters under cover of darkness. In lakes and ponds crayfish are eaten in large numbers, especially by small-mouthed black bass.

A word about the terms "shrimp" and "scud": many anglers use "shrimp" for both these crustaceans. The name shrimp is correctly applied to the large, true fresh water shrimp or prawn, *Palaemonetes* (Fig. 46, *A*). Shrimp are much larger than scuds, often being over two inches in length and quite distinctive in appearance. The so-called "Caledonia shrimp"* are not true shrimp at all. They were sold under that name to angling clubs for stocking private waters, and the use of the name probably spread from that beginning. (Fig. p. 120)

TABLE IX

SCUDS OF TROUT WATERS

Names		Maximum Length	Recognition Characters	Distribution
Common	Scientific			
Scud	*Gammarus fasciatus*	1 inch	1st antenna usually longer than second and *with* secondary flagellum. With groups of hairs on upper side of last three abdominal segments. Small posterior appendages on abdomen with inner branch shortest.	Scattered lakes and streams both east and west. Usually common in watercress beds in spring-runs or plant beds in some lakes. Prefers water of high lime content.
Scud	*Eucrangonyx gracilis*	½ inch	As above but lacks groups of hairs on upper side of last three abdominal segments. Small posterior appendages on abdomen with inner branch rudimentary.	General; usually in bog waters of low lime content.
Scud	*Hyalella azteca*	⅛ inch	1st antenna usually much shorter than second and *without* secondary flagellum. Often two spines on upper side of hinder abdominal segments. Lacks hairs here too.	General over the United States in both streams and lakes.

Fresh water scuds are much smaller than crayfish and of very different appearance. They rarely are found over an inch in length. Their bodies are flattened from side to side, curved in side view and look much like

* Abundant at Caledonia, New York.

large fleas. The jumping "sand-fleas" of the seashore are very similar in appearance, larger in size and very close relatives. Their color is generally pale yellow or green.

Scuds love the weed beds of both slow-moving and quiet waters and find their livelihood among the interlacing stems, leaves of aquatic plants and bottom trash where they feed on decaying matter of all kinds. There are three common kinds of scuds that are often abundant in trout waters (Table 9).

The scud *Gammarus fasciatus* (Fig. 47)* is usually scarce or absent from waters showing less than seventy-five parts per million calcium carbonate. It also seems to grow best in streams showing slight fluctuations in volume. It is usually very abundant in spring-runs in watercress beds. At the Hot Creek Rearing Ponds near Bishop, California (Fig. 49) in 1934, over one-quarter of a pound of these animals containing over 5,000 individuals was taken from an area of one square foot in the center of a watercress bed. Such enormous masses of them are exceptional. Widely distributed in the United States and Canada, this scud is usually found in the colder waters of spring-fed streams, ponds, and lakes. Its ability to survive in any given body of water depends apparently upon low maximum water temperature, hardness of the water, and the presence of aquatic plants such as *Elodea,* watercress, and *Chara.* (Fig. p. 124)

In lagoons of coastal streams in California, a closely allied brackish water scud, *Gammarus confervicolus,* is often abundant, furnishing large amounts of food to young steelhead and salmon.

The scud *Eucrangonyx* (Fig. 46, *B*) is somewhat smaller than *Gammarus* and usually lives in bog waters or in other waters known to be very low in lime content. On account of its comparative scarcity it is unimportant in most trout waters. (Fig. p. 120)

The smallest of the three common kinds of scuds is *Hyalella azteca* (Fig. 46, *C*). This is generally distributed in both streams and lakes in most parts of North America. While much smaller than *Gammarus,* its wider distribution and range of adaptability to various types of waters make it an important food, especially for young fishes. Its small size limits its consumption by large fish, but small fishes consume large numbers. Like *Gammarus* it is a scavenger, feeding on decaying matter of all kinds. It is common alike in cold and warm waters, in silted bottoms of lakes, or in shallow weed bed areas of both streams and lakes. *Hyalella* can usually be distinguished from *Gammarus* by the presence

* Two common species of these large scuds are commonly reported: *Gammarus fasciatus* and *G. limnaeus.* Recent work by Smith (1933) has shown that both these species are subject to local variations in color, hairiness, and other characters commonly used to separate them. Smith further found both species in the same waters, and concluded that, in New York state at least, it is not always possible to separate them. Examination of these scuds from other states has also shown this to be true.

of two backward projecting spines on the upper side of the hinder abdominal segments. (Fig. 46, *C*.) These spines are sometimes lacking, in which case other characters given in Table 9 must be used to distinguish it. (Fig. p. 120)

In a survey of lakes in the Willamette National Forest in Oregon in 1935, scuds were found in thirty-eight out of seventy-three lakes examined. The large scud, *Gammarus,* was found in very few of these

FIG. 41.—Hellgrammites of trout waters. *A,* the alderfly larva, *Sialis;* B, the true hellgrammite, *Corydalus,* showing gill tufts on abdomen at bases of lateral filaments; and *C,* top view of the small hellgrammite or fish-fly, *Chauliodes.* Both trout and bass fishermen commonly use the large hellgrammite *Corydalus* for bait.

lakes, but the small one, *Hyalella,* was usually fairly abundant. It has been found in many lakes at elevations from 5,000 to 10,000 feet, and in such contrasting types of waters as Lake Tahoe in California (over 6,000 feet elevation) and in a small spring-run near sea level at Mission San Vicente on the Peninsula of Lower California in Mexico. It has also been recorded from Lake Titicaca, Peru.

The large scud, *Gammarus,* has long been used to stock private trout waters in an effort to build up better trout fishing by increasing the productive capacity of water. This has been a haphazard practice. Some introductions have been successful, according to popular report; but few investigations were made in advance to determine whether scuds were already present in the waters for which they were intended, or to find out whether conditions would be suitable for them. Most attempts to introduce them into waters in which they were not native have failed.

Asellus, the water sow-bug (Fig. 48), is a flattened, fourteen-legged fellow; it is common in both ponds and streams, of cold or warm water, where it crawls about eating mainly dead vegetation. It produces young in egg pouches underneath the thorax. *Asellus* is about an inch long when grown. In spring holes full of dead leaves it is often possible to collect *Asellus* by the thousands. It is cosmopolitan in its distribution. The sow-bug is taken readily by trout. (Fig. p. 125)

NOTE: *Mysis relicta,* the opossum shrimp, has been successfully transplanted from Waterton Lake to several deep lakes in western states in attempts to bolster the trout food supply.

SNAILS AND CLAMS

Mollusca

The snails, *Lymnaea* (Fig. 50, *C*) with its elongate, spiral shell, *Planorbis* (Fig. 50, *A*) with a flat-spiral shell, and *Sphaerium* (Fig. 50, *E*), a small bivalve clam, are the most widely distributed and common molluscs found in trout streams generally in the United States. Both *Lymnaea* and *Planorbis* lack the hard, disc-like operculum which, in snails such as *Goniobasis* described below, closes the shell aperture when the animal is drawn inside. *Physa,* another common fresh-water snail, looks much like *Lymnaea,* but its shell has a left-hand spiral while that of *Lymnaea* turns to the right.

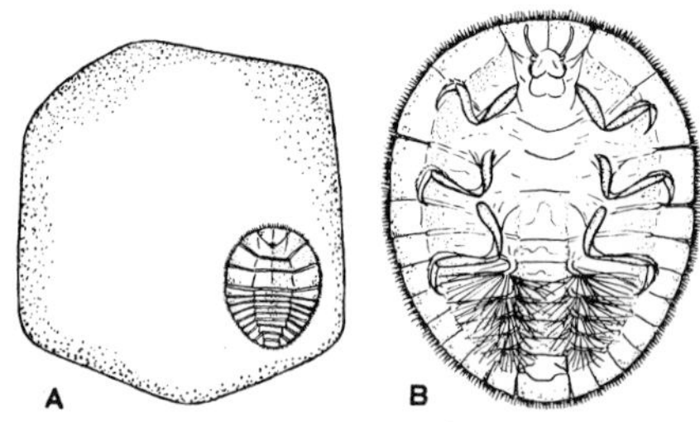

FIG. 42.—Two larvae of the water penny, *Psephenus; A,* top view of a larva on the surface of a stone (one and one-half times natural size), and *B,* underside of larva (enlarged five times). Common on stones in swift water.

An almost equally common snail is *Goniobasis* (Fig. 50, *B*), which is easily recognized by its rather heavy elongate shell, more or less pointed spire, and operculum covering the shell aperture. It is generally distributed in eastern and midwestern waters and is particularly abundant in streams of the Pacific slope. (Fig. p. 132)

Snails and clams are usually not abundant in eastern trout waters. In a few headwater tributaries and in waters heavily impregnated with lime, however, they often occur in large numbers, and trout in such waters eat many of them. Stomach examinations of four brown trout from this type of water showed snails to form over eighty per cent of their diet.

In acid, upland bog streams the small bivalve clam, *Sphaerium,* is often found in abundance. This and the closely allied *Musculium* are often found in the silt deposits of lake bottoms. Both snails and clams are usually found in quiet or slow-flowing waters having soft silt or mud bottoms in which they may burrow and feed. Occasionally, however, they will be found in abundance on stones in swift water. For instance, *Lanx altus* (Fig. 50, *G*), a limpet-like form limited to Pacific coast streams, is very abundant on rocks in swift riffles of the Klamath River in northern California. (Fig. p. 132)

Another typical west coast snail, one very abundant in the Klamath River, is *Fluminicola seminalis* (Fig. 50, *D*). *Lanx* is usually about the size of the thumb nail. It lives firmly attached to stones in rapids while *Fluminicola* is usually well hidden down among bottom trash close to the stream bottom. (Fig. p. 132)

Large bivalve clams are usually not abundant in trout waters. They show maximum development in larger, warmer rivers and their tributaries. However, Davis (1934a) records an interesting occurrence of the large clam *Margaritifera margaritifera* in the Truckee River in California. The young of this clam parasitized the gills of young trout in adjacent rearing ponds fed by river water. Large numbers of fingerlings were killed. He says:

> This mussel is abundant in certain sections of the Truckee River and the glochidia* had evidently been carried into the pools in the water supply which was obtained from the river. Practically every fish was infected with several glochidia, which appeared as small, rounded, translucent bodies attached to the gill filaments. The glochidia were easily visible to the naked eye and in some instances were so abundant as to prevent the gill covers from closing.
>
> The fish were suffering a heavy mortality, evidently due to the presence of the glochidia. A wild rainbow trout about 6 inches long was found dead in the river with the gills heavily infested. The fish in the rearing pools were said to have suffered heavy losses each year at this time which in all probability were due to infestation with glochidia.

The above discussion covers only a part of the lower animals (invertebrates) important as food for trout. Those who use this book will require no introduction to minnows, chubs, suckers, and other fishes that enter extensively into the diet of large trout, or to the frogs, salamanders, and tadpoles, a few of which are eaten by trout. Books giving careful and accurate accounts of these vertebrate animals are elsewhere available. A number of them are listed in the bibliography at the end of this volume. All these together, vertebrates and invertebrates, make up the animal population of cold-water streams and lakes.

Although immature insects make up the bulk of trout food, they live unseen below the water's surface and are little known to most fishermen, even though they may so easily be found. Halford says in his *Dry-fly*

* Young clams just released from the brood pouches of females are termed "glochidia." They live for a time parasitically on the gills and fins of fishes.

Entomology: "While floating food is caviar, sunk or midwater food is beef to the fish." Hence it has seemed preferable here to lay emphasis upon the under-water stages of insects. They are in some ways more interesting as well as more important. They are much easier to catch, and in some groups they show greater diversity of habit and form.

A better knowledge of the trout stream as a biological entity should prove useful by yielding a fuller enjoyment of the day's fishing. The "bugs" are there, and the delights of discovery await those who care to dip into the waters to find them.

IV

Food Selection by Trout

THE foods that trout largely depend upon are those just discussed in the preceding chapter. The underwater forms are available to them at all seasons of the year. Land foods supply a portion of the food during the warmer months of the year, but it is the aquatic animals that afford the bulk of their sustenance.

Having seen what food organisms are present in trout waters, anglers may be interested to know approximately what foods are eaten and in what proportions, to know the relative amounts of land foods eaten compared with aquatic foods, and also to know whether or not there is much difference in the feeding habits of brook, brown, and rainbow trout. The following answers to these questions are derived from microscopic examinations of 377 trout stomachs. They give a fair idea of food consumption by these three kinds of trout.

FOOD OF EASTERN BROOK TROUT

The following table lists the various foods eaten by brook trout and gives the numbers and percentages of each kind. These figures are based on stomach examinations of 251 specimens having an average length of five and one-half inches, and ranging from three to nine inches. Hence these fish may be considered as small adults. They were collected each month of the year from April, 1928, to March, 1929, and the figures given may be considered as average for a one year period.

Collection of trout through the winter months was a difficult task. The roads to the streams became impassable with drifting snow, and it was only with the greatest difficulty that trout were obtained in the smaller, warmer, head-water streams where the ice could be broken and a small seine used. Part of the trout were taken on rod and line and part with a small seine. All the trout were collected in the streams of central New York state near Ithaca. Trout in streams of the west or south would show similar foods present in their stomachs, but the proportions would be somewhat different. Feeding habits vary with local stream conditions.

The most important foods eaten by these brook trout were caddisflies, two-winged flies, and mayflies, in that order. These three groups taken together constitute over two-thirds (66%) of the foods eaten. Beetles were the fourth, making up 6.6% of the total. Water springtails, leaf hoppers, ants, bees, and wasps also furnished small amounts, varying from three to six per cent of the total. Other foods that made up around one per cent of the total were crayfish and shrimps, grasshoppers, stone-flies, true bugs, and earthworms.

In listing foods by number rather than by bulk, several questions might be raised by the reader. Recording food organisms by number does show

Fig. 43.—Adult (left) and larva (right) of riffle beetle. Both stages commonly found in crevices in bottom litter of swift riffles (enlarged twelve times).

the selectivity of the fish, since it is probable that each organism swallowed must first be secured by a definite selecting effort on the part of the fish. In bulk, one good-sized minnow or crayfish will equal perhaps fifty midge larvae or mayfly nymphs, or twenty to twenty-five caddis-fly larvae. Therefore, if we are to list organisms by bulk, naturally the larger foods will head the list. But the question of importance is this: what foods are a daily part of trout diet and furnish most of their sustenance? This question is answered by giving the numbers of each food. These are the organisms that are always present and may be depended upon. Minnows and crayfish, because of their large size and the relatively little indigestible material in them, probably furnish more nourishment per individual than any other forms upon which trout feed. However, these animals are not abundant, and while they may offer a feast to trout occasionally, their "daily bread" comes from the smaller but more abundant forms.

Only nineteen of the two hundred and fifty-one trout had eaten fish or salamanders. Of the twenty-one eaten, thirteen were small minnows, mostly the common brook sculpin, or miller's thumb, *Cottus bairdii,* which is usually common in brook trout waters. The remaining eight were two-lined salamanders, *Eurycea bislineata,* another common inhabitant of our smaller brooks. It is at once evident that insofar as these trout are concerned, fish and salamanders may be rated as minor foods.

It should be remembered that these trout averaged only five and one-half inches in length, and the larger foods are taken by the larger fish. Had these trout averaged fifteen inches or more in length (and provided these larger foods were present in the streams) they would very probably have constituted a principal item. Stomach examinations by many workers have given additional proof, and most anglers will agree to the statement.

Twenty-nine crayfish were taken from twenty-seven of the stomachs, or from 11 per cent of the fish examined. Other crustaceans found were the scuds, *Gammarus fasciatus* and *Hyalella azteca,* and a few copepods. These may be considered unimportant here because they were scarce.

TABLE X

FOODS CONSUMED BY 251 BROOK TROUT*

CLASS OF FOOD	NUMBER FOUND IN 251 STOMACHS	PER CENT OF TOTAL
Caddisflies	1,223	30.0
Two-winged flies	755	18.5
Mayflies	716	17.6
Beetles	268	6.6
Spring-tails	264	6.5
Leaf-hoppers	260	6.4
Ants, bees, wasps	123	3.0
Crayfish, scuds	69	1.7
Grasshoppers	66	1.6
Stoneflies	61	1.5
True bugs	48	1.2
Earthworms	47	1.1
Snails	35	0.8
Fish, salamanders	21	0.5
Miscellaneous	122	3.0
Total number eaten	4,078	

* Average length 5½″, maximum 9″, minimum 3″. Taken each month of the year from April, 1928, to March, 1929.

If we take each kind of food given in Table 10 and separate the land forms from the truly aquatic forms, it is possible to determine the amounts of food that came from these two separate sources.

Table 11 shows that a total of 1380 land animals was taken, which is

33.8 per cent of the 4078 items eaten. Aquatics supplied the bulk of the food, totaling 2698 items, or 66.2 per cent. This is a most important consideration, as it shows that wild brook trout, taken throughout the year, are dependent upon water-bred animals for two-thirds of their sustenance.

It will be noted that adult two-winged flies formed the largest single item of the terrestrial foods, or 22.1 per cent. These flies were of various kinds, such as midges, house-flies, bluebottle-flies, and crane-flies. These show why artificial flies make good lures. They are a staple, abundant, natural food and a part of the daily diet of trout in the summer time.

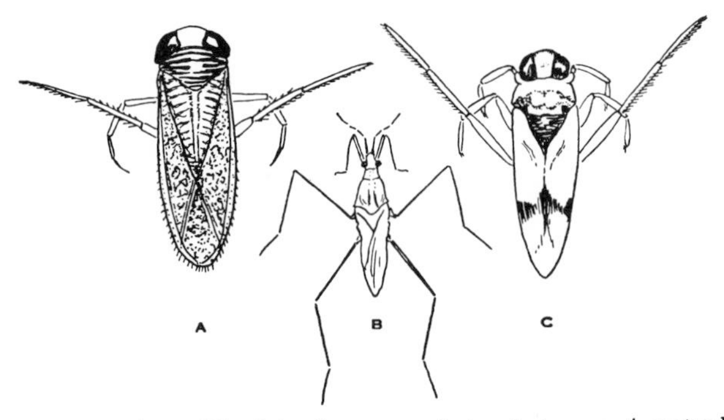

FIG. 44.—Three true-bugs (Hemiptera) common in trout streams. *A*, water boatman, *Corixidae; B,* water strider, *Gerris;* and *C,* back-swimmer, *Notonecta* (about one and one-half times natural size; after Hungerford, 1919).

Other important land foods eaten in some numbers were leaf-hoppers, forming 18.8 per cent, and beetles, 15.4 per cent. Adult mayflies, ants (with bees and wasps), grasshoppers, and earthworms were fourth, fifth, sixth, and seventh respectively in order of importance. Other land forms such as spiders, millipedes, etc., while occurring occasionally, are not important items.

Of all aquatic foods, caddisfly larvae and pupae were taken in larger numbers than any other food, forming 43.2 per cent of the total; and furthermore, they were found in 163 of the 251 trout. Mayfly nymphs were second, forming 19.9 per cent of total aquatic food, and fly larvae and pupae third, forming 16.8 per cent. Miscellaneous aquatic animals, including snails, dragon-fly nymphs, water striders, water boatmen, and aquatic beetles were scarce in the stomachs and may be considered as of minor importance.

Land organisms listed in Table 11 are mainly those animals which fall into the water accidentally. Many of these forms, such as adult caddisflies, mayflies, stoneflies, and other light-bodied insects, will float on the water surface if it is not too rough, and in this position are easily

TABLE XI

COMPARISON OF LAND AND WATER FOODS EATEN BY BROOK TROUT

CLASS OF FOOD	LAND INHABITING FORMS*		AQUATIC FORMS	
	Number	Per cent	Number	Per cent
Caddisflies	57	4.1	1,166	43.2
Two-winged flies	304	22.1	451	16.8
Mayflies	180	13.1	536	19.9
Beetles	213	15.4	55	2.0
Stoneflies	10	0.7	51	2.0
Leaf-hoppers	260	18.8	—	—
True-bugs	28	2.0	20	0.8
Ants, bees, wasps	123	8.9	—	—
Grasshoppers	66	4.8	—	—
Water springtails	—	—	264	9.8
Moth larvae	26	1.9	—	—
Spiders	29	2.1	—	—
Millipedes	32	2.3	—	—
Crayfish, scuds	—	—	68	2.5
Snails	3	0.2	32	1.2
Earthworms	47	3.4	—	—
Fish, salamanders	—	—	21	0.7
Miscellaneous	2	0.1	34	1.1
Totals	1,380		2,698	

* The adults of aquatic insects are listed as land organisms here because they have ceased to be aquatic in the adult stage; their gills are lost, wings fully developed for flight, swimming powers gone. It is only in their immature stages that these can be classed as truly aquatic and adapted to life in water.

seen and secured by rising trout. However, such land forms as earthworms, millipedes, and centipedes, being heavy-bodied, usually sink below the surface and are swept downstream with the current and secured below water by trout. These facts show us at once that sunken or mid-water food may be a mixture of both land and water-bred forms.

In this connection it is interesting to compare the numbers of adult aquatic insects with the numbers of their larvae or pupae that were eaten. A total of only 57 adult caddisflies was found in the stomachs as compared with 1166 larvae and pupae. Likewise, such large differences between numbers of adults and numbers of young eaten may be noted with the two-winged flies, mayflies, and stoneflies. The reason for greater consumption of the young of these insects by trout is that the immature stages are always present in streams. They usually have long developmental periods, and being associated with trout at all times of the year, is it only natural that they should be eaten more frequently. Furthermore, adult life is usually very brief, lasting only long enough for the mature forms to emerge from the water, mate, lay eggs, and die.

Floods eroding stream beds also materially assist trout to secure the aquatic forms by sweeping them from their hiding places into the open water where they are more easily taken.

Immature aquatic forms of mayflies, caddisflies, and two-winged flies are largely eaten at emergence from the water, when swimming to the surface to cast off their skins and take flight. At this time they are at the mercy of any fish that happens to see them. (Fig. 54.) At times they afford fish unlimited amounts of food upon which to gorge them-

Fig. 45.—Two dragonflies and one damselfly; nymphs common in trout waters. *A, Lanthus,* with grasping lower lip partly extended at front of head; *B, Cordulegaster;* and *C, Argia.* Note the two pairs of wing pads just back of the hind legs; also the three gill plates attached to posterior end of body of the damselfly nymph, *C* (enlarged about two times).

selves, and anglers begin a frenzied search of fly books in hopes of finding a true imitation of the emerging insects. (Fig. p. 144)

It is evident that brook trout feed to a considerable extent directly off the bottoms of streams. Many of the animals found in their stomachs could be obtained in no other way. This statement is supported by direct observations of fish feeding in clear water, where they may often be seen sorting bottom dwellers from their shelters with short, quick, sidewise, sweeping movements of their jaws over the surfaces of the stones and gravel on the bottom.

By rearrangement of our figures it is easy to determine what the trout's choice of foods was from month to month and season to season and also to show the relative proportions of land and water foods that were consumed each month of the year. In the accompanying Table 12 this has been done.

Certain salient facts at once become evident. Caddisfly larvae and pupae were first choice of the trout during seven months of the year, and were second choice only in the month of December. Mayfly nymphs were first choice in May and August, while leaf-hoppers were first in September and October. Leaf-hoppers are entirely terrestrial in habit and probably fall or are blown into the water. Water-bred foods were first choice each month of the year except September, October, and December. In the last named month, spring-tails were eaten in largest numbers.

In December the trout studied were taken on the 11th and 27th respectively. On the first date a few leaf-hoppers were present in the stomachs, while those taken on the 27th had only water-bred foods in their stomachs. Cold weather had either killed land organisms or driven them

TABLE XII

FOODS EATEN BY EASTERN BROOK TROUT EACH MONTH OF THE YEAR

Month	Number of Trout Examined	Foods Eaten*		Land Foods	Water Foods
		First Choice	Second Choice	Total Number Eaten	Total Number Eaten
January...	13	Caddisfly larvae and pupae	Aquatic fly larvae and pupae	2	158
February..	9	Caddisfly larvae and pupae	Mayfly nymphs	37	122
March....	4	Caddisfly larvae and pupae	Aquatic fly larvae and pupae	2	48
April.....	21	Caddisfly larvae and pupae	Aquatic fly larvae and pupae	181	738
May......	10	Mayfly nymphs	Adult mayflies	119	111
June......	25	Caddisfly larvae and pupae	Mayfly nymphs	122	165
July......	62	Caddisfly larvae and pupae	Mayfly nymphs	304	591
August....	40	Mayfly nymphs	Adult flies	302	276
September.	18	Leaf-hoppers	Grasshoppers	89	50
October...	18	Leaf-hoppers	Land beetles	94	53
November.	19	Caddisfly larvae and pupae	Land beetles	31	46
December.	12	Spring-tails	Caddicefly larvae and pupae	97	340
Totals....	251			1,380	2,698

* Choice determined by numbers consumed.

to cover. As would naturally be expected, land foods were also scarce in January, February, and March.

A variety of foods occurred as second choice during the different months. Aquatic fly larvae and pupae were second in January, March, and April, and made up a very large part (16.8 per cent) of total aquatic foods. Grasshoppers were abundant along the banks of streams in September and were second choice in this month. Land beetles were second in October and November, while adult flies appeared as second only in August and were never first choice.

FIG. 46.—Freshwater shrimp and scuds. *A*, the true freshwater shrimp, *Palaemonetes paludosus* (one and one-half times natural size); *B*, the scud, *Eucrangonyx gracilis;* and *C*, the small scud, *Hyalella azteca.* A commonly used recognition character for *Hyalella* are the two backward projecting spines shown on the upper rear surface (*B* and *C*, three and one-half times natural size; from Embody, 1912).

A comparison of the total numbers of land foods eaten each month with total water foods (Table 12) shows that in only four months of the year, May, August, September, and October, did land foods exceed water foods in numbers consumed. This is rather surprising. One might expect land foods to be secured more largely during the warmer months of the year, but to find them dominant in the stomachs in May, as well as in September and October, is rather unexpected. Doubtless part of the variation between land and water foods may have been due to seasonal variations in weather conditions, or in emergence periods of aquatic insects. More detailed studies of a larger series of stomachs taken during these months are needed. The figures given here show a large amount of land foods available during the fall months, the least amount occurring in the winter months of December, January, February, and March.

FOOD OF BROWN TROUT

The feeding habits of brown trout differ in some respects from those of brook trout. The most striking difference is the large number of mayflies consumed. Of the 2404 items taken from 46 stomachs, 1907, or about 80 per cent, were mayflies. (Table 13.) When it is remembered that with brook trout we found mayflies to constitute only 17.6 per cent (Table 10), it is evident that brown trout have greater liking for mayflies as food. Both were taken from the same streams.

TABLE XIII

FOODS EATEN BY 46 BROWN TROUT*

CLASS OF FOOD	NUMBER FOUND IN 46 STOMACHS	PER CENT OF TOTAL
Mayflies	1907	79.3
Caddisflies	230	9.5
Two-winged flies	61	2.5
Earthworms	51	2.1
Slugs	30	1.3
Beetles	28	1.2
Ants, bees, and wasps	22	1.0
Stoneflies	17	.7
Leaf-hoppers	17	.7
Crayfish and scuds	15	.7
Fish, salamanders	9	.3
Grasshoppers	7	.3
Miscellaneous	10	.4
Total	2,404	

* These trout had an average length of 8″ and ran from 5″ to 12″; they were taken mostly in May, June, and July.

Of the 1907 mayflies eaten by brown trout, we may note that 1714 were nymphs secured below water while only 193 were adults caught after they had emerged from the water. By way of comparison, the 251 brook trout ate only 716 mayflies, of which number 180 were adults. These made up only 4.1 per cent of the land forms eaten by brook trout, while with the brown trout adult mayflies made up 53.9 per cent. To put it in another way, 251 brook trout took 180 "dry" mayflies, while 46 brown trout took 193 of them. The above figures seem to indicate that brown trout feed more at the surface than brook trout.

Caddisflies, two-winged flies, and beetles apparently were much less acceptable to brown trout as they formed only 9.5 per cent, 2.5 per cent, and 1.2 per cent respectively, of foods consumed. Brook trout ate these three kinds of foods much more than did the brown trout. Of other foods eaten by brown trout, such as stoneflies, grasshoppers, leaf-hoppers, none were eaten in sufficient quantities to warrant further comment here. As shown in Table 13, 51 earthworms were eaten by the 46 trout. This unusually large number probably was due to high flood-waters washing them into the streams during the spring when these trout were caught. The same cause may explain the many "slugs" (land snails) that occurred in their stomachs. Of the nine larger animals eaten, four were small minnows and five were salamanders. Had these trout been larger, doubtless more would have been found in their stomachs.

As was true with the brook trout, most of the animals eaten (2046) were from the water, the smaller proportion (358) being supplied from the land.

FOOD OF RAINBOW TROUT

Rainbow trout feed upon the same common stream animals as do brook and brown trout, and the figures given here show that rainbows more closely resemble brook trout in their selection of foods. Furthermore, they show several dietary characteristics not shown by the other two species of trout.

For instance, in Table 14 the fresh-water alga, *Cladophora,* is indicated as being present in the stomachs by a plus sign (+). This alga occurred in 20 of the 80 rainbow stomachs and averaged 36 per cent, by bulk, of the stomach contents of the fishes in which it was found. No plant foods were found in any brook trout or brown trout stomachs. Rainbows either feed directly upon this alga or they secure it indirectly along with the animal foods, when feeding on rocky stream bottoms. This plant harbors many mayfly nymphs, midge, and other fly larvae. In capturing these animals, the trout would naturally get considerable amounts of algae.

Mayflies, caddisflies, and two-winged flies were the predominant foods eaten, forming 37.1 per cent, 18.7 per cent, and 17.8 per cent, respectively (Table 14). Of other foods listed in this Table, the beetles and ants, bees, and wasps were most largely selected. Of the latter group, more ants were eaten, bees and wasps occurring only occasionally. Five small minnows and one salamander were the only vertebrate animals found in these stomachs.

Of the 490 mayflies, 114 were taken as adults at the surface, while 376 were nymphs secured below water. This shows that rainbows, while not feeding at the surface as much as brown trout, do take considerable numbers of adult flies there. However, as with the others, the great bulk of their food is secured below water.

TABLE XIV

FOODS CONSUMED BY 80 RAINBOW TROUT*

CLASS OF FOOD	NUMBER FOUND IN 80 STOMACHS	PER CENT OF TOTAL
Mayflies	490	37.1
Caddisflies	247	18.7
Two-winged flies	234	17.8
Beetles	105	7.9
Ants, bees, and wasps	88	6.6
Stoneflies	44	3.3
Moth larvae	17	1.2
Snails	14	1.1
Leaf-hoppers	13	1.0
Crayfish and scuds	13	1.0
Alderfly larvae	11	.8
True bugs	11	.8
Grasshoppers	7	.5
Fish and salamanders	6	.5
Algae—*Cladophora*	+	+
Miscellaneous	23	1.71
Total	1,323	

* Average length 6″, running from 3″ to 12″. Most of these were taken in May, June, and July. All of these rainbows were taken from streams, none from lakes.

SUMMARY

Below is a tabular comparison of the percentages that adult mayflies, caddisflies, and two-winged flies made up of the land foods eaten by the three kinds of trout. It seems to show that brook trout preferred the members of the order Diptera, or two-winged flies (blue-bottles, deer-flies, horseflies, midges, etc.), while they were the second choice of rainbows and brown trout. Adult caddisflies took third place for each kind of trout, but more were taken by brook trout than by browns or rainbows.

TABLE XV

PERCENTAGES OF ADULT CADDISFLIES, MAYFLIES, AND TRUEFLIES EATEN BY TROUT

KIND OF TROUT	ADULT CADDISFLIES	ADULT MAYFLIES	ADULT TWO-WINGED FLIES
Brook trout	4.1%	13.1%	22.1%
Brown trout	1.1%	53.9%	2.8%
Rainbow trout	1.4%	27.7%	15.8%

The last meals of 377 trout having been recorded it may be of interest to note the average number of animals that were found in one stomach of each species of trout. Brook and rainbow trout averaged slightly over 16 per stomach. Browns, on the other hand, averaged better than 52 per stomach. These figures might be taken to show that brown trout are

FIG. 47.—Freshwater scuds, *Gammarus* (two times natural size).

more voracious feeders than the others, but this may not be the case, because first of all, the average length of the brown trout was eight inches, while both the brooks and rainbows averaged only six inches, and the larger trout took more food. Furthermore, the figures are based on three series of trout stomachs with widely varying numbers of individuals concerned (251 brook, 46 brown, and 80 rainbow), taken at varying seasons of the year. Also, empty stomachs were not included in the average.

In general, stomachs were found fully distended with food only during the summer months. Lowered water temperatures naturally tend to slow up feeding, and the trout examined in the late fall, winter, and early spring had much less food in them. Rainbow trout taken when the water temperature was 37°F. all contained food, but in relatively small amounts, the stomachs being filled to about 10 per cent of their capacity. Brook trout taken when the water was 40°F. all contained small amounts of food.

Trout from two or three pounds upward in weight seek the larger food, eat more at one time, and generally do not feed except at night. Exceptions to this statement could be made by almost any trout fisher-

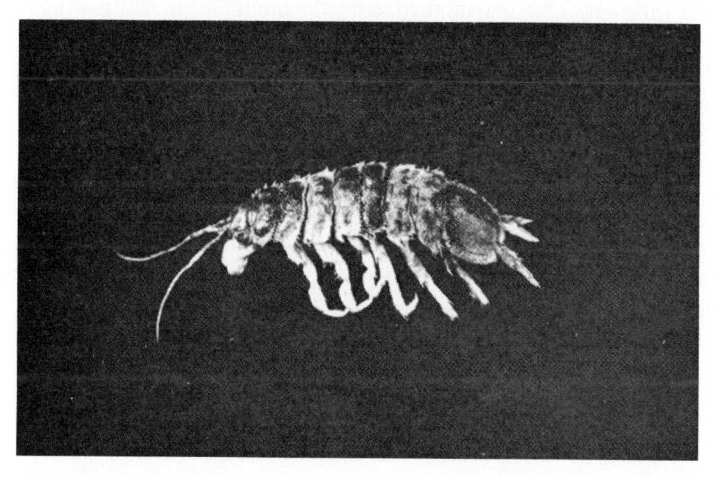

FIG. 48.—The water sow-bug, *Asellus.* This grey, flattened crustacean is common in the bottom of both ponds and lakes, particularly in eastern and mid-western waters. Rare in the west. An excellent trout food (photograph by courtesy of Raymond Redmond).

man, but generally speaking this is true. Foods taken by large trout consist mostly of the larger insect larvae, crayfish, minnows, and if the opportunity offers, their own kind. On one occasion a six-inch brook trout was taken from a twelve-inch brown trout. On another a four-inch brook trout was seen to try to swallow his two-inch brother, the latter sticking in his throat, killing both. Most anglers will agree that the big fish are the most predacious and will consume large numbers of smaller fishes, including their own kind.

It is a well-known fact that after a rain in the summer time, stream fishes begin to feed. This habit is easily explained. As the water begins to rise it sweeps bottom animals from their shelters and washes land animals into the water, the force of the rising current carrying them downstream. The fish know that the waters now carry an abundance of food and at once go "on the feed." Mr. E. R. Hewitt tells of taking trout on wet flies in meadows adjacent to streams during excessively high water. Bait fishermen usually take good catches when streams are on the rise after a fall of rain.

Large trout do most of their feeding after dark and at night are seldom found in the same places as in the daytime. Starting any time after sunset, they will leave their daytime shelters under cut-banks, stumps, stones, or logs, and forage in the shallow backwaters of pools or in shallow riffles or other places where they can secure a meal.

Roughage is supplied to most animals from waste materials in the foods they eat. This is true for trout; the undigestible chitin which gives the rigidity to the bodies of the insects that they eat passes through their intestinal tracts entirely unaffected by the digestive juices. Debris from caddiceworm cases furnishes another important source of roughage, sometimes far in excess of their needs.

The varied assortments of different organisms that fish pick up is little short of amazing. In one rainbow trout taken in the Ausable River was found part of a newspage with the print still quite legible. Feeding habits are entirely dependent upon local conditions. Trout are opportunists, and like all animals, in order to survive they must eat what they can get or go hungry.

V

Distribution of Trout Foods

TROUT STREAM animals show just as decided preferences for homesites as do human beings. Streams offer a variety in pool or riffle, in sand, mud, rubble, gravel or hardpan bottoms, in fast or slow, in cold or warm waters, in weed beds or bare rock ledges, in deep or shallow water, and in various combinations of these conditions. Most organisms select certain definite areas for their homes. Some range freely from one place to another while others will be found only in very restricted areas.

The stream is a rough-and-tumble environment. The seasons often bring sudden catastrophic changes in volume and speed of water that wipe out whole aquatic populations in a short time. Life is precarious in such unstable places and a fine degree of fitness is required for those that have ventured into them.

Roughly, the following five physical conditions largely determine the distribution of aquatic organisms: (1) type of bottom; (2) velocity of current; (3) depth of water; (4) temperature of water; (5) materials in suspension and solution.

Type of bottom is determined by the materials composing the stream bed. These may be hardpan, mud, muck, silt, sand, gravel, bed-rock, rubble, or large boulders. Seldom will one distinct type prevail for a long distance; usually one intergrades imperceptibly into another. Further, rubble will usually be mixed with gravel, gravel with sand, large boulders with small rubble, with only occasional pure bottoms of any given size of particles.

The type of soil drained largely determines the materials that compose the stream beds in any given region. If the soil is that of swamps or low-lands, the slow-flowing streams will have soft bottoms of mud or silt, perhaps intermixed with fine gravel and plant remains. In streams draining rocky hills or mountain ranges of quartz and granite, the swift streams will have rocky and boulder-strewn beds, composed only of materials that can withstand the powerful erosive action of water in such places.

The ability of water to transport solids is in direct relation to its volume and its speed. Fast water in large streams during flood time may carry bridges, boulders, and trees downstream, while quiet head-water rivulets will carry but fine silt and some plant debris. In any stream, as the gradient of its bed decreases, the heavier materials are dropped first, followed by the finer materials which settle more slowly to the bottom. Thus great deltas that are built up at the mouths of rivers offer abundant evidence of the carrying capacity of water.

Little is known about the temperature requirements of aquatic insects. However, streams that are too warm for trout contain few of the common mayfly and stonefly nymphs. Even unpolluted waters over 90°F. often contain practically none of them. The temperature necessary for best development of stream insects, regardless of winter conditions, seems to be that of our best trout waters, ranging from 65° to 75° F. in the summer time.

Fig. 49.—Water cress beds in a spring-run where fresh water scuds occur in enormous numbers. Hot Creek Rearing Ponds near Bishop, California.

As far as the distribution of stream insects is concerned, bottom materials, depth, and water speeds are the most important conditions affecting them. These three factors determine the presence of pools and riffles, which are the two main types of habitat to choose between.

Trout, as we well know, choose pools to pass their days in. Under the cover of darkness they range out to the riffles and shallow back-waters to feed. The riffles are the meadows, the pools the pastures of the stream economy. It is in the riffles that most organisms dwell, find their food, escape their enemies, and lay their eggs. Shallow, swift riffles produce more food than deep ones, and as will be noted below, the type of bottom exerts considerable influence upon the amounts present.

Width of stream is of itself unimportant as a physical factor. Wide streams produce less food per unit area, but it is not merely because they are wide but rather because of other factors incident to width such as severe floods, ice, and pollution.

CENSUS-TAKING IN STREAM BEDS

Let us now inquire more closely into the distribution of aquatic insects by actual measurements of their abundance in different situations. The "square-foot box" is used for taking quantitative samples. It consists of a galvanized iron box, 26 inches deep, open at both ends, exactly one foot square, inside measurements. The upper edges are rolled over a heavy-gauge rod, and the lower edges are strengthened by riveting a piece of band iron flush with the bottom all around. This edge is strong enough to withstand rough use when pushed into gravel or rubble bottoms.

In taking a sample, the box is pushed into the stream bed and the organisms enclosed are removed by means of sieves.*

When using the square foot box a 30-mesh handscreen is always held about the lower edges of it on the downstream side to prevent loss of animals due to irregularities of the bottom. In rubble bottoms in swift water, it is impossible to prevent some loss in taking the sample. Back washes from the current, even with the box edges pushed as far as possible into the substratum, cause them. However, one would expect the error due to roughness in securing the samples to be about constant in any given type of bottom. In gravel riffles, even when composed largely of small stones, the box often can be pushed quickly from three to six inches into the bottom, and quite accurate samples obtained.

Once the box is securely in the bottom with the handscreen in place, the larger stones are lifted out and the animals washed off into a bucket. The bottom is then stirred up, using a shallow 30-mesh sieve. The animals are washed off the sieve into a bucket and this process is continued until no more can be obtained. Any swept out of the box onto the handscreen are also dumped into the bucket and taken as part of the sample.

The bottom foods and trash in the bucket are now washed free of mud and silt by pouring the sample through a 30-mesh soil sieve. The catch is then washed off from the sieve into a quart fruit jar and brought indoors. While still alive, the animals are separated from the trash. After being sorted into a white-enamel pan, they are poured into a fine meshed tea strainer and held on blotting paper for one minute to remove excess moisture. The total catch is then weighed on torsion-balance scales.

The weight thus obtained is the wet weight (w.w.) in grams of the

* This simple piece of apparatus works well in water up to two feet in depth and where the bottom materials are sufficiently small to permit setting it properly. In streams having bottoms of large boulders and rubble it cannot be used. Under such conditions the only quantitative method (and that a rough one) used to date has been to make hand counts from stones offering measurable surface areas, as done by Needham and Christenson (1927) in the streams of Utah.

total bottom foods obtained. The figures submitted here giving pounds of food per acre are naturally based upon recalculations from averages of these figures.

Submitted below are the results of quantitative studies of the distribution of trout foods, carried on in the trout waters of central New York for the New York State Conservation Department* and continued in California as a part of the field program of the California Trout Investigations.

In brief the relative amounts of available fish food found per square foot in five types of riffle or fast water bottoms were as follows. Rubble produced the most, yielding an average of 1.84 grams of potential fish food per square foot, or approximately 176 pounds per acre. Coarse gravel and fine gravel were also fairly rich, while sand, hard-pan and bedrock were poor in food, each successively producing less.

TABLE XVI

FIVE TYPES OF BOTTOM AND THE AVERAGE AMOUNT OF AVAILABLE FISH FOOD PRESENT*

NUMBER OF SAMPLES	TYPE OF BOTTOM	WEIGHT OF FISH FOOD	
		Grams per sq. ft.	Lbs. per acre
112	Rubble	1.84	176
71	Coarse gravel	1.27	121
37	Fine gravel	0.93	89
1	Hard-pan	0.10	9.6
1	Bedrock	0.0065	0.5
	Average	0.82+	78+

* After Needham (1927, 1928b) and Pate (1931, 1932, 1933).

In reading these figures it is to be remembered that the "production per square foot" refers to the total weight of all the kinds of animals lumped together.

In slow-flowing water bottoms silt was found to produce the high average of 3.47 grams of food per square foot (333 pounds per acre). the highest average obtained for any type. Muck averaged 0.65 grams, while sand gave 0.37 grams: both were less productive than fine gravel in riffles.

The high figure obtained for silt bottoms is not very significant for the reason that silt bottoms are comparatively rare in most trout streams. We must consider as most important those bottoms which underlie the most miles of trout waters. These we know to be composed of largely

* Thanks are due to the Conservation Department, and particularly Dr. Emmeline Moore, Director of the New York State Biological Survey, for use of these data here.

gravel or rubble and not silt. However, it is interesting to note that silt may produce this great abundance of food where beds of sufficient purity and depth are deposited. Large burrowing mayfly nymphs, *Ephemera* (Fig. 26), and midge larvae (Fig. 36) are present in large numbers and are mainly responsible for the high average obtained.

TABLE XVII

THREE TYPES OF SLOW WATER BOTTOM AND THE AVERAGE AMOUNT OF AVAILABLE FISH FOOD PRESENT*

NUMBER OF SAMPLES	TYPE OF BOTTOM	WEIGHT OF FISH FOOD	
		Grams per sq. ft.	Pounds per acre
36	Silt	3.47	333
1	Muck	0.65	62
8	Sand	0.37	35

* After Needham (1927, 1928b) and Pate (1931, 1932, 1933).

The average production per square foot for pool bottoms was 0.26 grams, or 25 pounds per acre. This applies to pools in which the water practically comes to a standstill, variable in depth, but deep enough to offer good cover for trout; the type of pool which, when seen by an angler, hastens his step and raises his hopes. On the other hand swift water riffles averaged 0.82 grams per square foot, or 78 pounds per acre, approximately three times as much. These figures are significant. They show the value of riffles as the food-producing areas in trout waters and give weight to the idea that pools are more valuable as cover for trout and catch basins for food organisms swept downstream.

On the other hand some parts of pools at certain seasons of the year will be found tremendously rich in foods. These places are whirling eddies in which numerous caddicefly larvae, mayfly nymphs, and other food organisms carried down stream settle to the bottom, and where they may be easily secured. Over 10 grams of food per square foot have been taken in such situations. However, this one square foot included most of the organisms in the whole "eddy." They were concentrated at one place by the swirling current. Samples taken within three feet of the same spot in the same pool showed only the usual low amount. These rich "settling basins," "whirling eddies" or whatever they be termed, are quite scarce in pools. Many pools lack them entirely, so that in relation to total pool bottom areas they represent but a very small fraction, and hence not too much importance should be assigned to them.

Greater productivity of the riffles in foods is probably due to the protection afforded aquatic animals in these areas. Pools are apt to be scoured out during severe floods, while the fast water areas, if their beds are studded with good-sized, fixed stones, are less likely to be swept clean. The stones afford organisms a "port in the storm" on their lee sides as the waters rise. Also the feeding habits of some of the commonest aquatic insects make it necessary that they live in flowing water where they can strain food particles out of it by means of various devices. Stream insects are safer in riffles than in pools, as their enemies, the trout, have largely chosen the latter for residence.

Fig. 50.—Snails and clams common in trout waters. *A, Planorbis,* top and side view; *B, Goniobasis,* with enlarged operculum of same at left; *C, Lymnaea; D, Fluminicola; E, Sphaerium; F, Margaritifera; G,* top and side view of the limpet, *Lanx* (*A, B, F,* and *G* about natural size; *C* and *D* slightly, and *E* greatly, enlarged).

With both the fishes and the insects, doubtless the two problems of securing food and escape from enemies have largely determined their selection of home-sites. Much further investigative work will be necessary to determine the true value of different kinds and sizes of pools as food-producing areas.

DISTRIBUTION IN POOLS AND RIFFLES

In Table 18 are shown the percentages of the various groups of aquatic animals found in riffle and pool bottoms. Here it is seen that mayfly nymphs, caddice larvae and pupae, stonefly nymphs, and fly larvae and pupae were the dominant riffle organisms. These four groups made up over 86 per cent of all potential food organisms of swift waters.

Pools on the other hand showed but two groups of insects to be abundant, fly larvae and pupae and mayfly nymphs, which formed 46.7 and 41.2 per cent respectively of the pool inhabitants collected. Mayfly nymphs were the second most abundant food of pools (41.2 per cent). That they were the dominant element of the riffles shows that mayfly nymphs have a decided preference for flowing waters. Crayfish and scuds preferred fast waters, as did the beetle larvae, while *Sialis* larvae, dragonfly and damselfly nymphs showed preference for quieter pool waters.

TABLE XVIII

COMPARISON OF AVAILABLE FISH FOODS FROM RIFFLES AND POOLS
(Given in percentages by orders, based on collections of 1927)

ORDER	RAPID WATER BOTTOMS Per cent	POOL BOTTOMS Per cent
Mayfly nymphs	36.9	41.2
Caddisfly larvae and pupae	21.3	1.2
Stonefly nymphs	14.7	4.1
Fly larvae and pupae	13.8	46.7
Beetle larvae and pupae	7.6	2.6
Crayfish and scuds	3.7	.2
Sialis larvae (Neuroptera)	.9	2.1
Snails and clams	.2	.2
Dragonfly and damselfly nymphs	.1	.5
Miscellaneous	.7	1.1

Studies made on distribution of potential foods in relation to stream width have not been in close agreement. Léger (1910), after work done on the productivity of streams near Grenoble, France, stated that the food elements decreased by one-half from the shoreline to the middle of the channel in streams above five meters (16.4 feet) in width. Subsequent work by Needham (1928b) and by Pate (1931) showed this not to be true for certain New York streams. In streams above 18 feet in width,* they found decreases from shorelines to mid-channels of 11.05 per cent and 16.66 per cent respectively. These results were obtained in trout waters near Ithaca, New York, and in the Oswegatchie and Black River systems in northern New York. However, later work by Pate (1932, 1933) in other streams of New York confirmed Léger's findings. Much further work will be necessary on this feature of the

* The division of streams into two groups, those above, and those below 18 feet in width was not made arbitrarily. Previous work showed this to be the stream width at which the nutritive elements were most evenly scattered over the bed, more food being found in the centers of streams narrower than this, and less being found in the centers of those wider than this.

distribution of aquatic fish foods. It has become quite evident that what is true for one drainage area does not by any means hold true for another. Each presents its own environmental peculiarities and each must be studied individually.

By averaging our sample weights from streams of varying width groups regardless of whether they had been taken at sides or centers of streams, several significant facts are indicated. This is shown in Table 19. Narrow streams belonging to the 1-6 ft. group averaged over 2.06 grams per square foot while those in the 19-24 ft. group averaged only 0.51 grams of food per square foot. It is also to be noted that there is a steady decline in the amounts of food found from streams of the 1-6 ft. group to those belonging to the 19-24 ft. group. Beyond this point in the wider streams, the rise is slight to the last or 30-50 ft. group.

TABLE XIX

WET WEIGHT IN GRAMS PER SQUARE FOOT OF FOOD ANIMALS FOUND IN RIFFLES OF STREAMS OF VARYING WIDTH-GROUPS

WIDTH OF STREAM IN FEET	NUMBER OF SAMPLES	WET WEIGHT OF FOOD PER SQUARE FOOT	POUNDS PER ACRE
1– 6	10	2.06	197
7– 12	26	1.67	160
13– 18	24	0.94	90
19– 24	9	0.51	48
25– 30	6	0.62	59
30– 50	9	0.67	64
	84 total	1.07 average	103 average

While the data submitted in Table 19 are based upon only 84 samples, nevertheless they indicate clearly the tremendous amounts of food that are available in the smaller spring-fed tributaries less than twelve feet wide. The average wet weight of food found in the samples listed in Table 19 was 1.07 grams per square foot, or 103 pounds per acre of riffle.

In order to obtain fair averages of food conditions at any point in a stream, it is necessary to secure a comparatively large number of samples, because of the great variability from place to place. For instance, the ten samples upon which the data for streams in the 1-6 ft. group in Table 19 are based ranged from 0.65 grams per square foot, the lightest sample in this series, to 4.19 grams per square foot, the heaviest sample. Other samples in this series ran as follows: 2.5, 1.5, 3.97, 0.98, 0.99, 1.98, 1.01, and 2.85 grams respectively.

The weights in all of the other groups were equally variable; as for instance in the 7-12 ft. group they ran from 0.55 to 5.36 grams. It is practically impossible to predict with any great degree of accuracy the amount of food that will be found at any particular point where a sample is to be taken, though, with experience, it is possible to gauge roughly the relative richness.

Comparing now the productivity of wide and narrow streams, the figures of the preceding table seem to show that streams six feet or less in width are over four times as rich per unit area as streams 19 to 24 feet in width. Thus small, headwater brooks are very productive in potential fish foods, and this is a major reason why such areas make good nurseries or feeding grounds for small trout. On the other hand streams over 12 feet averaged less than 1 gram of food per square foot. It is evident then, that wide streams have considerably less bottom foods per bottom area than small streams.

Fig. 51.—Netting eastern brook trout in winter for stomach examinations.

The important question that at once arises is, are narrow streams more productive of foods than wide streams when total areas are considered? By this is meant, would a mile of stream averaging six feet in width produce more trout foods than a stream of the same length thirty feet in width? The exact answer obviously depends upon a multiplicity of conditions, such as total riffle areas, pool areas, type of bottoms, water speeds, and water temperatures in each. A rough answer may be obtained by a few simple calculations from the figures given in Table 19. These will show that wider streams produce more food over total areas, other things being equal. Although the wider streams produce smaller amounts per square foot, their greater areas more than compensate for the high production per square foot of the narrow streams.

In the cold spring runs that are the sources of our main rivers, living conditions are ideal both for the insects and fish. The main advantages of these headwaters as homes, in contrast to the big streams, are: little seasonal or daily fluctuation in volume and temperature, better protection from enemies, abundant food of the right sort, and clean waters in which to live. Here young trout find the best growing conditions. Here they can attain good size before seeking wider waters.

But not all wider streams are as poor in potential food as the figures in Table 19 would indicate. Later investigational work has shown that certain very wide streams are more productive of foods than many narrow ones. For instance, work in the Klamath River in northern California, near Hornbrook, a section of stream that averages about 200 feet in width, has shown an average of 5000 pounds of food per acre of riffle area. This is a very rich stream and the amount of food present is almost unbelievable. In one sample covering exactly one square foot, there were obtained over 4000 living animals. Such amazing production is probably due to the several unusual conditions present in this stream. It is very rich in suspended organic matter that the water picks up as it flows through the extremely rich tule-bordered Klamath Lake and Copco Dam, and upon which numbers of insects such as caddisfly larvae feed; it is not subject to severe flooding, and numerous fine cold-water tributaries flow in at frequent intervals along its course. Rotting king salmon that have died after spawning, and such steelhead as fail to survive the long spawning migration from the sea some 250 miles distant, both contribute considerable amounts of decaying organic matter to the water in the winter and spring. A small amount of pollution often enriches a stream. This is a perfect example of where "natural" pollution is the immediate cause of extremely high production of fish foods.*

The figures submitted in Table 19 were obtained in good trout waters in central New York state and represent fairly average conditions for trout waters in most semi-cultivated regions.

SEASONAL ABUNDANCE OF STREAM FOODS

All the foregoing figures were secured in the months of June, July, August, and September. No studies were made at any other season. In 1932 the writer was assigned to California by the United States Bureau of Fisheries to conduct similar investigations, and there the mild winter climate permitted investigation of stream foods throughout the year. The following data are based upon seasonal studies carried on in Waddell Creek, a small coastal stream about forty miles south of San Francisco. This stream averages about three feet in width at the end of the dry season in late October and early November. In the rainy season it

* Phinney and Peek (1961) estimated that in 1956, during August, 2300 tons of organic material were exported from upper Klamath Lake. Organic enrichment by salmon carcasses can be significant. J. R. Donaldson estimated yearly contributions of from 4 to 169 metric tons of phosphorus by sockeye salmon to Iliamna Lake, a deep, 1000-square-mile body of water. Similar figures were obtained for several other Alaskan lakes. Effects of slight amounts of artificial organic enrichment have been studied by Katz and Howard (1955) and Warren et al. (1964).

is subject to severe floods when it will flow up to 500 cubic feet of water per second. Its average annual width is about twenty feet. Silver salmon and steelhead trout are abundant, adults of both species running in from the ocean during late fall, winter, and spring. The bottom is largely of gravel and small rubble, with fine, deep pools at frequent intervals. The stream rises in the Santa Cruz Mountains and flows some 15 miles southward into the ocean. Before reaching the ocean it flows through a lagoon for approximately one mile. Here brackish water conditions prevail, depending upon high tides, flood conditions, and wave action. The food samples were taken at a series of stations in the first three miles above the lagoon.

In an effort to determine the amount of fish foods present at the various seasons, six series of from 11 to 14 samples each were taken at varying periods. It is to be noted in Table 20 that there is considerable fluctuation in the amount of food present from season to season. The May series of samples was the richest of any obtained, giving an average of 18,254 organisms per square meter or 472 pounds of food per acre. This extreme richness was largely due to a superabundance of blackfly larvae (*Simulium*), which literally covered the stones in the shallow, swift riffles at this season of the year. The lowest amount obtained was in the February series, in which an average of only 2862 organisms per square meter was found, giving the calculated amount of 70 pounds of food per acre.

It seems probable that the paucity of stream foods found during February was due to floods. The rains start in December and continue intermittently to March and April. Many are severe and cause heavy outwash in the streams, cutting away banks and trees and carrying large amounts of debris downstream.

It will be noted in several instances in Table 20, that high average number of organisms per square meter does not necessarily indicate high poundage of foods per acre. For example the February series averaged 2862 organisms per square meter and only 70 pounds per acre. The August (1932) series, on the other hand, showed 159 pounds of food per acre with but 2787 organisms per square meter. Such apparent lack of correlation may be easily accounted for by difference in the body weights of the organisms taken in each series. In the February series many animals of small size were taken and their body weight was low, while in the August series fewer but heavier animals were taken. Mayfly nymphs were dominant in the February samples while caddicefly larvae and pupae were dominant in August.

The data in Table 20 indicate roughly two peaks of seasonal abundance of stream foods: one in the spring and one in November-December. Whether similar seasonal variations would occur in streams elsewhere under more severe winter conditions remains to be seen.

TABLE XX

SEASONAL ABUNDANCE OF BOTTOM FOODS IN WADDELL CREEK RIFFLES, 1932–1933

DATE	NO. SAMPLES	AVE. W.W. OF FOOD PER SQ. FT. IN GRAMS	AVE. NO. ORGANISMS PER SQ. METER	W.W. POUNDS OF FOOD PER ACRE, RIFFLE AREA	DOMINANT FOOD ORGANISMS
Aug. 23, 24, 25, 26, 1932	14	1.66	2,787	159	Caddisfly larvae and pupae
Nov. 28, 29, 30, Dec. 1, 2, 1932	12	2.14	6,531	205	Mayfly nymphs
Feb. 14, 15, 16, 1933	14	0.733	2,862	70	Mayfly nymphs
March 30, 31, April 3, 4, 1933	12	0.907	2,324	87	Mayfly nymphs
May 16, 17, 18, 19, 22, 23, 1933	13	4.92	18,254	472	Two-winged fly (Diptera) larvae and pupae
Aug. 29, 30, 31, Sept. 1, 2, 1933	11	1.94	6,262	186	Caddisfly larvae and pupae
Totals and Averages	76	2.05	6,503	196	

It is to be remembered that the dry season in California extends from late April to November, when the streams become quite low. Undoubtedly this factor is of prime importance. Winter conditions in Waddell Creek and other coastal streams are quite mild and are in no way comparable to winter conditions in streams in northeastern states.

For the steelhead trout of the coastal streams of California it is exceedingly fortunate that an increase of stream foods occurs in the spring of the year. This is the time that the normal stream population is greatly augmented by steelhead fry hatching from eggs naturally spawned in the stream during the previous winter and spring months. The demand for foods is correspondingly increased at this time of year. General observations on other coastal streams in California have shown that similar spring increases of foods occur.

Surber (1936), after sampling foods each month over a year period using somewhat similar methods in Big Spring Creek in Virginia, found an average standing crop of approximately 485 pounds (w.w.) of food per acre of riffle area, between August, 1933, and August, 1934. From August, 1934, to August, 1935, the average was 643 pounds (w.w.) per acre of riffle area. As shown above, the average annual standing crop for Waddell Creek riffles was 196 pounds (w.w.) per acre. Thus Surber's figures show from about two and one-half to over three times as much as was found in Waddell Creek. With regard to reasonal abundance of foods Surber (*loc. cit.*) says: "The peak of production during 1934 was attained on June 8, at 1020.2 pounds per acre wet weight. . . ." Surber does not indicate that a peak is also reached in the fall season, as is roughly shown above in the Waddell Creek studies. It is interesting to note, however, that both the Waddell Creek and Big Spring Creek figures are in general agreement as to a tremendous increase in total available standing crops of food in the spring season.

Winter food conditions in streams are generally misunderstood by anglers, fish culturists, and others, who are often heard to object to the planting of trout in the fall because of the lack of foods for them for

FIG. 52.—Stomach contents of brown trout. This eight and one-half inch fish had eaten mostly mayfly nymphs of the genus *Baetis*. Part of a caddis worm case made of pebbles is seen just above the left center; just below is a stonefly nymph with the rear end of the body missing; and on the lower right, the dark outline of a beetle is seen (photograph by courtesy of Mr. J. H. Wales).

overwintering. This idea is not based on fact. While there is apparently less food available then, ample food is still present, as shown above.

In the Merced River in Yosemite National Park* in the Sierra Nevada Mountains where severe winter conditions prevail, there was found an average of 103 pounds of food per acre of riffle area in February, 1933. Samples from the same riffle in August, 1933, gave a production of only

* Thanks are due the National Park Service for hearty cooperation in furthering field investigations in streams and lakes of the Yosemite Region.

85 pounds per acre, or 18 pounds less. These figures are based upon four samples taken in each of these months. The Waddell data show a decrease of foods in winter and the Merced figures just the reverse, but these figures are too inadequate a basis for definite conclusions. Nevertheless they do show that while the fluctuation may be considerable in either direction, there still remains abundant underwater food available to the trout. In addition, the demand for foods by trout will be much less in the winter time, particularly in a stream like the Merced River where the water temperatures range close to 32°F. for December, January, February, and March. In cold-blooded animals such as fish, where the temperature of the medium in which they live determines the temperature of their bodies, the demand for food is greatly lessened by lowering of the rate of metabolism as the freezing point is approached. In the Merced River, rainbow trout have been seen feeding when the water temperature was 33°F. They were not very active, but they were rising occasionally to feed on a few scattered midges that were emerging in the bright sunlight of a fine February morning.

With regard to fall plantings of trout, more important than possible lack of food for them is their migratory habits, particularly if legal-sized fish are being planted. If young steelhead two or more years old are planted in the fall, they will migrate downstream in the early spring seeking the ocean or large lakes in which to mature, and when the fishing season opens they will be elsewhere.

Variable amounts of food are found from season to season in the same riffle. In Table 21 this is shown for one riffle in Waddell Creek. The figures for February, April, and May are the average weights of three samples taken in each of these months, but all the other figures are the weights obtained from single samples only.

TABLE XXI

AMOUNT OF FOOD FOUND IN ONE RIFFLE* AT VARYING SEASONS OF THE YEAR

DATE	NO. SAMPLES	WIDTH	DEPTH	WT. OF FOOD IN GRAMS PER SQ. FT.
August 25, 1932	1	8 ft.	6 in.	3.63
November 28, 1932	1	8 ft.	5 in.	5.23
February 15, 1933	3	20 ft.	6 in.	0.648
April 4, 1933	3	21 ft.	7 in.	1.14
May 17, 1933	3	21 ft.	4 in.	5.00
August 30, 1933	1	12 ft.	3 in.	1.67

* This riffle was located about one mile from the ocean in the lower part of Waddell Creek. Its length was approximately 100 feet and the water was swift in it at all times. The bottom at all times consisted of coarse gravel mixed with fine gravel and sand. Seasonal variations in volume of flow account for varying widths and depths listed.

Here the same seasonal trends are evident as were shown in Table 20 for the whole stream. The fluctuation in weight of foods found from time to time is greater here, and this would naturally be expected when production from individual samples is recorded rather than averages from a series of samples.

A study of weight as compared with numbers was undertaken in the spring of 1934. Instead of weighing together all the animals taken in each sample as had been done previously, the aquatic insects of the four major groups, caddisflies, mayflies, two-winged flies (*Diptera*) and stoneflies, were sorted and weighed separately to determine their contribution by weight as well as by numbers. This was done in thirteen samples and the data are submitted in Table 22. Here it is at once evident that larger numbers do not by any means indicate greater amount of food. Caddisfly larvae and pupae which formed only 22.2 per cent of the total number of organisms taken in the 13 samples formed 43.9 per cent of the total wet weight of all organisms, thus offering the most food in actual bulk of the four groups. Mayfly nymphs, on the other hand, were most abundant, forming over 55 per cent by number but only 28 per cent by weight. Stonefly nymphs were third in weight at 12.2 per cent and fourth in numbers at 7.8 per cent. Trout stomach examinations by many other workers have shown that the caddisflies are the most important single group of trout food insects. This is assuming equivalent nutritive values for all groups.

TABLE XXII

MAJOR GROUPS OF AQUATIC INSECTS AND THEIR CONTRIBUTION BY WEIGHT AND NUMBERS TO AVAILABLE FOOD SUPPLY OF WADDELL CREEK RIFFLES*

	Total No.	Per Cent	Total Wet Weight in Grams	Per Cent
Caddisfly larvae and pupae	891	22.2	6.79†	43.9
Mayfly nymphs	2,224	55.5	4.33	28.0
Diptera larvae and pupae	412	10.3	1.22	7.9
Stonefly nymphs	312	7.8	1.89	12.2
Miscellaneous	164	4.1	1.22	7.9
Totals	4,003	—	15.45	—

* Based on 13 samples taken Feb. 14, 15, 28, Mar. 1, 2, 20, 22, 1934.
† Weight of caddisfly larval cases not included.

In order to learn what trout select for food from what their environment offers, a study was made of available bottom foods as compared with those consumed. The results are given in Table 23.

Generally speaking, the insects most abundant in stream bottoms were eaten most largely. Mayfly nymphs formed 36.9 per cent of total available foods and 30.1 per cent of foods eaten by the 147 trout. On the other hand, mayfly nymphs, although the most abundant aquatic food, were second choice to caddisfly larvae and pupae. The reasons for larger consumption of a less abundant food would seem to lie in the following conditions: *viz.*, mayfly nymphs are much smaller in size than caddisfly larvae or pupae and therefore harder for trout to see; mayfly nymphs live closely attached to stones and gravel in swift water while the larvae of most caddisflies live in quite conspicuous places where they spin their nets or build their cases and in such positions are more easily found. Caddisfly pupae, when swimming to the surface to emerge as adults from the water, are entirely at the mercy of any fish that happens to see them.

TABLE XXIII

COMPARISON OF AVAILABLE BOTTOM FOODS WITH THOSE CONSUMED BY TROUT

Order	Available Aquatic Foods Per Cent	Aquatic Foods Eaten by Trout Per Cent*
Mayfly nymphs	36.9	30.1
Caddisfly larvae and pupae	21.3	44.7
Stonefly nymphs	14.7	3.5
Fly larvae and pupae	13.8	15.8
Beetle larvae	7.6	2.8
Crayfish and scuds	3.7	1.1
Miscellaneous	1.9	1.9

* Per cent based on number of each eaten. From stomach examination of 147 trout; 32 rainbow, 6 brown, and 109 eastern brook trout taken in streams of central New York state. Length from 4 to 10 inches.

A great assortment of aquatic insects may be found in a typical riffle bottom. Table 24 lists the insects that were collected from one square foot in the center of a riffle in a trout stream near Ithaca, New York, on August 22, 1927. The stream at the point where this study was made flowed down a swift rubble riffle about eight feet in width,

TABLE XXIV

LIST OF ORGANISMS FROM SAMPLE SQUARE FOOT OF RIFFLE BOTTOM

Order	No. Taken	No. Kinds	Names
Mayfly nymphs	58	4	*Baetis* dominant
Caddisfly larvae and pupae	82	5	*Hydropsyche* dominant
Two-winged fly	49	6	7 cranefly larvae, others midges
Stonefly nymphs	33	4	*Leuctra* dominant, 2 large *Perlas*
Beetles	36	3	5 adult and 31 larval riffle beetles (Parnids)

emptying below into a wide, deep pool bordered by willows. Here were found, crowded close together in one small area, a total of 258 specimens of 22 kinds of insects. Their total weight was 2.13 grams. The amazing feature is not their total weight, but the large and varied assortment of forms that can occupy so small an area as one square foot of stream

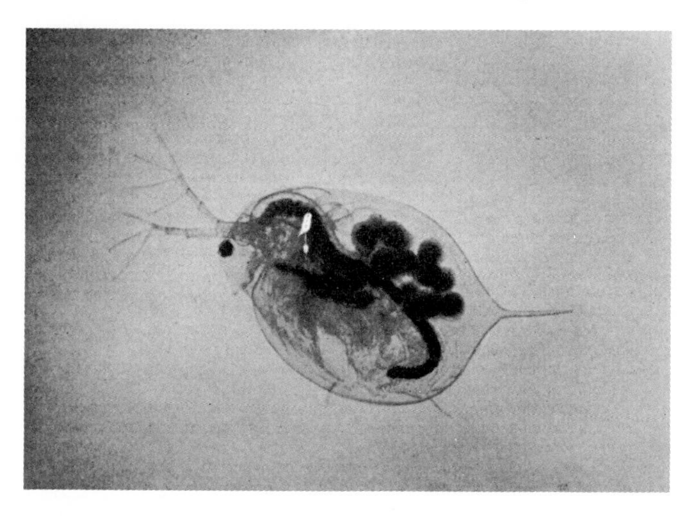

FIG. 53.—Water-flea, *Daphnia;* very abundant seasonally, and a major food item of small trout in lakes. The black wavy line is the alimentary canal full of food. Above this is the brood chamber with eggs. These produce living young (fourteen times natural size).

bottom. If this minute area supports successfully such an abundance of life the number of organisms produced over miles of trout streams must be enormous. At certain times of the year persons who reside by the water's edge are made aware of their numbers by the sudden appearance of the adults when they swarm by the million from the water, covering everything, houses and trees alike, in solid mats of drab grey or brown fluttering insects; or at the time of their mating flights when they are seen dancing over the water, rising and falling, dipping into the water to release their eggs; or after they have died, and the wind has blown windrows of them in dark lines along the shores.

AQUATIC PLANTS AND STREAM PRODUCTIVITY

Our concern here is to ascertain the effect of plant beds on stream productivity in fish foods. The figures given above were concerned with bare stream bottoms, or rather, with bottoms in which none of the larger, rooted, vascular plants were growing. Quiet or semi-quiet shallow waters with silt or mud bottoms are the places in streams that permit the best weed-bed development. Such situations most nearly approach pond conditions. On the other hand few aquatic plants have been able to withstand the force of the current in swift water, and there we find the plant populations limited to algae and a few mosses.

Plants must have light in order to grow, and shallow well-lighted areas are the zones of highest weed-bed development. None of the

FIG. 54.—Diagrammatic sketch of trout feeding on caddisflies rising from water. Caddisfly pupa leaving case at bottom; pupae swimming to surface; and adult shedding pupal skin to take flight from surface of the water.

plant bed studies recorded here was made in water over 12 inches deep, and only three were made in swift water.

A number of bottom studies were made in plant beds in trout streams. From the weight of animals found in various types of plant beds, has been calculated the production in pounds of food per acre (Table 25). The bottom fauna as well as the animals among the leaves and stems of the plants was taken in each case and therefore the available food is that found in both.

In production of food per acre the stonewort, *Chara,* was found to yield the most, giving the large total of 3553 pounds per acre (Table 25). Watercress was second with 1229 pounds; long-leaved and curly pondweeds were third at 566 pounds each, while water buttercup and the sago pondweed produced only 336 and 307 pounds respectively. All of these figures are based upon weighed collections from slow-flowing waters.

Of the plants in swift waters, a mixed growth of the alga, *Cladophora,* and moss produced the most animal food, 403 pounds per acre. Moss and horned pondweed gave the lowest productions obtained in any of the studies, 297 pounds and 288 pounds each, respectively. Horned pondweed usually grows in slow water but in this particular case it was found growing in swift water.

The scud often called "Caledonia shrimp" (*Gammarus*) (Fig. 47) made up 61.4 per cent of the total number of organisms taken in the stonewort bed. This is an excellent trout food and one that is in constant demand for replenishing the food supply of private waters. "Bloodworms" or midge larvae, another good food, formed 31.9 per cent of the

TABLE XXV

COMMON PLANTS OF TROUT WATERS AND THEIR PRODUCTIVITY IN FISH FOODS*

Name		Water		Type of Bottom	Dominant Organism % in Each Bed Studied	Pounds of Food per Acre
Common	Scientific	Depth	Speed			
Stonewort	*Chara* sp.	8″	Slow	Silt & muck	Scuds, 61.4%	3,553
Watercress	*Nasturtium aquaticum*	8″	Slow	Sand & gravel	Scuds, 81.4%	1,229
Long-leaved pondweed	*Potamogeton nodosus*	5″	Slow	Mud	Water-boat-men, 67.7%	566
Curly pond-weed	*Potamogeton crispus*	12″	Slow	Silt & muck	Sow-bugs and Scuds, 57.9%	566
Water But-tercup	*Ranunculus aquatilis*	2″	Slow	Silt & gravel	Midge larvae, 44.1%	336
Sago pond-weed	*Potamogeton pectinatus*	5″	Slow	Silt & gravel	Water-boat-men, 75.9%	307
Algae and moss, mixed	*Cladophora* and *Fontinalis*	8″	Swift	Gravel	Midge larvae, 59.8%	403
Water moss	*Hygrohypnum dilatatum*	3″	Swift	Bedrock	Beetle larvae, 43.8%	297
Horned pondweed	*Zannichellia palustris*	6″	Swift	Silt & gravel	Scuds, 60.6%	288

* Based on one sample square foot taken in each type of bed in streams of central New York state.

animals from stonewort. These two constituted 93.3 per cent of the total catch. Other animals less abundant here were beetle larvae, caddis-worms, snails and leeches. Of the two most abundant foods, scuds were collected largely from the stonewort itself while bloodworms were entirely restricted to the bottom silt and muck underneath the plants.

Watercress likewise was very rich in scuds and midge larvae. Here they formed 81.4 per cent and 9.8 per cent respectively and over 91 per cent of total foods.

Among long-leaved pond weeds water-boatmen, *Corixidae* (Fig. 44, *A*), were most abundant, constituting 67.7 per cent of the total collected. Snails, mostly the common pond form, *Lymnaea,* were also fairly common here. Curly pondweeds supported numerous sow-bugs, *Asellus* (Fig. 48), and scuds, these two forming 57.9 per cent of all available foods. This is the only type of plant bed in which sow-bugs were found to be at all numerous. These crustaceans often are staples in the diet of trout living in ponds.

Water buttercup yielded 453 (44.1 per cent) midge larvae and pupae, and 300 (29.2 per cent) mayfly nymphs. Most of the latter nymphs were the common soft-bottom dweller, *Tricorythodes,* similar to *Caenis*

TABLE XXVI
TOTAL AVAILABLE FISH FOODS FOUND IN SUBMERGED PLANT BEDS

KIND OF FOOD	PER CENT
Scuds and sow-bugs	47.8
Two-winged fly larvae and pupae	23.9
Water-boatmen	8.9
Mayfly nymphs	6.1
Caddisfly larvae and pupae	3.9
Snails and clams	3.1
Beetles	3.1
Miscellaneous	3.2

shown in Figure 28, *D.* In Sago pondweed again we find water-boatmen abundant, forming 75.9 per cent. In warm waters, bass often eat large numbers of water-boatmen.

Of the plants in swift water in a mixed bed of the alga, *Cladophora,* and moss, midge larvae occurred in large numbers, making up 59.8 per cent of the foods. In a pure bed of moss, *Hygrohypnum,* beetle larvae were dominant, forming 43.8 per cent. These were all riffle beetle larvae, and because of their minute size and secretive habits they offer but little food to trout. In horned pondweed scuds were again the most abundant food, forming over 60 per cent of the total. Blackfly larvae and pupae, *Simulium,* were also fairly common in this type of bed; they were found fastened upon the leaves of the weed as it trailed gracefully downstream in the current. These two groups formed over 90 per cent of total foods.

It is evident from the foregoing discussion that typical pond-inhabiting animals such as sow-bugs will establish themselves in weed beds in trout streams where sufficiently quiet waters prevail. Quiet waters of streams resemble pond conditions but are in reality a mixture of both types of environments. As a result, both stream and pond inhabitants are found. Some mayfly nymphs, scuds, some fly larvae, and others may inhabit either pond or stream, though most such animals seldom occur in both.

If we total the animals from all weed beds in which quantitative collections were made (Table 26) it is seen that scuds and sow-bugs were most abundant, forming 47.8 per cent. Fly larvae and pupae were second in number, making up 23.9 per cent, while water-boatmen were third at 8.9 per cent. These three groups taken together constitute over 80 per cent of the animals collected.

It will be recalled from the figures submitted in the first part of this chapter that the average food production per square foot in bottoms of bare pools was 0.26 grams, and in riffles was 0.82 grams. For all types of plant beds the average production was found to be around 12.0 grams per square foot. The reasons for the greater richness of stream bottoms in which plant beds have developed are obvious. Plants provide an abundance of food in their leaves; and what is more important, they furnish the finest kind of hiding places for aquatic insects, scuds, etc., among their interlacing leaves and stems. There these animals can escape their enemies and find fairly safe living conditions.

Fig. 55.—Drift net set in position to catch drift organisms that fall from the land into trout streams (photograph by courtesy of Dr. Myron Gordon).

From angling and aesthetic points of view, abundant plant growths oftentimes become a distinct nuisance. Trout ponds may become filled with masses of floating green algae in the summer, producing unsightly scums and bad odors. The larger rooted aquatics may completely fill the ponds, leaving no open fishing water. When choked with vegetation the natural circulation of water is retarded and summer temperatures often rise above the normal limit for trout, causing large losses.

In the more northerly latitudes little trouble is experienced with excessive plant growths, for low water temperatures and short growing season combine to limit weed-bed development. Lily pads in shallow, forest-bordered ponds, will often occlude all open water, spoiling what otherwise might offer good dry fly fishing. A moderate amount of vegetation can be very useful, but it is often difficult to establish and maintain plant growths in properly controlled abundance. In our best trout waters, those clear, cold, "lean" mountain streams, larger rooted aquatic plants are very scare. It is only in the warmer waters at low elevations that plant control becomes a major problem.

LAND FOODS SUPPLIED TO TROUT WATERS

Thus far in this discussion we have been concerned with underwater foods, those that live and grow submerged. Aquatic animals, while they furnish the bulk of sustenance to trout, do not supply it all. Land insects, spiders, millipedes, earthworms, and other land forms which fall into the water accidently furnish a fair proportion of trout diet in the warmer months of the year. This class of food has been termed "drift food" (Needham, 1928a). Land foods fallen into the water drift downstream with the current to pools where they can easily be secured by trout.

Stream drift foods upon which trout feed fall into the following categories:

1. Land inhabiting animals, principally insects, which fall into the water.
2. Aquatic larvae, nymphs, and pupae, that are dislodged from their hiding places in streams.

The first class includes, beside typical land organisms, the adults of aquatic insects that are swept downstream when attempting to emerge from, or to lay eggs in, the water. The second class is, as a rule, present most largely during flood times when high waters sweep these aquatic forms from their hiding places and wash them down stream.

The amount or number of organisms that fall into the waters of trout streams depends upon a number of conditions. The first, and most important, is the type of environment along the banks of the stream. If the banks are lined with green vegetation upon which many insects feed, more of these insects will fall into the water than if banks are bare.

Trout stream banks can be classified roughly into four types, each of which may be determined by the amount of vegetation present. These are: (1) forest-covered, (2) brush-covered, (3) semi-exposed, and (4) exposed.

These four types more or less intergrade, but are sufficiently distinct for general comparisons. In the forested type the stream banks are bordered by a growth of tall trees. Such an environment shelters large numbers of terrestrial insects. Usually it shades the water from the sun during part or all of the day, thereby assisting in keeping the water temperatures within safe limits for trout. Most of our better wilderness trout streams flow through wooded regions. The excellent fishing afforded by these streams is due largely to the forests that line their banks, offering food to the fish, low water temperatures, and a minimum fluctuation in volume. Few streams in the more cultivated regions now have forest growths on their banks, most of the timber having been cut, though they may still flow through small farm wood-lots for short distances.

The second type of stream habitat is that with low-brush-covered banks. Here is a dense growth of alders, hawthornes, willows, low herbs, and grasses that have developed along the stream, usually some years after the original timber was cut. Generally such streams are clogged with logs, sticks and debris of all kinds rotting in the water. Fly fishing is impossible in such places and bait fishing is difficult. However, the large amount of vegetation furnishes much food for insects, which in turn become food for the fish. The banks of many of our smaller and a few of our larger streams are of this sort. Most streams of this type are narrow headwater tributaries in which adult trout spawn. They should not be fished at all, for they serve as nursery streams for young trout.

Semi-exposed streams are usually wide, bordered partially by pasture and cultivated or bare uncultivated terrain, and partially by scattered trees at intervals along their margins, but not in a solid unbroken wall of vegetation. The trees are often willows, sycamores, poplars, or scattered conifers. These are remnants of former forests. Naturally, along the larger streams which drain considerable land areas, no one type of habitat will predominate over the entire course, but from source to confluence with other waters, the stream will flow through a variety of habitats.

Exposed streams flow entirely through pastures and meadows, their banks lacking the larger shrubs and trees. Grasses and low herbs are the only vegetation present on the banks. They are generally subject to high floods that continually erode the banks, change the course of the water, and work all manner of havoc with the bottom animals. Also, as is shown below, this type of environment furnishes but small amounts of drift food to streams.

DRIFT-NET STUDIES

In order to learn the amount of drift food present in streams, in 1927 a drift net was devised (Fig. 55) with the aid of which it was possible to collect this material quantitatively. This fine-meshed 3x30 foot net, when set crosswise in the stream, strained the drift animals from the water. The accompanying table gives some of the results obtained with it.

Forested stream margins supplied the most food, 5.66 grams per surface acre of water. Low brush-covered streams gave the second largest production in 4.14 grams. Semi-exposed and exposed streams produced the least, giving 3.96 grams and 3.22 grams respectively. These figures are based on drift net catches made during the months of June, July, and August, 1927, in the streams of central New York.

The average amount of drift food found per surface acre in streams regardless of type of environment was 4.23 grams. Since this is average production from a 1-hour period, over a period of twenty-four hours an average of 101.76 grams would be available as food for trout or approxi-

Fig. 56.—A serious barrier to upstream migrations; an old "splash dam" used in lumbering operations in Humptulips River, Olympic National Forest, Washington. The central portion of the apron and middle gates above it were removed by P.W.A. labor in 1933. Note figures of two men for comparison with size of logs (photograph by courtesy of U. S. Forest Service).

mately four ounces a day. This would seem to be a rather small amount of drift food to fall into an acre of water, but when total water areas are considered, it is at once evident that a very considerable amount of food is supplied from the land adjacent to streams.

As a general rule, the wider the stream, the more area there is for land insects to fall into, and more drift foods will be found in the wider streams. In the above calculations the amounts of drift foods found are based entirely upon amount received per surface acre of water, regardless of width, in each of the four types of stream environments.

One fact clearly brought out by these drift studies is the great value of marginal stream vegetation in supplying land animals to the water. This fact offers a further convincing argument against cutting away trees along the margins of trout streams.

This work also showed that pools on the average contain more land foods than do riffles. Pools are generally wider than riffles and offer larger surface areas for the reception of land foods, and one would naturally expect to find more drift foods in them on that account. Larger amounts of drift foods therefore compensate somewhat for the scarcity

TABLE XXVII

DRIFT FOOD FOUND IN STREAMS FLOWING THROUGH FOUR TYPES OF STREAM ENVIRONMENTS

TYPE OF ENVIRONMENT	AVE. WEIGHT IN GRAMS OF DRIFT FOOD FROM 1 SQ. ACRE OF WATER*
Forest-covered	5.66
Brush-covered	4.14
Semi-exposed	3.96
Exposed	3.22
Average over all types of Environments	4.23

* Amounts determined from 1-hour catches with the drift net. A "stop net" was always placed in the stream 250 yards above the "drift net." This strained all the drift food from the water that was carried downstream from other types of stream environments than the particular one being sampled. The "stop net" was always set well in advance of setting the "drift net."

To eliminate stream width as a factor, the drift food was calculated from the formula: $\frac{\text{grams}\times 100}{\text{square ft}}$ = wt. in grams of drift food per 100 square feet of water surface. In the above table the original results have been recalculated to show amounts per square acre.

of bottom foods in pools. The greatest value in wide, deep pools is not their value as food-producers but in the protection and shelter that they afford to game fishes.

Many kinds of animals are taken drifting. Two-winged flies (midges, gnats, blue-bottles, etc.) formed the largest single class found, and made up nearly 40 per cent by number of all taken. (Table 28.) Mayflies were second in abundance, giving 28.94 per cent of the total, and with the two-winged flies constituted over two-thirds of the available drift foods. Both of these are very acceptable to trout. Stoneflies formed 3.43 per cent and caddisflies 1.43 per cent. These two latter groups along with mayflies, being abundant in streams in their immature stages, and also being found in considerable numbers in the drift as adults, offer food to trout during their entire life cycle. Ants formed 4.33 per cent. These have long been known to be readily taken by trout. Beetles and true-bugs occurred in about the same numbers in the drift. Aphids or plant-lice made up 14.91

per cent numerically, but they offer but little real food on account of their exceedingly small size.

Grasshoppers were very scarce during the summer these collections were made, and none were found in the drift. Under the miscellaneous list are included a few leeches, hair-worms, spring-tails, millipedes, earthworms, and a few caterpillars.

TABLE XXVIII

MONTHLY AND TOTAL DRIFT FOODS FOUND IN STREAMS IN JUNE, JULY, AND AUGUST, 1927*

KIND OF FOOD	JUNE Per Cent	JULY Per Cent	AUGUST Per Cent	TOTAL Per Cent
Two-winged flies	30.95	51.20	24.42	38.46
Mayflies	26.97	27.19	37.03	28.94
Plant-lice	23.77	9.52	9.18	14.91
Ants	5.02	1.54	9.49	4.33
Beetles	4.92	2.84	3.94	3.84
True-bugs	4.18	1.09	3.94	2.80
Caddisflies	1.33	0.96	2.73	1.43
Spiders	0.89	0.52	0.81	0.72
Stoneflies	0.84	4.54	6.16	3.43
Miscellaneous	1.13	0.65	2.31	1.15

* Based on a total of 5,314 drift organisms; percentage by months based on total number taken each month.

Dry-fly fishermen will be interested to know something about the monthly abundance of drift foods. The summer month in which each class of insects is most abundant on the water is shown in Table 28. The true-flies (Diptera) reached their highest percentage in July, when they formed 51.20 per cent of the so-called "dry" foods. Imitations of blue-bottles, black-gnats, midges or other true-flies should therefore be more acceptable to trout during this month. A mayfly should be more acceptable in August, as this group reached its maximum in this month at 37.03 per cent. Red ants were most abundant in August, but since mayflies formed the dominant fly on the water in this month, a mayfly imitation should be more acceptable than an ant. Caddisflies and stoneflies likewise were most abundant in the drift in August. Spiders varied but little from month to month. Beetles were most abundant in June. The possible inferences from Table 28 are many, and using the data in this manner is likely to start more arguments than it finishes. Let each angler interpret it as best suits his own experience.

Of all drift foods taken, 93.02 per cent were adult insects terrestrial in origin, while 6.98 per cent were aquatic in origin; i.e., nymphs, larvae, or pupae that normally live on the stream bed, but which happened to be washed from their hiding places and swept downstream.*

* Anderson (1966), Waters (1969) and others have studied drift of aquatic insects in relation to the daily cycle and have found much greater activity at night—especially in the dark of the moon.

The above findings on the distribution of trout foods can be considered as applicable to the streams of central New York state and of California where these studies were conducted, or to streams similar in kind. The more general features of foods distribution discussed above will be found applicable to most trout waters. The greatest usefulness of work of this kind will lie in its application to stream improvement. Knowing the conditions that make for richness of foods and abundant fish, it should be possible to assist nature in bringing these conditions back in barren waters.

VI

Propagation, Stocking, and Protection

THE FOUR major activities involved in stream and lake management are *propagation, stocking,* and *protection* of trout and the *improvement* of trout waters. The first three of these are discussed in this chapter; improvements and related matters are taken up in Chapter VII.

We have learned from hard experience that our trout fishing is continuing to decline in spite of increased stocking, greater restrictive measures, and the building of stream improvements. That it has declined in many waters open to the public, I think all will agree. Improved highways, faster cars, and shorter working hours have so increased the spread of fishing and consequent "kill" of trout that many formerly productive streams now offer slim sport. They serve only as sources of discontent and criticism aimed at conservation officials by dissatisfied sportsmen. Trout streams in which I had fine brook trout fishing as a boy in central New York state I found on a recent visit to be practically troutless, in spite of continued yearly replantings. Pollution, droughts, poaching, and other factors have played their part, but by far the most important single cause has been increased intensity of angling. This has made it an almost impossible task for hatcheries to maintain a proper balance between stream populations and "take."

Frequent complaints are voiced by the older anglers who bemoan the passing of the "good old days" when it was possible to take a basketful of trout in an hour's fishing. This is futile. The "good old days" of easy fishing are gone for good, and in the sense of easy slaughtering of large numbers of game-fish at one time, the "good old days" are better past. Our task now is to salvage what remains of our game-fish from such angling orgies. If the same conditions prevailed today in our streams as prevailed in earlier decades, we might be able to bring back fishing to its former excellence. But modern commercial, industrial, and recreational activities have so altered conditions that in many streams we are lucky to have any fishing at all.

Happily, there remain some wilderness areas. Abundant stocks of fish and game are still to be found in places that are largely untouched and undeveloped by man. Here excellent sport is still to be had by the few sportsmen able to get into back country, and the kill is now moderated by helpful restrictive measures. But it is only a question of time until these areas too become accessible and depleted unless adequate conservation measures are adopted.

A few heavily fished streams offer better sport than formerly because they have been managed with foresight and intelligence. For examples, the Beaverkill, Willowemoc, and Esopus near New York City have held their own in spite of extremely heavy fishing. Private clubs or individuals own and control the better fishing areas on these streams, and this has permitted careful independent management. By stocking heavily and enforcing rigid regulations as to size and seasonal and creel limits the fishing has been saved. It is about as good today as it was ten or fifteen years ago. Likewise, streams in New Jersey offer good sport today, due to the planting of large, legal-size trout from the state hatchery.

Our problem is to maintain those waters that are still productive, and to bring back those already stripped of their trout population.

PROPAGATION OF TROUT

NOTE: This section reflects the conditions facing biologists from the 1930's to early 1950's. Although most of the abuses have been corrected, the section has been altered but slightly so that its impact from the historical standpoint has been preserved.

It has become a comparatively simple matter to raise trout. Hatchery methods of caring for eggs, fry, fingerlings, and larger fish have been well developed over a long period of years. Most of the common parasites that infest trout can readily be controlled by simple means, but diseases still cause considerable losses in hatcheries. In recent years research work on fish diseases has shown many new and practical methods of both prevention and control. Likewise nutrition research has produced new and cheaper diets for trout of all ages. These reduce production costs and cause more rapid growth and higher coloration. Larger numbers of trout can be carried to good planting size in the new types of circular ponds that are replacing rectangular ones. Selective breeding experiments at the New Jersey State Hatchery with eastern brook trout for more rapid growth and higher egg yields make it possible to obtain fish between six and seven inches long at the end of eleven months in water at 52° F., and egg yields have so increased per individual brood female that it is necessary to feed and rear only about one-fourth the former number of females to obtain the same number of eggs as were annually taken at the start of the experiments.*

Egg-taking from wild trout has had decidedly bad effects on the trout fishing in many areas. The wild males and females are trapped on their spawning migrations and the eggs are stripped by hand and placed in hatcheries for rearing. Usually but few of the resultant young are returned to the parent waters to maintain the supply; and intensive egg collecting coupled with intensive angling usually results in serious depletion within a few years. Young fish so reared when broadcast into other waters to which they are totally unsuited are a total loss.

* Chris Jensen of the Oregon State Game Commission reports that fall spawning rainbows are reared to 8 inches in 9 months at Oak Springs Hatchery where there is a constant temperature of 54°F. Some four-year-old brood rainbows at Oregon hatcheries produced up to 8 to 10 thousand eggs each in 1968. L. R. Donaldson, of the University of Washington, has developed rainbow trout which, under proper conditions, produce up to 25,000 eggs at first spawning.

Land-locked salmon, formerly found in apparently unlimited abundance in the Sebago Lakes in Maine, offer a clear example. The spawning fish were trapped and both eggs and fry were shipped to many states (and even to foreign countries) to persons who wanted to establish these gamy fish in new waters. A few of those hatched were returned each year to the waters from which they had come. But too few were returned to the native waters, as later years fully demonstrated. The strain of

Fig. 57.—An excellent type of stream improvement work; Civilian Conservation Corps workers removing old water supply dam which blocked upstream migration. Snow Creek, Olympic National Forest, Washington (photograph by courtesy of U. S. Forest Service).

intensive angling combined with intensive egg-taking so reduced the population of these fish that they steadily declined to a point where only a very limited supply was available. Coupled with the failure of the original source, most of the introductions of these fish into new waters also failed and represented largely wasted effort.

In streams on the Pacific Coast egg-taking from sea-run steelhead trout has been going on for years with similar consequent decline of sport fishing for these fish. As with the land-locked salmon, a portion of the eggs and young were returned to the waters from which they were taken each year, but most of them have gone to stock waters that do not offer free access to the ocean. Many are planted in waters where oceanward migrations cause large losses, due to power and irrigation developments.*

* Use of steelhead progeny for inland fisheries has been abandoned. The location of unscreened diversions is taken into account in most modern planting operations.

However, in the case of these fish, as contrasted with land-locked salmon, those planted in waters which give access to large lakes to which they can migrate and grow to maturity often do very well and offer fine sport fishing. A notably successful case is the introduction of steelhead trout into streams flowing into Lake Superior.

This whole problem is one of paramount importance at the present time. The same wastage is going on in the taking of wild eastern brook, cutthroat, stream rainbow, and brown trout eggs. Intensive angling coupled with excessive egg-taking is rapidly depleting waters of their brood fish.

There are several procedures that might be put in effect that would remedy the robbing of streams of their egg supplies until scientific study points out better measures. These are:

(1) To return the bulk of young to the waters from which eggs are taken.*

(2) To close and set aside entire small lakes or spawning tributaries, and in the case of sea-run steelheads, entire small coastal streams, as egg-taking sources.†

(3) To grow in hatcheries select domestic brood stocks of those species for which wild egg sources cannot be developed or obtained.

The first proposal would largely stop the present practice of robbing Peter to pay Paul. In most middle western and eastern states, sources of wild eggs failed long ago and domestic brood stocks now supply the necessary eggs. Depletion came sooner and has proceeded farther in the eastern states. With wild-egg sources gone for good, there was no other alternative than to develop domestic stocks. The Rocky Mountain and Pacific coast regions still depend on wild-egg sources to a considerable extent. These are being rapidly reduced, along with the fishing value of the waters wherein the eggs are obtained. In the west, depletion is following the same course as in the east, and it is only a question of time until the bulk of trout eggs will have to be raised in hatcheries. In anticipation of failing egg sources, many western states have begun to keep domestic brood stocks.

Eggs produced by fish that are fed on artificial foods naturally cost more per thousand than eggs taken from wild fish that have sought out their own food. The major costs involved in taking wild eggs are the labor of trapping, holding, and stripping the fish. Hatchery-raised eggs however do have the advantage of permitting far better management. Selective breeding for high egg-yields, for rapid growth, for resistance to disease, and for other characters, can be practiced with great improvement over a period of years.**

The second proposal, to close to angling and set aside entire small lakes or spawning tributaries as wild egg sources, can undoubtedly be of considerable use in supplementing the eggs secured from hatchery-raised

* In many instances, under rearing practices developed in the 1960's, the "bulk of young" would be more than necessary. Survival is sufficiently predictable so that an *adequate* number of young is returned.

† Closing sections of lakes adjacent to tributary spawning streams and sometimes the streams, has proven to be a good method. The Oregon State Game Commission maintains an annual egg take of more than a million on the Alsea River, a stream that produces 8,000 to 12,000 steelhead annually to anglers.

** Domestication of brood stock has been accomplished, but often there is a question of whether or not the changes in the stock detract from the ability of the trout to live in the wild. Vincent (1960) pointed out that hatchery strains tended to be less wary than the wild fish and showed several other physiological and behavioral differences.

brood stocks. The problems here will be: (1) to find lakes having a food supply sufficient to support a large number of adult fish of the species from which eggs are desired; (2) to select lakes that can be adequately protected from poaching, and yet are easy of access, and afford convenient means of trapping adult fish; and (3) to plant back into the same water each year sufficient numbers of young to maintain the brood fish population on a permanent egg-producing basis.*

In the case of steelheads, the production of large numbers of eggs by artificial feeding in hatcheries would be expensive. If, by closure of a few selected coastal streams for egg-taking purposes and by proper protection of the young trout after planting, the ocean could be used as the "rearing pond," it might prove practicable to rely upon wild egg sources for these fish.†

It would be well to add at this point that we do not yet know the number of fish that must be returned to any given water to maintain the supply, though studies on the salmon of the Pacific both by American and Canadian investigators are now presenting facts on this fundamental conservation matter.** Such facts as this are of prime importance in the development of sound management programs.

Great losses of trout result from irrigation and mining diversions. At present the most important single source of destruction to both hatchery-produced and naturally propagated steelhead and salmon on the west coast is unscreened ditches. Unscreened power diversions likewise take their toll of migratory species: oftentimes fish will be chopped into pieces as they pass through the turbines. Power dams on the lower course of westward-draining Sierra streams in California, such as the Merced, San Joaquin, Tuolumne, and Mokelumne, coupled with numerous irrigation projects, have practically exterminated salmon and steelhead runs in these streams. Rapid economic development with little thought or care given to the preservation of these extremely valuable natural resources has practically obliterated them. Irrigation and mining diversions in the arid portions of western United States destroy more fish than are ever taken by anglers. On the Klamath drainage alone a United States Bureau of Fisheries stream survey party found over two hundred and fifty ditches, about one hundred and thirty of which were in need of adequate and properly operated screens. (Taft and Shapovalov, 1935.) Instance after instance could be cited where young steelhead and salmon migrating downstream have been spread over fields, serving as an excellent but costly fertilizer. Few persons realize the immense losses of young fish that occur annually in this manner.

Strange as it may seem, even today few facts are at hand showing the efficiency of various types of screens. The best type of screen to use with any given amount of water flow, the original and maintenance cost of such screens, the best place and method of installation, and the

* East and Diamond Lakes in Oregon have small closed areas to protect congregating spawners. The combined egg take is nearly 5 million per year, and the combined angler harvest about 400,000 fish per year.

† Management of steelhead in the Northwest involves rearing hatchery fish for about a year to a length of 6 to 8 inches and releasing them at the proper physiological time for migration (March to May) See Wagner, 1968.

** Repeated experiments have shown that 1–3% of migrants planted as yearlings can be expected to return to the river as adults, with some returns exceeding 10%. Superimposition of redds, predation, disease, effects of climate and weather and lack of sufficient food all reduce the population. One of the most important regulatory mechanisms in some species is territorial behavior that limits the number of juveniles that can be reared in a given space (Chapman, 1962).

minimum size of fish held back, are problems of major importance in screening operations, and it is high time some basic facts were produced along this line. The United States Bureau of Fisheries and various state departments are giving serious attention to screening problems. They are of paramount importance if the remaining remnants of our former splendid steelhead runs in west coast waters are to survive present destructive conditions working against them.*

FIG. 58.—South Umpqua Falls at low water in August. The white water at the extreme right is flowing down an improvised fish-ladder blasted in the rock (photograph by courtesy of U. S. Forest Service).

AIDS TO PROPAGATION

Having discussed some of the major drawbacks working against successful propagative efforts, whether natural or artificial, let us inquire for the moment into recently developed means of assisting propagation in various areas. One such aid that is especially useful in places remote from hatcheries is rearing ponds by the streamside. Transportation of large fish is expensive, for few can be carried per can or tank as compared to small fry or fingerlings.† Inadequate water supply, pollution, high temperatures, and other conditions often make it impossible to locate hatcheries so that the transportation of large trout will not become a prohibitive expense. The construction of rearing ponds on level places next to the stream with water supplied from the stream itself may be the means of obtaining larger fish for planting. Such ponds save the cost of moving large fish long distances from hatchery ponds. They have been successful in Arkansas, California, Oregon, Pennsylvania, New York, and other states. Success or failure depends upon the care and feeding of the trout

* A considerable technology has built up around screening devices (Clay 1961). Many self-cleaning devices have been adapted to ditches of all sizes. Perforated plates and revolving drum screens are most often used on small ditches, whereas louvers and link-belt screens are used on large diversions.

† Improvements in road systems, along with research and developments in the physiology and technology of transportation of fish has made possible the use of "fish tankers" of up to 1350 gallons capacity, some of which successfully haul about 6000 to 7000 catchable trout (2000 lbs.) for periods up to 10 hours. These trucks carry their own refrigeration system and aerate water by circulation through a venturi device.

in such ponds. State fish and game departments could assign trained fish culturists to projects of this nature where enough ponds are operated to warrant the full-time efforts of one caretaker.

In the far west, at high elevations where water temperatures never become dangerously high, excellent trout ponds can often be constructed in old stream beds. Water can be diverted into former channels that usually more or less parallel present water courses, and after being properly screened and protected from floods these can be stocked with trout. After the fish have grown to proper size they may be planted in the stream supplying the water by merely removing screens at both ends of the diversion. Side-channel ponds at low elevations, on the other hand, may not prove successful because of warm water. Spreading water out and slowing it up in ponds is certain to cause increase in temperature when it is fully exposed to the sun's rays.

If artificial food is to be fed trout in rearing ponds by the streamside, much larger numbers can be reared than in ponds where trout are planted and left to forage for themselves on natural foods. In the latter case the stocking rate must be consistent with the food supply of the pond concerned, or only thin, poorly conditioned fish will result, and losses will be high, because the larger, faster growing individuals will eat the smaller ones. When trout are planted and left to forage for themselves during the summer months (July, August, and September) survival rates of 50 to 70 per cent may be considered successful. There are three basic requirements to be met in such an undertaking: (1) abundant natural foods; (2) water of good temperature for growth; and (3) a location with adequate space for natural ponds, affording protection from floods and easy of access. Also, protection from predatory birds, snakes, etc., is highly essential in trout rearing ponds.*

Cooperative rearing ponds run by sportmen's clubs (the fish being supplied by state fish and game departments) have assisted materially in stocking some waters. Here too the success or failure of rearing operations, if water and ponds are suitable, depends entirely upon the skill of the man feeding and caring for the fish.

Holding ponds are another aid. Strategically located holding ponds in the centers of heavily fished areas that lack hatcheries are of much assistance in planting of trout. The trout for planting are trucked or "packed" to points where the fish are rested (but not fed) in pure cold water ponds for a time, after which they are planted in nearby waters. Such ponds permit trout to recover from the effects of long hauls from hatcheries: generally they can then be planted in much better condition. Further, much of the rush to get trout out of cans or tanks is eliminated. They can be planted leisurely, following a carefully planned program of allotments. Trout often arrive at their destinations in a dazed, helpless condition. To dump them at such a time into wild waters, there to cope

* Rearing ponds at a distance from hatcheries are used extensively in the Pacific Northwest to rear anadromous salmonids to migratory size. Some of the rationale of using natural or fertilized impoundments is presented by Pressey and Smith (1958). They emphasize the economy of planting and letting nature take its course, except perhaps for predator control or fertilization. Results, not all favorable, are discussed by Coche (1967).

Good success has been enjoyed in feeding large numbers of young salmonids in ponds large and small. For instance, the Fish Commission of Oregon reports the release of 1,741,000 fall chinook migrants from a 20-acre impoundment after 80 days of rearing. Several such operations are documented by DeWitt (1969).

with numerous predators, is needless waste of expensive hand-reared fish. They should be permitted to recover their strength and to become used to their new environment. In California and other western states holding ponds have proved highly successful.

PLANTING OF TROUT

The planting of trout from hatcheries to lakes and streams is today the weakest link in the chain of events leading to the angler's creel. In

FIG. 59.—Members of survey party in air-inflated boat taking bottom food samples with an Ekman dredge. Purple Lake, Sierra National Forest, California, 1934.

most states this is a haphazard process at best, and it is doubtful if any feature of trout work offers greater chance for improvement. The greatest gap in our information lies in not knowing very much about what happens to trout between the time they leave the hatchery and the time they are caught.*

As carried on at present the allotments as to numbers, sizes, and species to be planted in the various waters are usually made up in the state fish and game headquarters or by district supervisors, hatchery superintendents, or others connected with the work and they are usually based, at least in large part, upon requests for fish by the anglers. Then the fish are either planted by those who raised them, the hatchery men, or they

* Although the complete answer is by no means available, the question of what happens to trout after planting has been pursued to the point where fishery agencies are in little doubt as to the practical use of their hatchery products. The *Transactions of the American Fisheries Society* and other journals contain the story of what happens to trout after planting by bits and pieces. Test streams and special studies have produced knowledge on relationships of survival to size at planting, to time and place of planting, to type of hatchery food, to the strain of trout used and many other aspects (Cooper, 1959). Some important points gained are (1) planted trout survive much better in lakes than in streams; (2) in streams, winter mortality is generally great; (3) in streams, migration of legal-sized fish and mortality from fishing and other causes combine to make most of them disappear after a month or so.

are turned over to special planting crews, or as is usually the case, to wardens, forest or park rangers, sportsmen, packers, anglers, or other persons interested in lending a hand. In other words, anybody may take a hand in it even though not well informed as to how or where any given species should be planted.

What has been the result today of this system (or lack of system)? The most important evil has been the mixing of incompatible species: warm-water predacious fish such as bass, perch, pike, etc., in trout waters; Loch Leven in rainbow or eastern brook trout waters; lake trout in cutthroat waters, etc.; so that today many lakes and streams contain heterogeneous mixtures of both non-native and native forms. These misguided introductions have so upset the balance of nature in many waters as to ruin almost completely the sport-fishing in them. For example: from New York in Lake Ozonia the introduction of bass has ruined the trout fishing even though bass are less adapted to this water than trout; in the Chateaugay Lakes yellow perch have spoiled much fine trout fishing; in Upper Saranac Lake northern pike have done nothing but harm. Also, in high, cold, mountain lakes in various sections of the west the introduction of Loch Leven or brown trout has largely had bad effects when they were planted in waters too cold for good growth. There they offer poor sport, and they consume large numbers of better adapted trout.

The whole question of correct and adequate stocking is one of balance. The fish that are found naturally in any water are the fish adapted to that environment. When man steps in to upset the balance, however good his intentions, the results are usually harmful. In waters lacking fish, the problem is to select the most adaptable species and to prevent the planting of others. Many careless and unintentional plantings have been made by anglers in throwing unused bait minnows into waters when they were through fishing. Some states now have laws making it illegal to fish with non-native minnows. This is one means of protection against planting of undesirable species.

To quote Dr. John R. Greeley (1929):

> In view of the many cases in which introduction of non-native species have proven detrimental to productivity, it is apparent that care should be exercised to prevent unwise introductions. The safest policy is to encourage native species which have been successful in the past and to avoid introducing others unless it is apparent that they will not be harmful. This is the "ounce of prevention" in this case. There may be no "pound of cure," for it is probably impossible to remove all individuals of an undesirable species from a large body of water. There is no simple means for restoring balance, once it is upset.*

One of the worst features of the introduction of new, non-native forms to improve angling is that, for the first few years, it is often apparently highly successful. Fish so introduced, lacking the normal population

* Fish eradicants have been used to rid ponds, lakes and even streams of all fish life, so that new starts could be made. Rotenone, endrin and toxaphene pesticides have been tried. See Applegate et al. (1961), McPhee and Ruelle (1968), and Gilderhus et al. (1969).

The sea lamprey population of the Great Lakes is being reduced by systematic use of 3-trifluoromethyl-4-nitrophenol in tributary streams. "Squoxin" shows promise of reducing populations of the northern squawfish, an important predator, in the Northwest. Antimycin A allows small crews to carry out, in a short time, fish control operations that once necessitated many men and several days of effort.

checks found in their native environment, will often grow and reproduce at a high rate with what appear to be highly satisfying results. But as soon as their food supply is reduced they begin eating each other, and in the long run there results a large population of stunted fish offering poor sport. The next step is to try other species, and so the vicious cycle goes on.

Certain fishes are associated together naturally in any environment. In brook trout waters in eastern United States various minnows, suckers, sculpins, etc., are usually abundant and furnish large amount of food to the trout. Their reproductive capacity is usually sufficient to counterbalance losses of those eaten by trout, and their numbers tend to remain about the same from year to year. The trout in such waters may maintain themselves fairly well in spite of fishing as long as such natural associations are undisturbed by the introduction of exotic forms. All species in any such natural association will show periodic fluctuations in their numbers from time to time due to various factors, but in the long run their numbers will tend to remain fairly constant. None of the species present in any such natural grouping will exterminate another completely.

Odell (1930), writes as follows on the destructive effects of introducing non-native forms:

> The introduction of one or more of these non-native species results in a disappearance of the trout and minnows along with an increase in the number and size of the individuals of the introduced species. Then this species, having no natural check on its rate of reproduction and having destroyed its natural food, becomes a stunted race unfit for practical use. The balance has been upset with dire results. These results may have been brought about by the foreigner through preying upon the native species or eating their spawn or by competing with them for food. In any case the results are bad as measured by the fish catch.

Many other instances could be cited to show the evil of indiscriminate planting. Suffice it to say here that such have been the major results of lack of definite, well-organized planting policies.

STREAM SURVEYS AND STOCKING POLICIES

Since each body of water presents its own problems and must be handled individually, the question now arises as to how one may obtain the necessary information upon which sound stocking and management policies can be based. The answer lies in biological stream and lake surveys. Surveys by trained aquatic biologists make a host of the necessary facts available.

With this object in mind, various states and federal agencies have actively engaged in such work. Embody (1927), in his *Outline of Stream*

Study and the Development of a Stocking Policy, first pointed out the necessity for measuring such basic factors as species present, water temperatures, food, and shelter. Surveys open up problems; they usually do not solve them, though in some instances the cause of the failure of various waters to produce fish has been discovered at once by survey crews and the proper corrective procedures recommended. A survey is exactly what the name implies—a general study of conditions.

FIG. 60.—Survey workers taking measurements and scales of trout for growth studies. Sierra National Forest, California, 1934.

The objects of stream and lake survey work as now conducted may be listed as follows:

1. To determine the best species, size, and numbers of fish to plant annually in relation to food, angling intensity and other environmental conditions found in each water surveyed.

2. To determine what improvements, if any, may be made to better the natural environment.

3. To locate suitable rearing pond and hatchery sites, if any, in each area surveyed.

4. To determine whether or not existing fishing regulations are suitable, and if not to recommend changes or additions to present laws relating to bag, open season, size limits, lures, methods of angling, and other restrictions.

5. To open up significant fish cultural problems in any given area that should receive further intensive study for their solution.

The major objective is of course the development of a scientific stocking policy. The ideal stocking objective is to maintain the largest population consistent with normal growth and available food supply. Nor is it by any means always possible to formulate truly balanced stocking policies in the present state of our knowledge. However, those today based on surveys are a long step ahead of past ones based on guesswork. Every bit of information that can be obtained by the survey personnel is brought to focus on the final stocking recommendation for each lake, stream, or section of stream. Facts are the prime requisite. Although the guesswork of "barber-shop" fish culturists must be eliminated at the start, yet the past histories of numerous waters must be obtained from men who have known and have fished in them for years: the testimony of experience must not be ignored. This evidence must be sifted carefully and fitted into the final picture prior to the development of the stocking recommendations.

Survey crews can assist materially in locating rearing pond and hatchery sites. They can analyze chemically all springs or stream water supplies that seem to offer sufficient adjacent flat or gently sloping ground for pond construction or hatchery sites. Naturally such recommendations must be checked later by experienced fish-culturists to determine the true value of sites so recommended for development. Occasionally survey crews will find excellent sites for holding or rearing ponds that have been overlooked by fish-culturists.

Recommendations from survey work on specific legal fishing regulations as to protection (seasonal, size, bag limits, and stream closures) for trout often provide facts which indicate that drastic changes in existing regulations are necessary if the protection intended is to be really provided. For instance, in one area a survey crew found trout spawning in small lake tributaries up to two months after the season had opened, with anglers catching large numbers of breeding trout. These fish were killed before they had completed breeding. Naturally the recommendation was not to shorten the season but to close all adjacent spawning and nursery tributaries for full future protection of breeding adults and resultant young. Since the tributaries were small, usually less than ten feet wide and less than half a mile in length, and since the lakes were the only places in the district where fishing was done (except during spawning periods as noted above), their proposal was sound and would go a long way in assisting natural reproduction to maintain good trout fishing in the lakes.

In states where surveys are run as a regular part of a planned series operated on an annual basis, then the director may cooperate closely with the hatchery department to make the most of the findings. If on the other hand the results of surveys are turned over to officials with little or no training along fish cultural research lines, and who in addition may be quite skeptical of the aid to be derived from surveys, the chances are that the data presented will largely be ignored.

Forbes (1928) says concerning the kind and value of the materials which the survey biologist offers to the aquiculturist:

They seem to me to be not very unlike the materials which the soil surveyor and the crop specialist give to the agronomist and through him to the

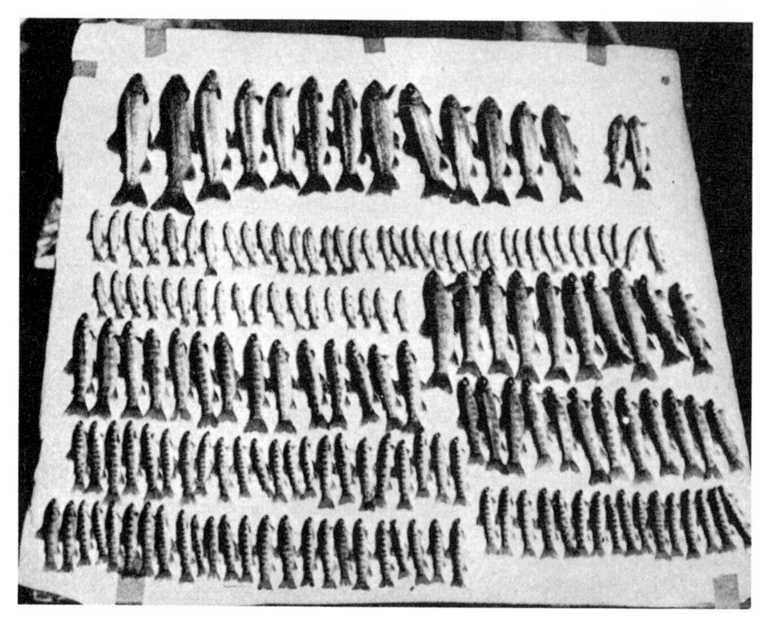

FIG. 61.—Seventy rainbow trout and ninety-eight eastern brook trout netted from a one-hundred foot section of the upper West Carson River, California. This study showed over 8000 small trout per mile in this section of this stream. Only six of the fish shown above were over six inches in length. This population study was made by U. S. Bureau of Fisheries Survey Party operated in the Mono and Inyo National Forests in 1934.

actual farmer; but their assortment, selection, and practical application is altogether a different matter from their accumulation, and calls for a liaison agency now non-existent . . . one competent to sift out from our bulletins and reports the facts, generalizations, inferences, and speculations even, which may be brought to bear on aquiculture as an art, and so to rearrange, assimilate, and present them as to bring them within the reach and comprehension of the fisherman, the fish culturist, the conservation office or department, and the legislative committee on fish and fisheries.*

* The type of liaison mentioned by Forbes has largely become a reality. Trained fishery biologists are employed by all the states and most of the federal agencies involved in land or water management. Their activities go far beyond surveys into research of all kinds. District management biologists form an excellent link between research and stream-side activities, and are usually available for public contact. Information and education sections have been organized within most Game and Fish Commissions.

Hand in hand with hatchery activities should go continual scientific investigations to determine basic facts that we now lack, so that the greatest possible return may be had from fish planted. New facts point the way to more economical and efficient procedures.

Any stocking program in order to be successful must adhere constantly to a long-time policy of stocking with naturally adapted species of fish. Stream and lake survey workers, if they do nothing else at all, aid in determining the best species to plant in any given water. They also place in the hands of the officials concerned a host of detailed facts that can be referred to at a moment's notice when requests for allotments of trout are made.

LARGE TROUT VERSUS SMALL TROUT

A controversy of some proportions has arisen within recent years between those who believe small fingerlings only should be planted and those who believe in planting large fish. Both would seem to be partly right, according to the waters to be stocked. For intensively fished waters near large cities and summer recreational centers, the planting of large, legal-sized trout is necessary if any sport fishing at all is to be maintained for large numbers of anglers. The biological capacity of such waters is seldom if ever sufficient to produce the necessary poundage to meet angling demands. Large trout immediately improve the fishing. They are put in with the expectation that most of them will be caught before the season is over.

New Jersey, Connecticut, Pennsylvania, New York, and some other states found, after years of experience in stocking intensively fished waters with large numbers of small fingerlings, that it was extremely difficult to maintain any decent sport with small fish. New Jersey was the first state to adopt a large-trout planting program. The results as judged by anglers' reactions would seem to have justified the added expense of rearing larger fish. The writer spent one year working at the New Jersey State Hatchery at Hackettstown in cooperation with Mr. Charles O. Hayford, Superintendent, and had ample opportunity to observe the results of a large-scale, legal-trout planting program from all angles. On a simple demand and supply basis, the planting of large, hatchery-reared trout is the only way to maintain any kind of trout fishing in the streams of northern New Jersey, or any region with densely concentrated populations.

But elsewhere there are other conditions to consider. In states of the Rocky Mountain and Pacific coast regions there are thousands of miles of fine trout water the greater part of which is still largely inaccessible and lightly fished. In such waters natural spawning plus annual or biennial planting of small trout will probably be sufficient to maintain the fishing for some time. Indeed, the cost of rearing and transporting large trout for such streams puts that method entirely out of question. Six-inch trout cost five or six times as much to rear as two or three inch fingerlings.

Roughly, it costs from twenty to thirty cents a pound* for food alone to produce a pound of trout. If fish averaging six inches are to be planted, they will run about twelve to the pound. If 100,000 six-inch fish are desired, and if the pond space, trained personnel, etc., are available for rearing them, these fish then will cost, at an average of 25 cents a pound, some $2,200 for food alone, excluding labor, depreciation, and other incidental expenses. When one considers that 100,000 six-inch fish are about one-seventh of the number of legal trout that the state of New Jersey plants annually in its some seventeen hundred miles of trout water alone, some idea of the magnitude of the task becomes evident. In California for example, there are over 5,000 miles of stream in the Klamath River drainage alone much of which is still unreachable by road.

The place where large trout should be planted depends on the *intensity* of the angling. In a few lakes of the west and in sections of some streams within the national parks and forests, large trout should be planted if good angling is to be had by the many anglers visiting such areas. Great scenic and recreational gathering places like the Merced River in the floor of Yosemite Valley in California, the Kaweah River in Sequoia Park, the Upper Stanislaus River in the Stanislaus National Forest, are such places. The anglers pay the bills and usually are willing to meet the costs of rearing and planting large trout. It is essential that special licenses and special restrictive measures as to bag limits, lures, and seasons be adopted to control the kill.

The problem of whether to plant legal-sized trout in spring or fall has caused considerable discussion in recent years. Discussion has arisen especially with regard to the planting of rainbow trout, because these fish are generally known to be more migratory than eastern brook or brown trout.

It is well known that some strains of rainbow trout are more migratory than others. Steelhead, for instance, undertake long migrations, while other forms of the same species are known to remain more or less as permanent residents of wide, deep, swift streams. Such similarity of appearance linked with such dissimilar migratory habits has naturally resulted in much indiscriminate inter-breeding and mixing of different races or strains through fish cultural activities, until today it is pretty much anybody's guess as to the genetic constitution of most domestic hatchery-reared brood stocks. This point is brought up here as it is important that the migratory habits of any given strain of trout be carefully considered in connection with both times and places of planting.

* The Oregon State Game Commission reports that total cost of rearing and releasing trout in 1967 was $0.81 per pound, with about $0.20 of that for food.

One eastern fish culturist stopped the fall planting of large rainbow when it was learned that the fish were being caught in shad nets enroute to the ocean as they attempted to fulfill their age-old migratory habits. Reports of similar emigrations of steelhead are often heard when these fish are planted into water where they are supposed to stay.

Aside from the migratory instincts of the fish to be planted, two other problems of importance with regard to time of planting must also be considered: (1) the added costs of holding large fish in hatcheries over the winter for spring planting; and (2) losses of fall-planted compared to spring-planted trout. Nesbit and Kitson (1937) from tagging experiments* with rainbow and brown trout in Massachusetts, present valuable data on these problems.

These workers found that in terms of fish recaptured by anglers far heavier losses occurred among trout planted in the fall. The difference averaged approximately 5 to 1.

They estimate that it has cost 5 cents per fish to rear a trout to an average length of 8 inches on December 1. The additional cost of holding it over winter until April 1 would be approximately 2.5 cents, giving a cost to April 1 of 7.5 cents. They find, however, that only 7 per cent of the fish planted in the fall survive to be taken the following summer, while 35 per cent of those planted in the spring are caught by anglers. Thus, even though the cost per fish is only 5 cents apiece to December 1, if only 7 per cent survive to be caught the cost per fish in the creel will in the end total 71.5 cents per fish. On the same basis spring-planted trout would cost only 21.4 cents per fish because of the higher survival obtained.

As a result of this study, the Massachusetts Division of Fisheries and Game now holds as many legal trout as the capacity of hatcheries permit, for planting in the spring.

MORTALITY FOLLOWING PLANTING

Dr. G. C. Embody (1927) of Cornell University was the first person to publish a mortality table† showing losses that may be expected when planting trout of various sizes. His table is as follows:

Size (in inches)	1	2	3	4	6
Mortality	95%	65%	40%	20%	0%

Thus it appears that excessive losses of small trout may occur before

* Internal tags described by Nesbit (1933) were used in these experiments. One of the conclusions from the experiment was that this method of tagging was unsatisfactory for trout. For further discussion of tagging methods see Shetter (1936) and Rounsefell and Kask (1946). Many new methods of fish marking are available. These range from cold and heat branding, through nearly microscopic coded wires inserted in the snout to sprays of fluorescent materials, and periodic feeding of materials that cause spaced fluorescent bands in bones (Chadwick, 1966).

† These mortality rates were modified somewhat by Davis (1938) and are given in the Appendix, p. 211.

reaching a size of six inches. That such losses may be obviated is one of the principal reasons for planting of legal-sized trout.

White (1929), in planting experiments with eastern brook trout in Canada, showed losses of fry planted ranging from 54% to 85%, depending upon varying conditions under which each planting was made. White says concerning losses of fry over a three month period in stream sections stocked with varying intensity:

> When 1,000 fry were planted in a section the loss was 85 per cent, when 333 were planted the loss was 79 per cent, and when 111 were planted the loss was 55.8 per cent. Since small trout fry migrate very little (White, 1924, p. 140), these results show that, at least within the limits of this experiment, when planting fry there is an advantage in scattering them. When large numbers are planted at one place the competition for food must become acute and the rate of growth slow. Moreover, it appears that the mortality is higher among the smaller fry than it is among the larger fry (White, 1927, p. 375); thus the critical period is greatly lengthened when the fry do not get enough food for rapid growth.

These are significant data and clearly show the advantages to be gained in scattering fry carefully in streams during planting operations.

With regard to the survival rates of trout planted from hatcheries, the results of catch records taken on Squaw Creek by the United States Forest Service during the fishing season of 1937 will prove of interest. Squaw Creek is a comparatively small tributary of the Pit River lying in the Shasta National Forest in northern California. It originally contained only native rainbow trout and has long been noted for its excellent fishing. A total of 2504 trout were reported caught. Of this number 2497 were rainbow, and only seven were brown trout. No eastern brook trout were reported caught. In the preceding five years, 1932 to 1936, reports show that there were planted in this stream approximately 20,000 eastern brook, 134,000 rainbow, and 130,000 brown trout. Since over ninety-nine per cent of the fish caught were rainbow trout, one might well ask what happened to the brown trout and eastern brook trout that had been planted in this stream in the previous five years. If environmental conditions were unsuitable for these species, possibly they migrated down into the Pit River below; possibly predators destroyed part of them—or floods, or other unfavorable conditions.

Since rainbow trout were dominant in the catches it is apparent that this species at least is well suited to Squaw Creek conditions. Another question of importance is, what proportion of anglers' catches consisted of naturally propagated rainbow trout as compared to hatchery-planted fish of the same species? This answer can be determined in future years by planting tagged or marked hatchery rainbow so those that survive can be recognized when caught later. True, some may migrate out of

Squaw Creek and contribute to catches from the Pit River or other lower waters, but at least the effect on the productivity of Squaw Creek itself can thus be measured.

MEASURING THE PRODUCTION* OF TROUT WATERS

In terms of pounds or numbers of trout produced per acre of water area, but few figures are available today. Surber (1936) in work on a trout stream in Virginia over a four-year period reports the following annual production in pounds of trout produced per acre of water area: 1933, 29.7 pounds; 1934, 27.7 pounds; 1935, 34.8 pounds; and in 1936, 30.2 pounds. Average annual production was slightly over thirty pounds. It is of interest to note in this connection that when Surber doubled the planting rate in the fall of 1935, production remained the same, although, as he points out, a flood that occurred in the middle of March, 1936, may have had some effect on the number of fish that survived.

Mr. Russell Lord of the United States Bureau of Fisheries, in a personal communication to the writer, states that the Furnace Brook "test stream" in Vermont showed an average production in trout caught by anglers of approximately thirty-four pounds per acre.

Production determined from catch record work of the United States Forest Service (unpublished) on Fish Lake in the Umpqua National Forest in Oregon in 1937 shows somewhat similar production. Fish Lake lies at the headwaters of the South Umpqua River at an elevation of approximately 3,300 feet, and has a surface area of about ninety acres. It can be reached only by trail some eight miles from Camp Comfort at the end of the road. In spite of its inaccessibility, a total take of 5946 trout is reported for the 1937 season, of which about 99 per cent, 5878, were rainbows, and the remainder, 68, were eastern brook trout. A production rate of approximately 66 trout per acre of water area is therefore indicated: since the fish taken would run about three and a half to the pound, or about nine and one-half inches long, a production of roughly twenty pounds per acre is calculated.

An interesting comparison can be made here between fish caught in the season of 1937 and fish planted from hatcheries. From 1934 to 1937, inclusive, the following trout were planted in Fish Lake: 1934—20,000 cutthroat; 1935—20,000 eastern brook; 1936—20,000 eastern brook; 1937—20,000 rainbow. As noted above, out of the total of 40,000 eastern brook planted only 1.15 per cent, or 68 fish of this species, were reported taken. Some cutthroat may have entered the catches as "rainbow," since they closely resemble the latter. Since the rainbow planted were not

* "Production" is used here in the sense of "yield." The usual modern usage of production includes all flesh formed during a given period whether it is harvested or not.

marked, naturally it was impossible to distinguish these from naturally propagated fish in the catches.

The above illustrations show a few of the present-day efforts that are being made to find out what trout waters are actually producing. A small start has been made. Most of the figures determined to date from both non-trout and trout waters merely indicate what is being produced. What is more important to find out is what they should produce under any given type of aquatic conditions.

Common objections heard against planting legal-sized hatchery trout are that they are not good to eat and that, being liver-fed "softies," they lack fighting ability. Such objections cannot be sustained of trout which have been reared under sanitary conditions in hatcheries and properly fed and cared for. Experiments in planting marked adult eastern brook and rainbow trout (Lord, 1935a) have shown from stomach examinations after recapture that these trout readily take to natural foods soon after planting, and their fighting ability is just as keen as that of wild trout in the same stream. As for their edibility, after the hatchery fish have been in the stream a short time, it is practically impossible to detect any difference. Trout reared in natural ponds secure much natural food and if scientifically balanced diets are also fed them, they will taste almost the same as wild fish.

NATURAL SPAWNING

Fish populations in many of our less accessible waters today are being maintained largely by natural reproduction alone. Everything possible should be done to encourage breeding, by adequate protection during spawning periods, by making spawning beds easy of access, and by mechanical improvements to the redds where practical. As an instance where natural propagation is bearing successfully the burden of maintaining angling, Smith (1936) cites the case of Dry River in New Hampshire. This is a small stream, some ten miles in length, accessible only by trail. It contains only small eastern brook trout. This stream had not been stocked in recent years and catch records taken in 1935 showed an estimated total harvest of 1500 legal eastern brook trout. The actual measured harvest was 1039 fish taken by ninety-three anglers; an average of 11.17 fish per angler.

A "yardstick" has been furnished for measuring the returns received per dollar spent in hatchery operations by the pioneer work of Foerster (1936), on the sockeye salmon of Cultus Lake in British Columbia for the Biological Board of Canada. His work demonstrated that,

In an area such as Cultus Lake, where a natural run of sockeye occurs with a reasonable expectancy of successful spawning, artificial propagation, for the purposes of continuing the run in that area is unnecessary and, if producing any additional results over natural spawning, these would not appear to be in any way commensurate with the cost. This conclusion may not apply to areas where there is no reasonable expectation of successful natural propagation.

Foerster's work showed a survival rate of from 1 to 3 per cent in three tests of natural spawning, while returns of from 2 to 4.5 per cent were obtained under artificial propagation where free-swimming fry were liberated. In brief, Foerster's work demonstrated that while a slightly higher survival of returned migrants was obtained from hatchery-planted sockeye salmon the cost involved more than over-balanced the slight benefits produced. On the basis of Foerster's ten-year study, all sockeye hatcheries in British Columbia were abandoned in the summer of 1936.

Fig. 62.—Chemist of survey party analyzing lake water for oxygen with portable chemical field kit.

This work of Foerster's is a classic piece of research on a single species of salmon. It at once pointed the way to better management methods for sockeyes, at least in British Columbia. But to return to trout, we have a similar question with regard to steelhead trout. Heavy egg-taking of steelhead eggs from any given stream, coupled with intensive angling and the replanting of but a small proportion of the young back into their parent waters, gives a story of continually lowering angling values. We might well ask ourselves just what we are getting out of our investment in steelhead propagative activities. The same question is involved, but the answer may be different.*

If we turn to resident trout, trout that live their entire lives in freshwater streams and lakes and that migrate only short distances between feeding and breeding areas, the problem is different, and also much more complex. There are two schools of thought here: one believing that if it were not for hatchery propagation our streams would be barren of fish life, and the other as firmly convinced that hatcheries do but little good, naturally spawned fish providing and maintaining the sport fishing. It seems evident that both are partly right. Some waters afford

* The answer appears to lie in the technique of rearing young steelhead to migratory size and releasing them at the proper time before the migratory urge is lost. Yearlings so released have provided enough adult escapement past the fishery in the Alsea River of Oregon that the fish have occasionally been trucked, on an experimental basis, from the hatchery downstream to be run through a second time. Stocking fish at sites low in the stream systems appears to show promise in keeping returning adults available to anglers for longer periods of time (Wagner, 1969).

This type of management is expensive but acceptable to anglers on many streams.

good, natural spawning facilities, whereas some do not; some are hard of access and lightly fished, and with good spawning conditions would not need hatchery-planted fish. I personally believe that natural spawning is more successful than hatcherymen generally concede it to be, but just what may be the ultimate percentage of survival to the angler's creel from a thousand eggs laid by wild fish, as compared to a thousand eggs started in a hatchery, remains to be determined.

In lakes barren of fish life because of impassable falls or other barriers to natural distribution, one original planting will start, and natural spawning will often maintain a good stock of trout. Eyed eggs of rainbow and cutthroat trout have been used successfully to make the original plantings in some such lakes. The necessity for future plantings will depend entirely upon the intensity of angling and the extent of natural propagation.

NEW PLANTING SYSTEMS NEEDED

Stream and lake survey findings make possible more careful planting than has been practiced in the past. That the correct species, sizes, and numbers of trout recommended be planted in the specific waters for which they are intended is absolutely essential if long-time, consistent policies are to prevail. Competent workers must see to it that the trout are well scattered in the areas where the best shelter and food are available.

All too often the hatcheryman's interest ends when the fish leave the hatchery. This is not as it should be. In many cases the vicious result is a "paper record" of huge numbers planted. Just what was their condition and where they were planted is not told. Hatcherymen are usually interested in their work, and if they were given more responsibility in seeing the fish they have raised properly planted, the result should be a higher survival to the angler's creel. But the job is too big for them alone. Wardens, forest and park rangers, sportsmen and club workmen should all cooperate. Check-ups should be made by responsible persons connected with the work. In the national parks and forests, individual rangers with adequate fisheries experience should be in charge of planting work. Within recent years fish and game management has been given a large place in the work of both the forest and park services and great improvements have already been brought about.

If a larger proportion of the angler's dollar were spent in developing a more efficient planting system it would undoubtedly give greater returns and would compensate somewhat for the lesser amounts of money that would then be available for hatchery activities alone. There is no good reason why public fishing waters in general cannot be so managed as to offer as fine sport as private waters, once the problem is understood and the cooperation of fishermen at large is obtained.

TABLE XXIX

WATERS RECOMMENDED FOR PLANTING TROUT OF VARIOUS SIZES

SIZE OF FISH	RAINBOW TROUT	BROWN OR LOCH LEVEN TROUT	EASTERN BROOK TROUT
Advanced fry to 2″ fingerlings	Smaller tributaries of streams preferably with unobstructed access to deep, cold lakes or to the ocean.* Lightly fished streams with ample shelter.	Small warmer streams, lakes and tributaries with ample shelter and lightly fished, if already well established there.	Cold, headwater brooks or tributaries and ponds or lakes lightly fished and affording ample shelter.
3″ to 5″** fingerlings	Moderately and heavily fished lakes and streams, preferably with access to deep, cold lakes or to the ocean; wide rugged, mountain streams.	Moderately and heavily fished streams and lakes where already well established.	Moderately and heavily fished cold water ponds, lakes, or streams lacking predacious warm water species and where food supply is rich.
6″ or larger** yearlings or older.	Large streams and lakes heavily fished. Preferably "white-water" mountain streams near recreation centers or large cities and towns.	Heavily fished warmer, quieter main reaches of streams where already well established near recreational centers or large cities and towns.	Upper portions of cold streams and lakes intensively fished near recreation centers or large cities and towns.

* Rainbows have become well established in many streams both east and west that do not give access to the ocean or to large lakes. Whether or not rainbows will remain in such waters depends to a large extent upon the migratory instincts of the particular strain of rainbow to be planted. Certainly the offspring of sea-run or lake-run steelheads should not be planted where downstream migrations will lead to their destruction.

** In many heavily fished streams and lakes with rich food supplies, it may be advisable to plant three- to five-inch fingerlings along with legal fish. This combination has proved quite successful in some waters.

PROTECTION

Present-day legal restrictions relating to seasonal, bag, and size limits are relics of the days of "meat fishing." These days are now largely past in our inland waters, and it is sport fishing that offers the attractions. True, food is obtained in any case where fish are caught, but with modern refinements of tackle and methods of fishing, the angler is usually more interested in the sport than in the food obtained. Since it is apparent that increased stocking is failing to maintain continued good fishing, it is obvious that drastic changes in our fishing regulations are needed to make the supply more nearly consistent with the demand.

Bag or creel limits allowing twenty-five or more trout per day are absurdly high when applied to the average, accessible trout stream. In remote streams and lakes where abundant stocks of trout remain and where fishing intensity is usually extremely light, such creel limits are not out of reason. A limit of fifteen per day or five pounds and one fish should be more than ample for the average angler and his family. Where legal-sized trout are planted on heavily fished streams it is imperative that small bag limits be imposed to obtain greater spread of trout among larger numbers of fishermen.*

Most of the fish caught in any open season are usually taken by a comparatively few expert anglers. The average license holder, on the other hand, fishes only occasionally and usually makes but small catches and seldom gets a "limit." To reduce daily bag limits is essentially to reduce the catches of the expert anglers, making possible greater survival of trout for the less expert fishermen. Also, some fish surviving uncaught would augment the population with additional offspring from natural spawning. (Needham and Hanson, 1935.)

Size limit restrictions have long caused much controversy among sportsmen.

There are two good features of size limits. In the first place they protect the young growing trout until it has become older, wiser and harder to catch, thus preventing easy wholesale destruction of immature fish. They also make for greater poundage and less fish per catch per angler, which is more desirable than the large catches of small fish so often seen. From the angler's standpoint, the greater sport in taking larger fish is also highly desirable.

One benefit that the imposition of size limits is supposed to give is that they will protect young fish until they have had a chance to spawn at least once. That this idea is in error can be shown by the following facts.

Legal size limits, to be effective in protecting young trout until their first spawning, must set the minimum legal size for each species above that at which the average fish spawns for the first time. This makes it necessary that different size limits be imposed for the different types of waters, because trout reach breeding age and spawn at varying sizes depending upon the environmental conditions of the various waters in which they live. For instance, studies on golden trout of the high Sierra have shown that these fish usually spawn at the end of their third or fourth year when eight or more inches in length. A size limit to protect these fish to their first spawning therefore would have to be eight inches or higher. The size limit now in effect of five inches, while it does prevent wholesale slaughter of small trout under this length, fails to protect these fish to their first spawning. Other work on rainbow trout in the high Sierra [California] has also shown a size limit of at least eight inches would be necessary to afford protection to a breeding age, though even this size limit would not completely protect either species, as many spawn for the first time in their fourth year when they exceed this

* Regulations emphasizing "low kill" or "no kill" angling are justified and accepted in some populous areas (Hazzard, 1954; Sport Fishing Institute, 1964).

length. It is therefore evident that the principal function of a size limit is not that of protection to a breeding age but rather that of protecting immature fish to a respectable, catchable size. (Needham and Hanson, 1935.)

One of the arguments advanced against the enforcement of size limits is that more work is involved in check-up by wardens, since small fish near the minimum size limit must be measured. Whether size limits are imposed or not, violators can hide or throw away small fish and replace them with larger specimens after the legal bag limit is reached.

Both larger size, and lower bag limits are very necessary to modern conditions. They tend to cause anglers to seek larger trout to obtain greater poundage in lieu of the lesser numbers creeled. Trout waters are thus benefited by the removal of large, cannibalistic adults, for such fish feed extensively on young, recently planted fish, especially in lakes lacking adequate shelter in their shallow water areas.*

Seasonal limits should be such as to completely protect all species of resident stream trout over the breeding season. Nature carries on not as ordained by state legislatures, but on her own unswerving natural processes. Conservation measures must be developed in accordance with these natural processes or they are foredoomed to failure. For example, rainbow trout spawn in the spring in the eastern states from early March until the end of April. The season may open the fifteenth of April and many unspawned rainbows may be caught before the eggs are deposited. This is equivalent to killing the cow before the calf is born.

The same criticisms might be leveled at seasons which close too late in the fall to protect fall-spawning brown or eastern brook trout that may be caught near spawning beds before their eggs have been deposited. Of course all trout are potential spawners, but it seems needless waste to kill trout that have reached the threshold of the spawning period.

Sea-run or lake-run steelhead are not generally available to stream fishermen until the urge of their reproductive instinct starts them on their up-stream migration. Such fish offer some of the finest sport fishing available today and to deny such sport completely is not to be recommended. But a sufficient number must be allowed to escape capture and to spawn each season if we are to be assured of a continuous supply. Low bag limits or from one to two fish per day offer one possibility for protection. The facts have not as yet been determined as to just what percentage in relation to the kill must be allowed to spawn.†

Summer fishing for young steelhead and winter or spring fishing for the adults are burning the candle at both ends. Formerly in the Klamath River in California a summer season of six months, May 1 to October 31, coupled with a winter season of four months, November to February, allowed protection to these fish only for the months of March and April. A bag limit of five adults regardless of weight was allowed per day in

* The McKenzie River in Oregon has benefited from a maximum size limit of 14 inches, imposed to protect the brood fish of the local "Redside" strain. Returning the large fish to the water has resulted in an increase in naturally hatched trout in the fishery.

Also in Oregon, an eight-inch minimum limit is used in coastal streams to protect downstream migrants of salmon and steelhead.

† Escapements of about one-half of the individuals in Oregon steelhead fisheries seem to be quite sufficient to maintain wild stocks. Some biologists estimate that much smaller percentages of escapement are needed for artificial maintenance of runs—perhaps only 10 to 15%.

the winter fishing, and in the summer the bag limit was twenty-five or ten pounds and one fish. Such generous limits are entirely out of line with modern conservation needs.

It has been customary in the past to close various streams to angling in order to permit resident fish populations to build back, and after a time to open them again. This practice tends to concentrate the fisherman on open streams, giving an erratic balance between open and closed waters. Such streams when re-opened to fishing greatly benefit the early season fishermen, who so reduce the fish supply that late comers find the stream about at a level with others that have not been closed at all.

FIG. 63.—Ekman dredge ready to be dropped to lake bottom to take sample of bottom foods. The jaws of the dredge are tripped and closed by the messenger dropped from the left hand of the operator. Detailed studies of bottom foods of both lakes and streams are among the most important of survey activities.

The smaller spawning and nursery tributaries of intensively fished lakes should be closed entirely so that natural propagation may be given its opportunity. Likewise the smaller spring-fed brooks less than three feet in width, the spawning and nursery tributaries of main fishing streams, might well be closed permanently as a precautionary, protective measure until further facts become available as a basis for more efficient methods of management.

Where size limits are imposed, bait fishermen often kill many small trout in releasing them from deeply embedded hooks. The way to meet this problem is to designate a minimum hook-size for bait fishing, one that trout under, say, six inches, cannot swallow. Fly hook-size would not need to be regulated, as most fly-caught fish are hooked in the mouth.

It would not seem wise to eliminate bait fishing as many fly-fishing "purists" propose, for it is the principal method of fishing employed by the plain, "garden variety" of licensee. He represents a very large group of contributors to fish and game funds. In recent years a larger variety and much cheaper grade of fly tackle is being sold, with the result that many fishermen have "graduated" from the ranks of mere bait fishing to the more skilled activity of wet- and dry-fly fishing. Perhaps the better way to regulate methods of fishing is by means of restricted seasonal, bag, and size limits.

Administration of fish and game laws is another matter, and the suggestions submitted above are merely with regard to more important restrictive measures that are in serious need of revision to meet modern needs. Local problems differ with each area, and must be solved on factual bases if the fishing is to be maintained and perpetuated.

VII

Stream and Lake Management

LIKE MOST of our methods of fishing, stream improvement came to us from England. There individual care has been given trout waters for generations. It is only within recent years that stream management has come to receive any considerable attention in the United States. Large amounts of relief funds made available to various governmental and state agencies during the 1930's made it possible to carry on experiments in a large way with various types of installations designed to improve conditions for trout. Unfortunately the great amount of publicity given this work has led anglers to the unwarranted conclusion that here, at last, is a panacea for our troubles in keeping trout fishing from further decline. Although stream and lake improvement is a useful method of providing better conditions for the trout, other measures must also be taken.

In brief, the objects of stream improvement are: (1) to provide additional shelter for trout, (2) to improve the food supply, (3) to improve spawning conditions, and (4) to prevent extreme seasonal changes in volume and temperature of the water.*

Long, flat, shallow riffle areas, no matter how productive in bottom foods, will be deserted by large trout for more adequate shelter. They may forage here at night from deep pools above and below, but during fishing hours such areas offer scant sport and most anglers do not even bother to fish them. The better type of stream, both as to shelter for fish and for angling, usually has about 50 per cent of its area made up of pools and 50 per cent of riffles. Deep pools, but not too long, interspersed with frequent riffles, make ideal conditions. Riffles produce the greater part of the food; pools, the shelter. Both are essential, and properly arranged, form the ideal fishing stream.

Using this standard as a measure, most eastern streams flowing through semi-cultivated, marginal lands offer only from 20 per cent to 40 per cent of fishable water. Floods and consequent erosion often fill pools with silt, sand, or gravel, and if the gradient of the bed be low, long, flat, useless stretches result, with pools few and far between. Much good improvement work can be accomplished in eastern and mid-western

* White and Brynildson (1967) state that a major aim of trout habitat improvement is to enhance the capacity of the stream for self-repair.

waters by the installation of low dams, deflectors, etc. This has been demonstrated by Hubbs, Greeley, and Tarzwell (1932) in Michigan, by Mr. E. R. Hewitt in the Neversink River in New York state, and the United States Bureau of Fisheries and Forest Service work (1935) in the National Forests.

Streams of the Pacific coast drainage are different. Insofar as stream improvements are concerned, they must be divided into two groups. West slope streams draining directly into the Pacific from the high coastal ranges of California, Oregon, and Washington do not afford

FIG. 64.—A simple type of stream improvement. A single log dam that has created a good pool on its downstream side.

much opportunity for the installation of standardized types of barriers. Extreme seasonal fluctuations in volume occur, and shelter is usually already abundantly supplied. The lower courses of large rivers in Washington and Oregon usually contain shifting bars of gravel and sand that make the installation of dams or deflectors an uncertain procedure at best. In streams of the Olympic Peninsula this is particularly true. There the rivers occupy practically entire valley floors, shifting annually from one side to the other, and carrying large amounts of materials during flood periods. The cost of improving such areas by methods employed in the east is entirely out of proportion to the results obtainable. Stream improvement work by the United States Bureau of Fisheries in cooperation with the Forest Service, in the summer of 1935, clearly demonstrated this fact. Of more practical value in these streams are (1) the removal of barriers to sea-run salmon and trout on their spawning migrations, (2) the screening of irrigation and power diversions to prevent losses of seaward migrants, and (3) the installation of storage or check dams at the outlets of head-water lakes, to create permanent flow in dry seasons over spawning and nursery grounds.

Eastward draining streams, on the other hand, in the Pacific coast states as well as in the inter-mountain states of Utah, Nevada, Arizona, and New Mexico, offer good opportunities for stream improvement work. Streams in this drier, more arid inland region are on the whole small, show less seasonal fluctuation, and provide less natural shelter for trout than do the Pacific coast waters. Improvement work under the

FIG. 65.—An elaborate type of stream improvement structure. A double-truss log dam with wide central spillway. Temple Fork of Logan River near Logan, Utah.

direction of Dr. A. S. Hazzard in this region clearly demonstrated that much effective work is possible. Many streams may be in no way in need of improvement, and it should not be attempted without advance surveys by competent supervisors.

Two quite unsatisfactory features of many improvements made to date are first, their temporary nature, and second, their artificial appearance in the stream. In streams subject to severe floods it is extremely doubtful whether many of the types of improvements developed to date will withstand the force of flood waters. To replace them each year would involve expenditures out of proportion to benefits obtained. Artificial dams and cemented structures give streams an unnatural appearance inappropriate to trout waters. Where boulders, logs, stones, or other natural materials along the stream are carefully utilized, it is quite possible to put in effective shelters and at the same time preserve a natural appearance. No one would care to see concrete, log, or stone dams arranged in neat, park-like order on a wild stream. Such installations are useful in hatchery rearing pools, but are out of place on natural trout waters. Simple low dams or deflectors can usually be built with materials from the streamside to transform unproductive portions into pools which will furnish shelter for the trout. The ideal to keep in mind is frequent riffles with good pools between. Both are essential.

It is evident that dams, deflectors, rafts of logs or brush, or other types of shelter improvements will not in themselves increase the total fish population. They merely make for more even distribution of fish normally present, preventing concentration of them in a few of the better pools.*

Spawning-bed improvements, on the other hand, may actually increase the number of fish present by improving natural propagation.

A practical illustration of the value of simple improvements can be cited in the case of Lake Dorothy in the Inyo National Forest in California. This lake lies in a granitic cirque at an elevation of about 10,500 feet on the east slope of the Sierra Nevada Mountains, near Bishop, California. It contains golden and rainbow trout. Lacking spawning inlets, but possessing a good-sized outlet, the fish migrated downstream below the lake each spring to spawn. Unfortunately, some went down too far and many passed over a high falls about half a mile below the lake and were killed by landing on rocks in a talus slope at the foot of the falls. In the spring of 1935, gunny sacks of fine heavy fish could be picked up below the falls. Attention of the Forest Service was called to this problem and a parallel bar weir or fence was placed across the stream just above the falls in the summer of 1935. In the spring of 1936 this weir efficiently prevented the bulk of spawning fish from passing over the falls. They were restricted to spawning in the only areas available in the short stretch of stream above the falls. It saved many fine adult trout from destruction and illustrates the practical and useful types of improvements that may be recommended by improvement or survey workers.

CALIFORNIA CHECK DAMS

In the Sierra Nevada Mountains in California a new type of stream improvement to control excessive seasonal fluctuations has been developed, and it is proving to be a great boon to angling. As noted above, streams draining westward from the Sierra Range are already well provided with shelter. Their principal drawback is tremendous seasonal fluctuations in volume, varying from extraordinarily high water in the

* Protection and improvement of trout habitat on the Pacific Coast is reviewed by Calhoun (1966). Stream clearance and repair of logging damage appear to be more useful than elaborate improvement devices in the streams.

spring from melting snow and ice, to a very low run-off, or none at all, in many streams in late summer and fall. Very few streams of the south or central Sierras in California are fed by springs of sufficient size to maintain even flow the year round. In streams that dry up periodically enormous losses of trout occur annually.

Briefly, the plan calls for the construction of small check dams for water storage at the outlets of head-water lakes. The water is released in the dry seasons of late summer and fall, thus maintaining permanent

FIG. 66.—A simple, effective, three-log, semi-pyramid dam. Logs fastened together by long "drift" pins. Ends of logs are placed deep in banks of stream and covered with rocks. East Branch of Kaweah River, California (photograph by courtesy of U. S. Forest Service).

stream flows below the lakes so dammed. In this case, lake improvement becomes a direct means of stream improvement.

In 1931 five check dams were constructed as a test project on lakes at the headwaters of Cherry Creek,* a tributary of the Tuolumne River just south of the boundary of Yosemite National Park. Before the dams were installed, sportsmen who fish this region were greatly perturbed about the heavy annual losses of trout, and now, since the check dams have accomplished such a fine job, they are wondering if the trout population is becoming too heavy for the food supply.

* Mr. Fred Leighton, conservationist and sportsman of Sonora, California, was largely responsible for initiating the Cherry Creek work, the first of its kind to be attempted in California.

The total cost of the five dams constructed in 1931 was $5,200.* (See Table 30.) The average cost was $1,040 per dam. The average cost per acre foot of water stored was approximately $1.70. This last cost is amazingly low when it is known that the cost per acre foot of water† in numerous power and irrigation projects often runs to from twenty to fifty times this amount.** One major expense was the transportation of cement, tools, tackle, pipe for outlets, food, and camp equipment by pack train the twenty-five miles over steep trails.

FIG. 67.—One of the most effective and cheapest types of stream improvement devices: a rock and boulder dam. Note crest of dam upstream is built in shape of "V." This type of construction utilizes the force of current in wedging the rocks tightly together. Temple Fork, Logan River, near Logan, Utah (photograph by courtesy of U. S. Forest Service).

The geological formation of the country in which the lakes lie permitted construction of the dams at low cost. All of them lie in granite basins with or without meadows around their margins. Their outlets almost without exception are in narrow V-shaped glacier-cut channels of solid granite. These required only a little clearing of surface debris to secure bed-rock foundations, and only small dams in the narrow channels were required to store many acre feet of water. Rocks for the dams and granitic sand for the concrete were found right at the damsites. The five dams were built in about forty days' time by two crews of seven men each.

* This included donations from various helpful sources.

† An acre foot of water is an area of 1 square acre covered to a depth of one foot. One acre foot of stored water will give a flow of 20 miner's inches of water for 24 hours.

** During the 1950's more than one-half million dollars were authorized for maintenance dams in California. Some 50 dams are in operation (Calhoun, 1966).

At the time of construction, an eight-inch iron pipe with regulating valve is placed in the bottom of the dam. Operation of the valve is regulated by means of a rod extending from it to the level of the top of the dam on the upstream side; a padlocking device prevents unauthorized persons from changing the size of the openings. Eye-bolts embedded in the dam protect the rod from being knocked out of place, or bent by ice or by floating logs. Wire screen placed on supports on the inside of the dam prevents debris from settling and clogging the pipe opening. In winter and spring melting snow fills the lake and flows over the top of the dam. After the lake level has fallen below the crest, water continues to feed into the stream below through the bottom pipe.

In the fall of 1933 no more than about half the water stored had been utilized, even though a fine flow had been maintained from the dams all summer.

TABLE XXX

LAKES AT HEADWATERS OF CHERRY CREEK ON WHICH CHECK DAMS WERE BUILT IN 1931, SHOWING AREAS, COSTS, AND CONSTRUCTION DETAILS

Name of Lake	Area in Acres	Storage Capacity in Acre Feet*	Days to Build	Sacks of Cement Used	Length at Crest	Height	Width at Base	Width at Crest	Cost Including Donations
Bigelow..	59	460	17	51	28′	8′	8′	2′6″	$1,128.00
Emigrant.	213	1,491	12	38	35′	7′	8′	2′6″	788.00
Emigrant Meadow.	23	160	13	65	41′	6½′	8′	2′6″	852.00
Buck....	48	360	24	70	56′	8′	8′	2′6″	1,416.00
Long Lake	67	520	15	56	27½′	8′	9′	2′6″	1,016.00
Totals...	410	2,991							$5,200.00

* Amount of water stored above level of outlet pipe.

Later two more check dams were constructed by the National Forest Service with the help of boys of the Civil Conservation Corps at the headwaters of Clavey Creek, the next good-sized tributary of the Tuolumne River northwest of Cherry Creek. The upper portion of this stream used to go dry annually, causing large losses of trout. These two dams together store about 420 acre feet of water and supply about twenty miles of stream (including several miles of fine natural nurseries and spawning beds) with water the year around.

As for the headwater lakes themselves, these will require restocking to maintain fishing in them. Many of these were barren of fish originally, for numerous high, natural falls prevented fish in the streams below from entering them. Further, most of these uppermost lakes lack spawning grounds or streams above them, and in all probability natural reproduction will not be sufficient to keep them supplied with a good stock of catchable fish. In any case, stocking with hatchery trout should not be necessary. Small, naturally spawned trout are exceedingly abundant in the streams below and doubtless some of these can be netted and planted in the upper lakes each year at little expense and without great effort or serious detriment to the streams.

Fig. 68.—Another elaborate type of stream improvement. Log and board dam (right) with double deflectors below. Note large rocks placed at ends of both structures to prevent washing out during flood periods. Temple Fork, Logan River, near Logan, Utah (photograph by courtesy of U. S. Forest Service).

The fine thing about this type of stream improvement is that it is self-operating. Once the dam is in and the outlet valve adjusted, no further attention is required except for an occasional check-up. The fishing is light in the Cherry Creek drainage and its lakes, because of their comparative inaccessibility; and with natural spawning aided by stream flow maintenance, the trout supply has become entirely self-maintaining. No expensive stocking with hatchery-reared trout by pack train should be required unless the intensity of fishing becomes far greater than it is now. The dams are steadily paying for themselves by building up the trout population.

IMPROVING THE FOOD SUPPLY

This phase of improvement work is one that has received little attention in this country to date. Sporadic attempts to improve food conditions of various waters have been made by a few sportsmen, clubs, or other agencies. Of particular interest in England are "fly-boards" developed to increase the mayfly populations. Observations of Mr. J. W. Lunn, who for forty-seven years was "river-keeper" for the Houghton Club on the River Test, showed that many mayfly eggs were eaten by caddicefly larvae. The larvae crawl up on weeds, sticks, or the banks to reach the egg clusters. Lunn invented "fly-boards," which are merely floating boards anchored by wires in the stream. Mayfly (*Baetis*) adults lay their eggs on the boards, and caddicefly larvae cannot climb the wire to get at them. Major J. W. Hills in his *River Keeper* (1934) says of these:

> The value of boards in one's own river can, I think, be considered proved. They have been used for some years by Lunn and he has noticed a marked increase in pale waterys and most kinds of olive [mayflies]. I believe everyone who has knowledge of their use will confirm this. . . . I am quite sure they have done a great work.

The "fly-boards" would probably be an aid in increasing the numbers of mayflies on private waters in this country, but it is doubtful whether such improvements would be worth the expense involved on the average open trout stream.

It is often asked what results may be expected from the introduction of various aquatic food animals into trout waters. The answer to this question depends upon what food animals are introduced, whether or not the waters they are intended for are suitable, and whether or not they are already present. Much money has been wasted in attempting to stock waters with organisms which failed to thrive. Adult insects, being winged, are able to establish themselves wherever the environmental conditions they require are found. For example, nymphs of the large salmon-fly (stonefly, *Pteronarcys californica*) are abundant in streams of the central and northern Sierra Nevada Mountains in California and, so far as we have been able to determine, are absent from southern Sierran streams such as the San Joaquin, Kings, Kaweah, and Kern rivers. Adult salmon-flies are winged forms and would probably occur in these streams naturally if conditions were suitable. The reason for their absence is very probably the lack of much decaying organic matter such as leaves, bark, and twigs, upon which they normally feed. Spring floods of the more southerly Sierras pulverize and destroy such materials through the grinding action of granitic sand and smaller stones carried by high waters. More stable seasonal conditions exist in northern California streams, with the result that greater amounts and kinds of these food materials remain in the stream beds. This is probably a major reason for their greater richness in salmon-flies and other aquatic insects.

Non-winged forms such as shrimp, crayfish, snails, and forage minnows, which must depend for the most part upon water courses as their

Fig. 69.—Buck Meadows Creek above Buck Lake, Stanislaus National Forest, California. This stream goes dry in late summer and fall in dry seasons, destroying thousands of naturally spawned young rainbow trout or stranding them in shallow pools where predators and high temperatures may kill them.

Fig. 70.—Inlet to Huckleberry Lake, Stanislaus National Forest, California. Photograph taken September 24, 1933, at height of dry season shows fine flow of water. This is maintained over nursery and spawning beds by the Bigelow Lake check dam a few miles above. Check dams have been the means of saving large numbers of trout in streams that once went dry annually in this forest.

paths of distribution, may occasionally be introduced with success, but only careful biological investigation will reveal the practicability of this procedure. There is danger of introducing harmful forms which might upset the biological balance existing between the fish and the food supply already present. Claims of successful introduction of scuds and other animals are often made, but an examination of the results obtained usually fails to bear out these claims. A bit of aid to nature in providing better conditions for the life already present will often save much money that might be wholly wasted in introducing animals that cannot establish themselves.

As shown in Chapter V, the presence of plant beds in trout waters may increase the food supply many times. They also provide shelter. Caution must be exercised in introducing them, however, for they have been known to smother out all open water, making fly-fishing practically impossible. Such rooted aquatics as the pond weeds, water milfoil and Elodea may grow so densely as to slow down current speed to a point where water temperatures become dangerously high. A careful analysis of local conditions should be made before planting.

In swift "white water" mountain streams the larger submerged aquatic plants are usually scarce, but the water moss (*Fontinalis*) may often be found in them. It is only in the quieter portions of trout streams and in ponds or lakes that the larger aquatic plants become abundant.

Here again, naturally adapted plants will be found already growing. While it is easy to make new introductions, there is always the risk of making conditions worse instead of better. There is still great lack of experimental evidence to show the value of such work.

Tarzwell (1936), in the course of quantitative food studies made in Michigan streams to obtain experimental evidence of the true value of stream improvements, found that food production was greater on the types of bottom produced by the improvement structures than on the original bottoms. He states that the volume of organisms per unit area was increased from three to nine times by the improvements installed on three Michigan streams. These findings were obtained in sandy-bottomed streams where many wing deflectors were used which, with the aid of the current, uncovered good food-producing gravel areas, and in mucky areas in the backwaters where plant beds would grow.

LAKE IMPROVEMENTS

Lake work offers a different set of problems from an improvement standpoint. The objectives are the same as for stream improvement but the methods available are different. Various types of brush shelters or rafts sunk to the lake bottom by means of stones are the principal devices in use at present. These are to furnish shelter for young, growing

Fig. 71.—Lower Emigrant Lake, Stanislaus National Forest, California. A low check dam at the outlet of this lake stores up sufficient water for many miles of spawning and nursery grounds throughout the dry season in late summer and fall.

Fig. 72.—Lower Buck Lake Check Dam, Stanislaus National Forest, California. Note good flow of water coming from bottom of dam even though lake level is below crest of dam. Spring floods left the logs seen on the crest of the dam (photograph by courtesy of Mr. Louis Jensen).

fish where they can escape large predacious enemies. Rocks or brush placed in shallow water have also been used extensively to provide additional shelter. In some instances large pieces of sod bound together and containing various aquatic plants have been sunk in lakes lacking plant beds. The success obtainable is questionable, and some lake improvements used to date have been distinctly detrimental to the beauty of the waters concerned by littering up the shallow-water areas with unsightly and unnatural accumulations of debris.

If such shelters are to be installed it is essential that they be installed in goodly numbers; for where only one or two are sunk, they attract large numbers of fish, which in turn attract the anglers, who then quickly reduce the fish supply. Where many shelters are installed the fish remain scattered. It should be kept in mind that shelter is installed primarily for the fish, not to make catching them easier.*

SPAWNING-BED IMPROVEMENT

Suitable spawning grounds exist in most trout streams or their tributaries in the United States. Few are so rugged over their entire course as to prevent spawning migrations to suitable areas in their tributaries. Even in the high mountains of the western states where cascading, boulder-strewn streams abound, a careful examination will usually show adequate gravelly spawning areas at various points either along their course or in their tributaries. It is not lack of spawning grounds but lack of adult trout to utilize them that is the critical problem in most intensely fished areas today. As evidence of the fact that natural spawning alone can build up tremendous populations of trout where the hand of man has not interfered with the natural balance, witness the abundant stocks of trout in remote areas long distances from roads and where little or no stocking has been done. In such areas the "take" is far below production, and races of stunted, small trout sometimes result because populations are far too dense for the available food.

Lakes, particularly many of those in the high mountains of the west which were originally barren of trout, often lack adequate and suitable spawning beds in both the inlets and outlets. In such cases artificial improvements to provide suitable areas have been tried, with indifferent success. Where such are naturally lacking and where artificial beds cannot be supplied, periodic re-stocking with eyed eggs or young fish are the only methods available. The problem is to allow sufficient survival each year of adult trout so that such spawning areas as are available may be utilized to their fullest capacity.

* For a comprehensive discussion of lake improvement methods in relation to fish management, readers are referred to *The Improvement of Lakes for Fishing*, by Dr. Carl L. Hubbs and R. W. Eschmeyer, recently published (1938) by the Institute for Fisheries Research of the Michigan Department of Conservation.

Sometimes impassable falls prevent fish from reaching suitable spawning beds, in which cases, where the falls are low, a few shots of dynamite will often clear a way permitting their ascent. Unless good spawning grounds exist above any given obstructions there is absolutely no point in removing them. Barriers that have existed in streams for geologic ages and to which runs of migratory fishes have adjusted themselves naturally, might better be left alone. Proposals by angling clubs that certain falls be supplied with fish ladders or dynamited out often have little justification. The writer knows of two supposedly impassable falls that were commonly said completely to block upstream runs of steelhead and salmon. Examination of young fish in the streams above both falls showed abundant young of those salmonoids that, according to popular opinion, could not possibly have spawned above the falls. Man sometimes does more harm than good in attempting to improve on nature.

In many high lakes in California, where spawning inlets are entirely lacking or inadequate, trout will spawn in the lake outlets or descend them, often passing down steep, rock-strewn cascades to their destruction. In such lakes some means of permitting safer spawning, such as that used in Lake Dorothy (see page 183), would certainly seem desirable.

In England artificial gravel spawning beds have been constructed by dumping loads of gravel in shallow water areas of streams, though I do not know of any published accounts of the success obtainable with this method. Hubbs, Greeley, and Tarzwell (1932) say:

> It is of course advantageous to supplement the stocking of . . . streams with natural reproduction. We have already pointed out that, by the use of current deflectors, the sand can be washed off to expose gravel suitable for spawning in some such streams. When this may not be done, and no spawning facilities are available, gravel beds may actually be added. This should be done, for either brook or brown trout, in headwaters which do not freeze in the winter, when the eggs are developing (streams which remain well below 60°F. in hot summer weather will seldom if ever freeze over in winter). The best gravel is rather coarse and loose. Natural gravel where too firm to allow the trout to dig out the spawning pits may be made suitable for spawning by turning over the gravel with a fork, or better with a spike-toothed harrow drawn by a horse.

Here too, no mention is made of the results of such improvements. In fact we know practically nothing about this phase of improvement work. This problem presents a chance for some extremely useful fact-finding research.

In California, the United States Forest Service started experimental work along this line in the inlet to Medicine Lake in the Shasta National Forest during the summer of 1933. This work was the first of its kind in the far west. To date, while spawning fish have been observed using the artificial redds provided, no quantitative determinations have been made of the resultant young produced in such beds. In the summers of 1934 and 1935, similar improvements were installed on Gumboot and Castle Lakes in the Shasta National Forest, but no clear-cut conclusions are possible now on any of such work to date.*

This phase of improvement work will offer numerous possibilities once the requirements of trout are fully understood, and once really practical methods for providing substitute redds are developed in waters lacking natural spawning areas.

A good summary of this topic is the statement of Davis (1934b) of the United States Bureau of Fisheries regarding stream improvement work in general:

> Furthermore, there is the all-important question: How far are we justified, from an economic standpoint, in proceeding with stream improvement? Is it not possible that some of the money now being expended on this work would yield greater returns if used for the construction and maintenance of rearing pools, or for the development of a scientific stocking program based on adequate surveys and field investigations? There is remarkably little evidence to show that much of the stream improvement work will yield returns at all commensurate with its cost. . . . There is still room for improvement in our hatchery technique and much greater room for improvement in our stocking technique. In the development of any well balanced program of fishery management this fact must be recognized and each problem receive its proper share of attention.

The essence of all improvement work is to make trout comfortable by meeting in the fullest measure possible the fundamental requirements of adequate food, shelter, and fit conditions for reproduction.

MEASURING ANGLERS' CATCHES

With very few exceptions, the only criteria that fishery officials now have by which to judge the condition of any lake or stream are the praises or complaints of fishermen. If the fishing holds up and continues to be good, little is usually said about it. However, if the fishing becomes poorer or the fish harder to catch, then a cry goes up from the anglers and frenzied attempts may be made by planting the lake heavily to bring it back to its former productivity. But the complaints or praises of anglers are seldom based on sufficient evidence to warrant any given type of treatment. Where the fishing falls off in any lake it may merely be that more anglers are fishing it, and hence the fish are being shared by a larger number of fishermen. The basic productivity of a lake in game fish is not changed unless natural conditions change considerably. This they usually do not do from year to year unless man interferes to upset the natural balance. Any given lake will produce only so many

* Numerous spawning channels have been constructed in the Northwest and in British Columbia—many to take the place of natural spawning areas made inaccessible or inundated by dams. Success has varied, but there is much encouragement in what has been learned. Devices have been developed to clean the gravel of fine materials prior to the spawning season.

pounds of fish per acre of water area. If the take exceeds the supply then naturally the fishing will deteriorate. Our waters should be managed on a sustained yield basis. Catch records may furnish the needed facts to measure the trend of fishing.

Biological surveys have conclusively shown that each lake differs from most other lakes. Each presents its own unique management problems. Anglers know this. We all know it; and hence *general* conservation policies for wide areas must be replaced by *specific* policies for different waters.

Stream and lake surveys indicate at least the preliminary stocking policies needed. One way to check the results is to record anglers' catches by developing a system for securing voluntary returns. Another way is that of taking quantitative collections of fish from gill nets or seine hauls; but this method as used today usually produces rather incomplete and unsatisfactory results. More accurate methods may be developed. Records of anglers' catches will provide a measure of the annual trend of the fishing. This method has the added advantage of putting the licensees in direct contact with conservation agencies, thus stimulating their interest in conservation.

Various states have made sporadic efforts to collect angling statistics in inland waters. Such work has usually been directed toward determining the availability of fish to fishermen by measuring the catch per unit of effort. Michigan instituted its statewide creel census in 1927 and has continued it every year on a large scale. California in 1932 placed in effect a system for obtaining statistics relating to marine sport catches in the ocean off southern California. Clark and Croker (1933) say regarding the latter:

> In addition to obtaining total catch figures our system will enable us to record any changes in availability of the various species of fish to the fishermen. Because the amount of time expended by fishermen on barges and piers is relatively constant from year to year, and knowing the number of fishermen, we will be able to calculate the fish yield per unit of effort from one season to another. The catch per unit of effort put forth by fishermen on party and charter boats can be calculated readily because the exact number of passengers and hours of fishing are recorded with the catch. It is not absolutely essential to have figures on the entire catch of sport fish in order to determine accurately the trend of fluctuations. With an adequate representative sample, it is possible to ascertain the catch per unit of effort more accurately than the total catch.

Clark (1934) also points out further the desirability of securing sport catch records whether taken in salt or fresh waters, and says that any plan adopted must be tested carefully and modified as desirable. In his concluding paragraph Clark says,

We have put off too long this matter of a measure of the angler's catch Why not do some thinking about it and then act, so that at least a representative sample of the angler's catch may be used to measure the availability of fish to the fisherman by gauging the catch per unit of fishing effort? With definite knowledge of the supply in the various bodies of water, regulation and administration of our fish resources will be on a much firmer foundation. We will have facts, not just hearsay and poor estimates.

Lord (1935b) later reported that good returns were obtained through the use of a so-called "test stream" where all anglers were required by law to report their catches. He says,

. . . at the Pittsford Station (Vt.) there have been in the past several attempts to secure fishing statistics, by asking for voluntary cooperation from the fishermen. Fishermen however are somewhat loath to reveal much about their luck, especially if it is good, and hence the system of voluntary reports did not amount to much. For example during the summer of 1934 only 129 reports on fishing results in Furnace Creek [Furnace Brook] were received.

The subject was taken up with the Vermont Fish and Game Service and with certain sportsmen's associations, with the result that the 1935 Assembly of the State of Vermont passed a bill making it possible for the state fish and game service to cooperate with the Bureau of Fisheries in a program of "test water" investigation. The bill provides that up to four different bodies of "test waters" can be set aside in the state at any one time to be used in an investigation to determine the annual trout production. The Bureau of Fisheries is to carry on the necessary stocking and scientific work while the state fish and game service is to see that the regulations pertaining to the "test waters" are enforced. All fishermen are required to obtain a permit, issued without charge, and are required by law to report the daily catches on cards provided for that purpose in boxes at certain points along the test area in question. Violators are liable to a $10.00 fine.

During the past season just one stream, Furnace Brook, which flows through the hatchery grounds at Pittsford, was selected as a test stream. This is an excellent trout brook with plenty of food and shelter. It is about twenty-five feet in width throughout the four miles of stream selected as the test area. A good road follows it to the headwaters. As it is within a few miles of several cities and towns it is very heavily fished each season.

Lord also stated that, "8589 legal trout were taken" and "anglers averaged 7.2 trout per fishing attempt. Rainbows made up 34 per cent of the catch. This species is maintaining itself without stocking. Brook trout made up 66 per cent of the catch. The number of brook trout taken exceeded the number of fish planted before the first fishing month was over." Lord based recommendations for reduced bag limits and changes in the fishing season upon the excellent information derived from the "test stream" project. This same method is being used successfully to obtain marine sport catch records in the ocean off southern California. The California legislature in 1935 passed a law giving the

State Division of Fish and Game power to demand catch records from the operators of pleasure fishing boats. Making reports of catches mandatory by law is one method that seems to offer good results.

Another method used by the writer in connection with lake studies in California has been to secure the cooperation of resort owners in recording catches from lakes on which their resorts are located. By this method catch records have been secured from Convict Lake and Upper Angora

FIG. 73.—Ideal dry-fly water. The Owens River near Bishop, California. Many large brown or Loch Leven trout are caught by anglers in this stream (photograph by courtesy of Mr. Joe Mears).

Lake at high elevations in the Sierra Nevada Mountains. These lakes have but one resort each on their shores, and fishermen are easily reached here, since in both cases there is only one road or trail giving access to the lake, and anglers pass within a few steps of the resort entrances. Marked fish of various sizes and species were planted in both lakes. This was done to determine from the catch records how many of them land in angler's creels. Here some of the incomplete results obtained to date with regard to Convict Lake will be submitted (Fig. 74).

In the summer of 1935 there were planted 2014 rainbow trout averaging 5.67 inches in length in Convict Lake (Needham, 1937). These fish were marked with a pair of clippers by snipping off two fins from each fish, the adipose and left pelvic fins. This is a common method of marking both trout and salmon so that they can be distinguished when caught later. The one camp on Convict Lake leases boats on the lake. The owners of this resort gave every cooperation in securing records of the catch.* Accordingly the following system for securing returns from both fishing parties renting boats and anglers fishing from the shoreline was adopted.

For boat catch records, blanks of the type printed below were used and filled out completely by anglers upon returning the oars to the resort *at the conclusion* of a rental period for any one day. Persons renting boats for more than one day were asked to fill out one blank for each day that fishing was done. One person only filled out one blank for any given party in one boat and usually this was the person who returned the oars and paid the rental charges.

BOAT CATCH RECORD

Convict Lake—1935

Number of boat: Date:

Number of fishermen: Hours fishing:

Trout caught:

UNMARKED	Number	Estimated Weight	Estimated Length
†Brown or Loch Leven			
†Rainbow or steelhead			
Marked rainbows			

Remarks

(Signed) ....

Address ....

This blank took care of boat fishing returns. For shore fishing returns it was necessary to post conspicuous signs at all important camp sites, fishing points, and trails. These announced the fact that records were

* My thanks are due Mr. and Mrs. Bill Garner, operators of the Convict Lake Resort, for their help in obtaining daily records of the catches.

† Since Loch Leven and brown trout have been thoroughly mixed by fish culturists, all gradations may be found and hence both were recorded in one category on this blank. The same may be said for rainbows and steelheads. No other game fish are found in Convict Lake, except rarely a golden trout and a few cutthroat trout.

wanted of all trout caught, whether marked or unmarked, and stated the object of the work. Liberal use of the word "please" was very helpful. It is highly important in work of this kind that no antagonism be aroused. In large letters and underscored at the bottom of the signs a large "PLEASE RECORD YOUR CATCHES AT THE CONVICT LAKE RESORT" appeared. Special blanks for recording catches made by shore fishermen were placed at the front desk in the Convict Lake Resort. Here they were written in as reported by anglers.

Boat catch records are here estimated as being 98 per cent complete; it is doubtful whether the shore-fishing returns are over 65 per cent to 75 per cent complete. If it were not for the fact that this resort is located about one-quarter of a mile below the lake on the only road giving access to the lake and provides the only dining room, store, and gasoline pump within about six miles, the shore-fishing returns would probably have been even more incomplete. In this connection, it is rapidly becoming evident from the catch record work done to date, that where voluntary returns alone are expected from fishermen without the aid or help of persons especially assigned to follow-up and urge their cooperation, only very incomplete results will be had.

RECORDS OF THE CATCH FROM BOATS

Table 31 below gives a summary of all trout caught by boat fishermen in Convict Lake from July 20 to October 31, 1935. Since the experiment was begun July 20, 1935, when the marked fish were planted, no returns were received from May 1, when the season opened, to July 19.

TABLE XXXI

ANALYSIS OF THE RECORDS OF CATCH FROM BOATS IN CONVICT LAKE
JULY 20 TO OCTOBER 31, 1935

Month	No. of Boat Reports	No. of Anglers	Total Fishing Hours	Fish Taken				Catch per Unit Effort*
				Unmarked Browns	Unmarked Rainbows	Marked Rainbows	Total Trout	
July	34	62	270	12	19	4	35	0.13
August	51	99	414	23	45	25	93	0.24
September	10	19	83	0	11	0	11	0.13
October	2	4	29	23	1	4	28	0.96†
Total	97§	184	796	58	76	33	167	0.21

* One hour's fishing by one angler.
† Based on two returns made by four expert fishermen.
§ 106 blanks were returned, but 9 made out for 15 anglers could not be used in calculating catch per unit of effort as they failed to state the number of hours of fishing.

The returns for boat fishing submitted in Table 31 indicated the average catch per unit of effort to be 0.21 trout. In other words, a person fishing during the season of 1935 would have had to fish about five hours to catch one fish if his fishing ability was average. Evidence that expert fishermen get the bulk of the fish is shown by the fact that only half of the boats rented actually took trout. The average catch per boat of those taking trout was 3.6 fish. The average length of the rental or fishing period was slightly over four hours, approximately half a day.

If the catch per unit of effort by boat fishermen can be obtained in this lake annually, a very definite measure of the trend of its fishing will be had. It will serve as an accurate measure of the results of any management or stocking system put into effect. This is a method that may be applicable to intensively fished inland lakes generally.

TOTAL RETURNS FROM CONVICT LAKE IN 1935

The following brief summary of all returns received from both shore and boat fishermen in 1935 in Convict Lake should be considered as preliminary. It is given to demonstrate a method rather than for the facts determined.

A total of 337 anglers caught 848 trout in the lake (Table 32). Of the latter, 499 or 59 per cent were unmarked fish (25 per cent brown

TABLE XXXII

TOTAL RETURNS FROM SHORE AND BOAT FISHERMEN IN CONVICT LAKE
JULY 20 TO OCTOBER 31, 1935

Fish Caught From	No. of Anglers	Total Trout		Unmarked Brown Trout		Unmarked Rainbow Trout		Marked Rainbow Trout	
		No.	%	No.	%	No.	%	No.	%
Shore.....	134	650	76.6	138	64.1	199	70.0	313	89.6
Boat......	203	198	23.3	77	35.8	85	29.9	36	10.3
Totals....	337	848	—	215	—	284	—	349	—

trout; 34 per cent unmarked rainbow trout), and 349 or 41 per cent were marked rainbow from the planting of July 20. Approximately 77 per cent of all fish taken were caught by shore fishermen while 23 per cent were taken from boats. Boat fishermen caught the larger fish and hence the greater poundage, even though the actual numbers taken were less than from shore. Marked rainbows formed 48 per cent of shore catches and 18 per cent of boat catches. This shows that the smaller fish were most abundant in shallow water, as would naturally be expected.

A computation of the trout population in Convict Lake goes as follows. Of the 2014 marked rainbow trout planted, the 349 reported caught constituted 17.33 per cent of the total. The 284 unmarked rainbow trout formed 44.86 per cent and marked rainbows 55.13 per cent, respectively, of the total catch of 633 rainbow trout. By using these figures, it is possible to calculate roughly the total population of rainbow trout present in Convict Lake in 1935 as follows:

Let a = number of marked rainbow planted in lake July 20—2014
b = number of marked rainbow reported caught after July 20—349
c = number of unmarked rainbow reported caught after July 20—284
x = number of unmarked rainbow in lake July 20
y = total rainbow population July 20

On the assumption that the number of marked and unmarked trout reported caught bore the same ratio to the total population of both marked and unmarked fish in the lake, respectively, then:

$$(1)\quad \frac{a}{b} = \frac{x}{c}$$

By substituting values given above the number of unmarked rainbow (x) July 20 can be calculated directly by proportions. The total population of rainbow (y) July 20 can then be determined simply by addition: ($a + x = y$), or directly from the formula:

$$(2)\quad y = (b + c)\left(\frac{a}{b}\right)$$

If marked fish were planted more than once the computations would be more complicated but still not difficult. From the calculations outlined above, the rainbow trout population of Convict Lake may be summarized as follows in Table 33:

TABLE XXXIII

THE COMPUTED POPULATION OF RAINBOW TROUT IN CONVICT LAKE

	Population on July 20, 1935		Reported Caught		Remaining at End of Season	
	No.	Per Cent	No.	Per Cent	No.	Per Cent
Planted (Marked) Population	2014	55.13	349	55.13	1655	55.13
Calculated Unmarked Population	1639	44.86	284	44.86	1355	44.88
Total Population	3653	—	633	—	3020	—

The calculations shown in Table 33 can only be considered as extremely rough approximations by reason of the following sources of error:

(1) Incomplete returns. For this reason the computed number of fish remaining at the end of the season is certainly too high because of fish caught but not reported. Since marked fish predominated in the shore catches and since unmarked fish were taken more largely by the boat fishermen, complete returns would have raised the number of marked rainbow caught with reference to the number of marked fish planted, and therefore given a higher value for the number of unmarked fish present July 20.

(2) Marked fish may be more easily caught than unmarked fish. This is an assumption based on the general experience that young hatchery-raised trout freshly planted are more easily caught than wild trout of the same age. The marked rainbow averaged 5.67 inches in length when planted and fish of this size usually take bait or flies readily. This factor would make for imperfect sampling of the unmarked population, and for this reason also the number of unmarked rainbows in the lake was probably higher than computed, both on July 20 and at the end of the fishing season.

(3) Losses of fish due to predators, disease, and cannibalism. There was undoubtedly loss of fish due to these causes, and no allowance is made in the calculations in Table 33 for such losses. These factors would tend to lower the population remaining at the end of the season below the computed number.

(4) Lack of proof that in-shore and off-shore populations were representatively sampled by anglers. Since marked trout were taken chiefly near shore and no doubt were more numerous there, any disproportionate sampling of this population would distort the calculated values. These sources of error are quite unmeasurable, and today no ready means is apparent for estimating either their magnitude or their direction. Since the error may be great, these computations must be regarded as only very rough approximations.*

We are not justified in calculating the brown trout population from the proportion recorded as having been caught. In the opinion of most experienced anglers these fish are much harder to catch than are rainbows.

The measurement of trout populations can only be obtained by planting experiments with marked trout in "test lakes," where complete or nearly complete records of the catch are possible. From such experiments such basic facts will be determined as (1) mortality of planted trout of various sizes and (2) pounds of fish produced per acre of water area.

* An excellent review of population estimation is given by Overton and Davis (1969). Ricker (1958) goes into the subject in detail, as do Regier and Robson (1967).

Although a complete census is needed to determine accurately the trout population of a given lake, and is very desirable for "test lakes," it is not necessary to take complete returns in order to obtain data of value in fish management. The measurement of the catch per unit of effort affords a definite means of determining the trend of the fishing, and can be based on an annual random sample of the catch. The sampling should cover, without selection, both the parties catching many fish and those catching few or none, in order to obtain proper balance between returns of expert and inexpert fishermen. Enough records should be obtained every year to be statistically representative. The sampling should be random as to season and time of day as well as to the skill of the fisherman. This will avoid taking records in one year at a time when fishing tends to be better, and in another year at a time when few fish are caught. If the samples obtained are truly random in nature and gathered consistently from year to year by uniform methods and under uniform conditions, they will give accurate measures of the trend of the fishing and fish populations from year to year.

Determining the trend of fishing in streams presents greater difficulties. Through the use of "test streams," as demonstrated by Lord (1935), it is evident that satisfactory catch records can be obtained when the census is backed by appropriate legislative action. Before any system of recording the catch can be placed in operation, it should be decided whether total catches or merely random samples of catches are desired. Total catches are by far the more desirable, and are also more costly and harder to obtain. Many types of useful, pertinent data, that will prove of much practical use in the management of specific waters, can be obtained from complete catch records. For streams and lakes that have long been soures of discontent and criticism by anglers, the factual data furnished by total catch records should in the end more than pay for themselves. Measurement of annual trends by random samples should be sufficient for non-problem types of waters in which the fish are holding their own fairly well. Possibly it would be better to take total records or none at all, in view of the wider range of facts obtained.

To facilitate receiving reports from anglers, it might be satisfactory to furnish licensees with books or pads of blank forms of convenient size upon which could be written the catch records of separate fishing trips. These could then be mailed to the administrative office concerned at the conclusion of each trip. It would be important that the records be written down the same day the catch was made before memory of details had faded. Records of fish caught mean little or nothing if written some weeks or months after the event. There is no good reason why catch records should be obtained on remote, inaccessible streams and lakes where the fishing is light, and where no critical problems exist, unless it is desired to know for purposes of comparison how successful the fishing is in such waters.

As Clark (1934) has clearly pointed out, any system for obtaining voluntary records of catches must have the full support of the angling public. To obtain their support a constant barrage of publicity by articles, movies, talks to sportsmen's clubs and over the radio, would be needed.

It is difficult to get anglers to record their catches correctly and honestly. They are usually in too much of a hurry, or they find it too much trouble to study the blanks provided to learn how to fill them out

FIG. 74.—Convict Lake, near Bishop, California. A typical east slope lake heavily fished and easily accessible by road. The planting experiment with marked trout discussed in this chapter was carried on here (photograph by courtesy of Mr. Francis Hatch).

properly. In Michigan, game wardens and C.C.C. workers have been employed to gather the records and to fill out the blanks. Lord (1935) reported very poor returns until anglers were required by law to report their catches on "test streams" in Vermont. The work on Convict Lake reported here has inaccuracies caused by incomplete returns. It is beginning to appear that if adequate voluntary catch records are to be obtained, they must be taken under very close and capable supervision.*

Before concluding, I would like to quote Leopold on what he calls "Kill Ratios" in his *Game Management* (1933). His remarks, though made with respect to game animals, apply equally well to fishes. He says:

> Statistics based on experience are the only available means of arriving at the proportion of the game population which may be safely killed on any

* For additional information on creel census see Butler and Borgeson (1965) and Neuhold and Lu (1957).

given area without reducing the breeding stock or the size of subsequent crops. The subsequent crops are the best measure of whether the breeding stock has been unduly reduced. Consequently statistics must cover a defined area for a period of years, . . . if a kill-ratio is to be correctly determined. No single case is as yet known in which such a ratio has been derived in this country. There is in this fact a certain irony which should not escape notice. For decades our game literature was largely a record of kills. If there exists, in all these tons of bloody paper, a single accurate bag count applying to a specified population or area through a period of years, then I have failed to find it. Yet these same men [the men who wrote these records] every day of their lives, measured the yield of their fields, their herds, and their commerce in terms of principal and interest.

Appendix

I. NAMES OF TROUT

Anglers' arguments as to the kinds of trout caught are endless. The confusion of many names given to the same or to closely related forms has added to the difficulty of properly designating the various kinds caught. Anglers are not interested in the hair-splitting distinctions that have been used by systematic ichthyologists to separate various species.

Jordan, Evermann, and Clark (1930) in their check list of the fishes of North America list over forty distinct species of trout as occurring on this continent. All of these species fall naturally into the following four groups or series: rainbows, browns, cutthroats, and charrs. Many species are poorly defined and represent such a medley of intergrading forms that expert ichthyologists have trouble in separating one from another. And right here lies the cause of the endless confusion among anglers regarding the names of trout. As Dr. W. C. Kendall, for many years Senior Ichthyologist with the United States Bureau of Fisheries, said (1931):

> There are several causes for changes of names. One is that a species may have been described under different names by different individuals at different times. They may all stand as distinct species until it is found, or someone thinks, that they are all one species. When this is found to be the case, the oldest name is used for the single species and the other names are relegated to synonymy. On the other hand, another cause of change is that more than one species may have been found to compose what has previously been thought to be one species, or someone may think that is the case. Here is one factor conducive to instability, for while one thinks several species are perhaps combined under one name, another may continue to regard them all as one. Still another reason for change of names is that it may be found that the animal has been misidentified and has been given a name which belongs to some other animal, or someone thinks that is the case. In this instance, if the animal has not been previously described it is given a new name. Or, if someone else has previously described and named it, this name is used. If it has been described and named more than once, the oldest name obtains.

At another point Dr. Kendall remarks, "When doctors disagree, and especially when the same doctor disagrees with himself, to the uninitiated, uniformity and stability of nomenclature seem almost hopeless."

A reasonable explanation of the development of many closely allied species results from a study of the orgin of these fishes in North America. Dr. David Starr Jordan, in his *Fishes* (1907), says:

> It seems probable that the American trout originated in Asia, extended its range to southeast Alaska, then southward to the Fraser and Columbia, thence to the Yellowstone and the Missouri via Two-Ocean Pass; from the Snake River to the Great Basins of Utah and Nevada; from the Missouri southward to the Platte and the Arkansas, thence from the Platte to the Rio Grande and the Colorado, and then from Oregon southward coastwise and along the Sierras to northern Mexico, thence northward and coastwise, the sea-running forms passing from stream to stream.

Subsequent isolation in numerous drainage systems would seem to account for further variations, which in the course of time may produce more distinct types, however closely they may resemble each other today.

The native home of rainbow in California was in the rivers draining the west slope of the Sierra Nevada Mountains into the Sacramento and San Joaquin valleys. Early ichthyologists working in California gave most of their attention to the Kern and Sacramento rivers and described the Kern River and Shasta rainbows from these areas as distinct species. Had the trout populations of the lower Kaweah, San Joaquin, Kings, Merced, Tuolumne, Feather, Stanislaus, Mokelumne, American, Yuba, and other streams draining into the great central valleys received similar study, it is quite possible that the species described might have been discovered to be but local variations of the previously described species. It is logical to assume that there must have been some natural inter-stream mixing of races where there were no impassable barriers, however distinct they may have been originally. Inter-breeding of fish from the lower reaches of the different streams over a long period of time, before man appeared on the scene to change conditions, would tend to reduce differences in appearance and structure.

Dr. Jordan and others have pointed out that apparently the cutthroat or black-spotted trout, *Salmo clarkii,* has interbred in some waters with the coast rainbow, *Salmo gairdnerii,* notably in the Columbia and Snake rivers, and it is possible to find variously marked hybrids, of which some resemble the rainbow and others are more nearly like the typical cutthroat.

Further complications have been added by fish culturists who have crossed cutthroats with rainbows and stocked streams with the resultant hybrids. The transfer by fish culturists of fishes from one drainage area to another has added further chaos. For instance, in some waters it is possible to take four or five kinds of trout from the same stream on the same day. In Colorado it is possible to catch seven distinct species of trout and one species of salmon. It is no wonder that anglers may not be sure just what kind of trout they are catching.

Whether steelhead and rainbow trout are distinct species is one point where confusion has been endless. Equally competent observers have held both views. Various structural measurements and scale and vertebral counts have shown that it is almost impossible to distinguish the two by these means alone. Dr. J. O. Snyder said (1933) in this regard:

> Some observers hold to the belief that the steelhead is a distinct species of trout somewhat intermediate between the cutthroat and the rainbow. Such is not the case, and this statement is supported by a mass of observational and experimental evidence. A steelhead is a sea migrant of the particular species inhabiting the stream, and in our waters [California] it may be either a cutthroat steelhead or a rainbow steelhead.*

He also says, in speaking of the "coast rainbow": "Entering the streams as steelheads, they migrate to the uppermost tributaries, where they spawn and then return to the sea. The progeny of the steelheads remain for a time as stream trout drifting toward deeper water as they grow larger, some remaining three years or more before entering the ocean. In large bodies of water, lakes and river channels are resident trout which behave in their spawning migrations just as do the steelheads, seeking turbulent, well aerated water in which to deposit their eggs."

For all practical purposes, and to get rid of a lot of confusion in conflicting scientific and common names, it would seem logical to call the large sea-run fish that have returned to spawn "steelheads," restricting the term "rainbow" to the non-sea-run stream fish. I prefer to follow the classification recently used by Mottley (1936), Schultz (1936), and others for the trout of Oregon, Washington, and British Columbia. Both these workers use the name *Salmo gairdnerii* for steelhead or rainbow and *Salmo clarkii* for cutthroat or black-spotted. Geographic races or varieties within this species are indicated by the use of sub-specific names (trinomials). Thus either fresh water rainbows or sea-run steelhead of the lower and middle Columbia River and coastal area generally of Oregon, Washington, and British Columbia would be called *Salmo gairdnerii gairdnerii*. Mottley (*loc. cit.*), not finding any single character by which all adult Kamloops trout could be distinguished from all adult steelhead of British Columbia, used the name *S. gairdnerii kamloops,* placing this trout as a variety of *gairdnerii*. Similarly the coast cutthroat is called *Salmo clarkii clarkii,* while the Montana black-spotted or Montana cutthroat of the upper and middle Columbia basin is given the name *S. clarkii lewisi;* both are subspecific indicating merely different varieties of the same species.

* Dr. Snyder's designtion of anadromous cutthroats as steelhead has not caught on with anglers, who refer to them as "searun cuts" or "bluebacks." One occasionally hears the old-fashioned name "harvest trout."

II. INSTRUCTIONS FOR COLLECTING FISH SCALES* FOR USE IN AGE AND GROWTH STUDIES

Method of collecting.—The best place to take scales from fish is from the midregion of the body immediately above the lateral line. They may be easily removed by scraping against the outer free tips of the scales with a dull knife or scalpel. Scales should not be taken from the lateral line. With large fish over 12 inches long, it is well to wipe mucus off the side of the fish with a cloth before the scales are scraped loose. Large amounts of mucus make it difficult later to clean the scales for mounting. The scales should then be placed either in regular United States Bureau Fisheries scale envelopes, which are provided for this purpose, or they can be placed in scale-collection books where the edge has been cut and on which the scales are placed and the edge folded back against the other half of the sheet. The mucus secured with the scale samples is usually ample to attach them firmly in place. Extreme care should be taken to prevent the mixing of scales from different fish. The knife should be wiped clean after each sample is taken. Complete data as to date, name of water, species of fish, sex, total and standard lengths, etc., should be recorded with each sample taken. Where condition factors are also to be determined from the same fish, it is highly desirable that the fish be weighed fresh as preservation in formaldehyde changes the weights markedly.

Obviously, scales collected cannot be studied in the field owing to the time involved, but should be retained for later study in connection with the write-up of the survey findings. Scale reading requires special training and technique, and untrained persons should not attempt to read them.

III. PLANTING TABLES*

Table 34 indicates the number of 3-inch fingerlings to be planted yearly, and per mile, for streams of various widths and showing different combinations of food and pool conditions.

* Reprinted with permission of Dr. H. S. Davis from *Instructions for Conducting Stream and Lake Surveys* (1938). Tables 34, 35, and 37 are modified after Embody (1927). Regarding these Davis (1938) says:

"Dr. Embody's table was developed primarily for the streams of western New York which are subjected to very heavy fishing and in which there is very little natural propagation. Experience indicates that under ordinary conditions it is advisable to reduce the stocking rate somewhat and also make some readjustments in the estimated survival of fingerlings of different sizes. While it is hoped that a revised table will prove more serviceable for general use, it still remains true that the numbers recommended are purely tentative and will doubtless require considerable revision in the light of future investigations.

"Even though our knowledge is too limited to make it possible to outline a truly scientific stocking policy at this time, recommendations based on the results of the survey will do much to increase the efficiency of artificial stocking and be a great aid to any program of fish management." (Most state fishery management agencies now have their own stocking schedules built on many years of experience with the stream environments and the fishing pressure, but most probably started with some form of Embody's table.)

In order to use this table, one must first determine the average width of the stream, the number of miles suitable for stocking, and values for stream conditions (A, B, and C) and food conditions (1, 2, and 3) as already described. [The letters *A, B* and *C* refer to grade of pools and shelter in streams. *A,* better than average condition; *B,* average condition; and *C,* conditions below average. The numbers 1, 2, and 3 refer to food grade. If better than average and very rich in food the figure 1 is used; if average, the figure 2; and if below average, the figure 3. For a

TABLE XXXIV
PLANTING TABLE FOR TROUT STREAMS

WIDTH OF STREAM (FEET)	NUMBER OF 3-INCH FINGERLINGS PER MILE								
	A-1	A-2	A-3	B-1	B-2	B-3	C-1	C-2	C-3
1	80	65	50	65	50	35	50	35	20
2	160	130	100	130	100	70	100	70	40
3	240	195	150	195	150	105	150	105	60
4	320	260	200	260	200	140	200	140	80
5	400	325	250	325	250	175	250	175	100
6	480	390	300	390	300	210	300	210	120
7	560	455	350	455	350	245	350	245	140
8	640	520	400	520	400	280	400	280	160
9	720	585	450	585	450	315	450	315	180
10	800	650	500	650	500	350	500	350	200
11	880	715	550	715	550	385	550	385	220
12	960	780	600	780	600	420	600	420	240
13	1,040	845	650	845	650	455	650	455	260
14	1,120	910	700	910	700	490	700	490	280
15	1,200	975	750	975	750	525	750	525	300
16	1,280	1,040	800	1,040	800	560	800	560	320
17	1,360	1,105	850	1,105	850	595	850	595	340
18	1,440	1,170	900	1,170	900	630	900	630	360
19	1,520	1,235	950	1,235	950	665	950	665	380
20	1,600	1,300	1,000	1,300	1,000	700	1,000	700	400

more comprehensive discussion of these conditions in relation to stocking, see Davis (1938)].

Table 34 refers to 3-inch fingerlings only. To determine the required number of 1-, 2-, 4-, 5-, or 6-inch fish, multiply the number given in table 34 by the factor given in table 35.

Table 34 covers streams up to 20 feet in width. Values for wider streams may be determined by multiplying the number given for a stream 1 foot wide by the width of the stream in question.

Calculate the number of fish required of the sizes recommended. Recommendations as to size should take into account the sizes that are available for distribution at nearby hatcheries at the time the plantings are to be made. This information can usually be obtained from the hatchery superintendents. The sizes of fish available will vary, depending on water temperatures, the strains of fish at various hatcheries, and rearing facilities. Any stocking plan is much more likely to be followed if the number and sizes of fish recommended are available for stocking. When

TABLE XXXV

FACTORS FOR DETERMINING THE REQUIRED NUMBER OF FISH AND THE APPROXIMATE PERCENTAGE OF SURVIVAL

SIZE (INCHES)	FACTOR	SURVIVAL	SIZE (INCHES)	FACTOR	SURVIVAL
		Per cent			Per cent
1	10	5	4	0.7	70
2	2.5	20	5	.62	80
3	1	50	6	.55	90

legal-size fish are to be planted it is usually better to plant them at intervals throughout the season, rather than all at one time. In all cases the fish should be distributed more or less uniformly along the stream and not dumped in large numbers at a few easily accessible points.

These recommendations are intended primarily for streams that are fished heavily and in which there is relatively little natural propagation. In the case of streams which are less intensively fished, and in which there is considerable natural propagation, the numbers given in the table

TABLE XXXVI

PLANTING TABLE FOR TROUT LAKES; NUMBER OF 3-INCH TROUT PER ACRE

FISHING INTENSITY	GRADE I—FOOD ABUNDANT		GRADE II—FOOD AVERAGE		GRADE III—FOOD POOR	
	Good spawning	Poor spawning	Good spawning	Poor spawning	Good spawning	Poor spawning
Heavy......	180	240	90	120	50	60
Medium.....	90	180	45	90	25	45
Light.......	30	120	15	60	10	30

should be reduced 25 to 50 per cent, depending on the abundance of native trout of various sizes.

Table 36 indicates the number of 3-inch trout to be planted per acre of water surface in lakes of the three grades of richness and of various combinations of fishing intensity and spawning effectiveness. In estimating the acreage to be planted only water 50 feet or less in depth should be considered. This will include the entire area of shallow lakes, while in deep lakes it may happen that a considerable percentage of the total area will not be included in the estimated acreage for stocking purposes.

Table 36 refers to 3-inch fingerlings only. To determine the required number of 1-, 2-, 4-, 5-, or 6-inch fish, multiply the number given in table 36 by the factor given in table 35.

IV. ORGANIZATION OF STREAM AND LAKE SURVEY CREWS

One survey crew, as usually operated, consists of one leader assisted by from four to seven assistants. Both leader and assistants are selected wholly on the basis of fitness for their work. All, except the chemists assigned to any given crew, are usually college graduates trained for fresh water biological studies. All the men must be strong and in good health in order to withstand the rigors of working and camping under the oftentimes very difficult field conditions. Cooking in the field in camps is done either by men especially hired for the job or by the surveyors themselves taking turns at it. Hired cooks have proved more satisfactory.

Each survey crew is under the direction of a leader who is entirely responsible for the direction and accomplishments of his party. The leaders in turn plan and perform their work under the direction of the person who may be in general charge in any given state, national forest or park, or other territorial unit.

In my own experience in survey work, first in New York state and later in charge of surveys in California for the United States Bureau of Fisheries, the four-man party (one leader and three assistants) has been found quite satisfactory. Since two trucks are usually supplied each party for transportation, the men can work in pairs. This permits elasticity of organization and furnishes additional safety to the workers when in rough, mountainous country at high elevations. In well-roaded areas the two-men-per-truck arrangement also permits dropping a man off at any given point to follow a water-course either upstream or down to the next road where the man remaining with the truck can meet him, and in the meanwhile cover nearby tributaries reachable by road.

Equipment Supplied Survey Crews

Listed below is a partial list of scientific and camping equipment usually furnished a four-man survey crew by the agency carrying on stream and lake surveys.

Scientific Equipment

2 pick-up light ½ ton trucks

1 Ekman dredge for taking bottom samples with messengers for closing same
2 sets U.S.G.S. maps of area to be surveyed, mounted on cloth
1 map measurer
1 2-man air-rubber portable boat
2 Kapok life preservers
1 water sampler—1200 cc. for taking samples in lakes
2 plancton nets with buckets for collecting microscopic, free-swimming lake plants and animals
2 Secchi discs for measuring transparency of lakes
4 notebooks and field blanks for recording data
2 stream-bottom foods samplers
2 counting pans for stream foods
1 30-mesh soil sieve for straining out lake bottom organisms from silt
1 pH outfit for measuring hydrogen ion concentration of streams and lakes
1 chemical box containing materials and equipment for making water analyses in field
1 dozen field thermometers
3 wood kanakins for preserving fish
1 portable typewriter
1 1 meter steel tape
1 5 ft. folding rule
1 100 ft. tape
25 yds. cheesecloth
400 ft. #6 cotton sash cord for use with Ekman dredge
5 gallons formaldehyde for preserving fish
1 gallon alcohol for preserving fish foods
1 gross 4-dram vials with corks
1 stop watch
2 5-mesh size gill nets—125 ft. long x 6 ft. deep
2 30 ft. x 4 ft. minnow seines
2 10 ft. x 3 ft. minnow seines
1 100 ft. seine
Net mending needles and mending twine
8 prs. forceps (small, for sorting fish foods)
1 large pr. forceps for handling preserved fish
6 centrifuge tubes in case, for measuring volume of plancton samples, capacity 15 ml. x 1/10 cc.
1 reversing thermometer and case
2 hand tallies for counting fish
2 sounding lines with bobs
2 prs. waders
1 injecting syringe
4 12″ rulers
4 white enamel pans for sorting fish food organisms
2 prs. scissors
Miscellaneous: pencils, ink, office supplies, etc.

CAMPING EQUIPMENT

1 grub box
1 6-man cooking-eating kit
1 9 x 12 tent
2 ground cloths
1 cooking grid
1 reflector oven
1 gasoline lantern
1 camp table
2 tin wash basins
2 water buckets
4 folding canvas stools
4 compasses
4 canvas haversacks
2 2 gal. fuel cans
1 carborundum stone
1 axe
1 shovel
1 saw
1 first aid kit
4 pack boards for carrying equipment into inaccessible country
Miscellaneous: nails, rope, oil cloth, dish towels, mosquito netting, etc.

The above list will give some idea of the kind and number of items required for extensive stream and lake survey work. These lists are by no means complete. Types of equipment must be modified according to the character of the drainage basins in which the work is carried on and the types of field data required of the survey units. New problems constantly arise in the field and their successful solution depends on the ability and efficiency of the personnel of each party. Careful, accurate work is required and sound information will be obtained only if the workers are supplied the proper tools with which to make their observations, and if they are properly trained for, or experienced in, survey work.

COST OF SURVEY CREWS*

One four-man crew with one leader and three assistants will cost between $2,000 and $3,000 for salaries alone for from three to four months field work in the summertime. To date it has not proved feasible to operate surveys in winter because of weather conditions. Equipment cost per party including operations during field period for gas, oil, tires, etc., will run from $1,500 to $2,000. Thus the total for the first season's work will total between $3,500 and $5,000 per four-man party for a three to four month field period. A large portion of the equipment is good for several seasons' work, and after equipment is once purchased

* Compare 1969 costs of about $2,200 for three months of a biologist's time and $1,300 for seasonal aides with one or two years of college. Equipment costs have risen accordingly.

for two or three crews to be employed annually, the greatest cost of later surveys for several years at least will be largely in salaries.

V. METHODS OF LOCATING ON MAPS BOTH UNNAMED WATERS AND WATERS BEARING DUPLICATE NAMES

In any given drainage area to be surveyed, several lakes or streams may bear the same name, and others no name at all. This makes it essential that some system be adopted for designating waters, so that in future references to them they may be quickly and easily located in office files.

New York state, from the inception of the intensive surveys begun in 1926, has used a system whereby the tributaries are numbered in order from the mouth up. Tributaries of tributaries are similarly numbered. Lakes are similarly designated in order as they are encountered in numbering the streams. The tributary streams of lakes are numbered in clockwise order starting from the outlet, omitting the inlet if it bears the same name as the outlet.

Various other systems have been suggested but the writer personally prefers the numbering system, as all tributaries fall naturally and easily into one complete system. In surveys conducted by the United States Bureau of Fisheries in 1934 in the National Forests and Parks, the range, township, and section designations on the United States Forest Service maps were generally used. These are not entirely satisfactory, however, as a good many of the smaller lakes and ponds are not shown on these maps. The best maps available for survey purposes are the topographic quadrangles of the United States Geological Survey. However, these cannot be obtained for all areas, in which case park, forest service, water survey or other maps must be used. In the records, the names of streams, when available, are always used in addition to survey numbers. Final survey data sheets covering rivers, streams, sections of streams, lakes, and ponds, are filed in their proper order as they occur in any drainage basin.

In order to give an idea of the kind of information sought, given below are headings taken from the stream and lake survey forms of the United States Bureau of Fisheries. There are additional blanks (not shown here) covering chemical analyses of water, and seine or gillnet catches.

VI. BLANK FORMS FOR USE OF SURVEY CREWS*

U. S. DEPARTMENT OF COMMERCE, BUREAU OF FISHERIES
STREAM SURVEY

1. State River system Name of stream
   Forest or park Map Number
   County Tributary to
   Stream section:
   From:
   To:
   Length of section:

   Notes.—Sketches (show trails, roads, tributaries, stations, barriers, springs, etc.):

2. Name of stream .... Date ....

Region	Upper	Middle	Lower
Station:			
Altitude			
Average width and depth			
Volume			
Velocity			
Color and turbidity			
Alkalinity			
pH			
Air temperature			
Water temperature			
Hour and sky			
Pools:			
Size, type, frequency	S T F	S T F	S T F
Caused by			
Shelter			
Bottom type:			
Pools			
Riffles			
Shade			
Aquatic vegetation			
Fish food (per sq. ft.):			
Caddiceflies	Beetles		
Mayflies	Other insects		
Diptera	Crustacea		
Stoneflies	Miscellaneous		
Vol. in cc. per sq. ft.			

* Reproduced here by permission of the Commissioner of Fisheries.

Character of watershed: Canyons, mountainous, hilly, rolling, flat, swampy, wooded, open, cultivated, uncultivated.
Character of subsoil, bedrock and dip of strata.
Condition of stream: Low water, normal water, high water.
Fluctuation in volume:
Gradient:
Source:
Barriers (type, location, height):
Diversions (type, location):
Springs (location, volume, temperature):
Tributaries (number and size):
Fish (kinds, av. size, abundance, stations):
Enemies:
Degree fished (heavy, medium, light):
Spawning areas:
Fry, fingerlings seen (kinds, abundance, stations):
Accessibility of stream (by car or . . . miles by trail):
Previous stocking:
Pollution (source, type):
Rearing pool sites:
Fish recommended:
  Species:
  Reasons:
Remarks:
Improvements:

____
Investigator.

Average width: Pool grade: Food grade:

Stocking Program

Section to be stocked:
Species:
Size:
Number:
Frequency:

____
Authority.

U. S. DEPARTMENT OF COMMERCE, BUREAU OF FISHERIES

LAKE AND POND SURVEY

---

1. State River system Name of lake

Forest or park Map

County Tributary to Number

Notes.—Sketches (show soundings, station, weed beds, tributary streams, outlet, roads, and trails on outline map):

N

↑

Map

2. Name of lake: Date:

Altitude: Area:

Natural or artificial:

Height of dam: Fishway:

Character of shore line: Rocky, boggy, sandy, muddy, meadow, wooded.

Character of watershed: Mountainous, hilly, rolling, flat, swampy, wooded, open, cultivated, uncultivated.

Principal tributary streams (number and size):

Fluctuations in water level (causes and feet variation):

Approximate depth 100′ from shore ...., 200′ from shore ...., Maximum ....

Shoal areas 20′ or less .... % of lake:

Bottom—Mud, silt, sand, clay, peat, marl, detritus, hardpan, gravel, bedrock.

Deep areas: Bottom—Mud, silt, sand, clay, peat, marl, detritus, hardpan, gravel, bedrock.

Temperatures: Inlet ...., Outlet ...., Surface ...., Air ...., Hour ...., Weather ....

Color: Turbidity

Higher plants (show location on map): Abundance

Emergent:

Submerged:

Algae (kinds): Abundance

Vertebrates:

Kinds of fish: Abundance

Other vertebrates:

Invertebrates:

Shore (approx. no. per sq. ft.): Stoneflies ...., Mayflies ...., Caddiceflies ...., Odonata ...., Diptera .... Snails ...., Amphipods ...., Miscellaneous ....

Open water stations	1	2	3	4	5
Depth in feet					
Plankton:					
Length of haul					
Quantity in cc.					
Bottom (per ¼ sq. ft.):					
Midges					
Annelids					
Snails					
Clams					
Amphipods					
Miscellaneous					
Volume in cc.					
Type of sample bottom					

Spawning areas:

Young fish seen:

Accessible by car or . . . miles by trail.

Boats available:

Pollution: Source:
Type:

Degree fished (heavy, medium, light):

Rearing pool sites:

Fish recommended:

Species:

Reasons:

Remarks:

Improvements:

____
Investigator.

Stocking Program

Species:

Size:

Number:

Frequency:

____
Authority.

BIBLIOGRAPHY

Books having general popular interest are preceded by an asterisk (*).

ALLEGEIER, R. J., W. H. PETERSON, C. JUDAY, and E. A. BIRGE. 1932. "The Anaerobic Fermentation of Lake Deposits." *Int. Rev. d. ges. Hydrobiol. u. Hydrogr.*, Vol. 26, pp. 444-461.

*ARMISTEAD, WILSON H. 1908. *Trout Waters, Management, and Angling.* London, 203 pp.

BELDING, DAVID L. 1929. "The Respiratory Movements of Fish as an Indicator of a Toxic Environment." *Trans. Amer. Fish. Soc.*, Vol. 59, pp. 238-245.

*BERNERS, JULIANA, Dame (supposed author). 1496. "The Treatyse on Fysshynge with An Angle." From the *Book of St. Albans.* Originally printed by Wynkynde Worde. Edited by "Piscator," Edinburg, 1855, 36 pp.

*BREDER, CHARLES M. 1929. *Field Book of Marine Fishes of the Atlantic Coast from Labrador to Texas.* New York, 332 pp.

*BOCCIUS, GOTTLIEB. 1848. *Fish in Rivers and Streams: a Treatise on the Production and Management of Fish in Fresh Waters, by Spawning, Breeding and Rearing: showing also the Cause of the Depletion of all Rivers and Streams."* London, 38 pp.

*CALDERWOOD, W. L. 1930. *Salmon and Sea Trout.* London, 242 pp.

CARPENTER, KATHLEEN E. 1928. *Life in Inland Waters.* New York, 267 pp.

CLAASSEN, P. W. 1931. *Pleocoptera Nymphs of America (North of Mexico).* Thomas Say Foundation, Vol. III. Springfield, Ill., 199 pp.

CLARK, G. H. 1929. "Sacramento-San Joaquin salmon (*Oncorhynchus tschawytscha*) Fishery of California." Calif. Div. Fish and Game *Fish Bull.* No. 17, 73 pp.

1934. "The Need of a Measure of the Angler's Catch." *Trans. Amer. Fish Soc.*, Vol. 64, pp. 49-51.

CLARK, G. H., and RICHARD CROKER. 1933. "A Method of Collecting Statistics of Marine Sport Catches in California." *Trans. Amer. Fish. Soc.*, Vol. 63, pp. 332-336.

CLEMENS, W. A. 1935. "The Pacific Salmon in British Columbia Waters." *Rept. British Columbia Comm. Fish.*, 1934, pp. 103-105.

COMSTOCK, JOHN H. 1925. *An Introduction to Entomology*, 2d ed. Ithaca, N.Y., 1044 pp.

CONNERY, R. H. 1935. *Governmental Problems in Wild Life Conservation.* New York, 250 pp.

COSTEN, H. E. TOWNER; F. T. K. PENTELOW, and R. W. BUTCHER. 1936. *River Management; the Making, Care, and Development of Salmon and Trout Waters.* London. 263 pp.

COTTAM, CLARENCE, and F. M. UHLER. 1936. "The Role of Fish-Eating Birds." *Progressive Fish Culturist,* Jan., No. 14, Mimeographed Memorandum I-131, U. S. Bur. Fish., pp. 1-14.

*COTTON, W. HAROLD. 1935. *Aquaria and Garden Ponds.* London, 90 pp.

CREASER, CHARLES W. 1930. "Relative Importance of Hydrogen-Ion Concentration, Temperature, Dissolved Oxygen, and Carbon-Dioxide Tension, on Habitat Selection by Brook-Trout." *Ecology,* Vol. 11, pp. 246-262.

DAHL, KNUT. 1934. "Does Trout Stocking Pay?" *Salmon and Trout Mag.,* No. 74, pp. 18-26.

DAVIDSON, F. A. 1933. "Temporary High Carbon-Dioxide Content in an Alaskan Stream at Sunset." *Ecology,* Vol. 14, pp. 238-240.

DAVIDSON, F. A., and SAMUEL J. HUTCHINSON. 1938. "The Geographic Distribution and Environmental Limitations of the Pacific Salmon (Genus Oncorhynchus)." *Bull. U. S. Bur. Fish.,* Vol. XLVIII, pp. 667-692.

DAVIS, H. S. 1934a. "Care and Diseases of Trout." U. S. Bur. Fish., *Investigational Rept.* No. 22, Vol. I, 69 pp.

1934b. "The Purpose and Value of Stream Improvement." *Trans. Amer. Fish. Soc.,* Vol. 64, pp. 63-67.

1938. "Instructions for Conducting Stream and Lake Surveys." U. S. Bur. Fish., *Fishery Cir.* No. 26, 55 pp.

EATON, A. E. 1883-87. "A Revisional Monograph of Recent *Ephemeridae* or Mayflies." *Trans. Linn. Soc. London,* Sec. Ser. Zool., Vol. 3, 352 pp.

ELLIS, M. M. 1935. "Water Purity Standards for Fresh Water Fishes." U. S. Bur. Fish., *Special Rept.,* Mimeographed, 14 pp.

EMBODY, G. C. 1912. "A Preliminary Study of the Distribution, Food and Reproductive Capacity of Some Fresh-Water Amphipods." *Int. Rev. d. ges. Hydrobiol. u. Hydrogr.,* Suppl., Vol. 3, pp. 1-33.

1927. "An Outline of Stream Study and the Development of a Stocking Policy." *Contribution Aquicultural Lab.,* Cornell Univ., 21 pp.

1936. "Water Suitable for Trout Culture." *Fish Culture,* Vol. 2, No. 1, Mimeographed, N. Y. State Conser. Dept., pp. 1-5.

ESCHMEYER, R. W. 1935. "Analysis of the Game-Fish Catch in a Michigan Lake." *Trans. Amer. Fish. Soc.,* Vol. 65, pp. 207-223.

FARRELL, M. A. 1930. "Studies of the Bottom Fauna in Polluted Areas." A Biological Survey of the St. Lawrence Watershed, N. Y. State Conser. Dept., Supp. to 20th *Ann. Rept.,* pp. 192-196.

FOERSTER, R. E. 1936. "Sockeye Salmon Propagation in British Columbia." *Bull. Biol. Board of Canada,* No. LIII, Ottawa, 16 pp.

FORBES, STEPHEN A. 1928. "The Biological Survey of a River System—Its Objects, Methods, and Results." State of Ill., Div. *Nat. Hist. Surv.,* Vol. 17, Article VII, pp. 278-284.

GILBERT, CHARLES H. 1913. "Age at Maturity of the Pacific Coast Salmon of the Genus *Oncorhynchus.*" *Bull. U. S. Bur. Fish.,* Vol. 32, 1912 (1913), Doc. No. 767, pp. 1-22.

GILBERT, C. H., and W. H. RICH. 1927. "Investigations Concerning the Red-Salmon Runs to the Karluk River, Alaska." *Bull. U. S. Bur. Fish.,* Vol. 43, Part II, Doc. No. 1021, 69 pp.

GREELEY, J. R. 1929. "Fishes of the Lake Champlain Watershed." A Biological Survey of the Champlain Watershed, N. Y. State Conser. Dept., Supp. to 19th *Ann. Rept.,* pp. 44-87.

1932. "The Spawning Habits of Brook, Brown and Rainbow Trout, and the Problem of Egg Predators." *Trans. Amer. Fish. Soc.,* Vol. 62, pp. 239-248.

*HALFORD, F. M. 1897. *Dryfly Entomology.* London, 293 pp.

*HAWES, HARRY B. 1935. *Fish and Game—Now or Never.* New York, 332 pp.

HAZZARD, A. S. 1932. "Some Phases of the Life History of the Eastern Brook Trout, *Salvelinus fontinalis* Mitchell." *Trans. Amer. Fish. Soc.,* Vol. 62, pp. 344-350.

1933. "Low Water Temperature, a Limiting Factor in the Successful Production of Trout in Natural Waters." *Trans. Amer. Fish. Soc.,* Vol. 63, pp. 204-207.

HAZZARD, A. S. and R. W. ESCHMEYER. 1936. "A Comparison of Summer and Winter Fishing in Michigan Lakes." *Trans. Amer. Fish. Soc.,* Vol. 66, pp. 87-97.

*HEWITT, E. R. 1930. *Telling on the Trout.* New York, 216 pp.

*1931. *Better Trout Streams.* New York, 140 pp.

*1934. *Hewitt's Handbook of Stream Improvement.* New York, 82 pp.

1935. *Hewitt's Trout Raising and Stocking.* New York, 71 pp.

1936. "Fish Eating Birds Have No Place in Trout Waters." *Progressive Fish Culturist,* Mar., No. 16, Mimeographed Memorandum I-131, U. S. Bur. Fish., pp. 11-12.

*HILLS, JOHN WALLER. 1934. *River Keeper.* London, 227 pp.

HOBBS, DERISLEY F. 1937. "Natural Reproduction of Quinnat Salmon, Brown and Rainbow Trout in Certain New Zealand Waters." New Zealand Marine Department, *Fisheries Bulletin* No. 6, 104 pp.

HUBBS, CARL L., JOHN R. GREELEY and CLARENCE M. TARZWELL. 1932. "Methods for the Improvement of Michigan Trout Streams." *Bull. No. 1, Institute Fisheries Research,* Univ. Mich., 54 pp.

*HUBBS, CARL L., and R. W. ESCHMEYER. 1938. "The Improvement of Lakes for Fishing, a Method of Fish Management." *Bull. No. 2, Institute Fisheries Research,* Univ. Mich., 233 pp.

*INGRAHAM, HENRY A. 1926. *American Trout Streams.* New York, 140 pp.

*JENNINGS, PRESTON S. 1935. *A Book of Trout Flies.* New York, 190 pp.

*JORDAN, D. S. 1905. *A Guide to the Study of Fishes.* New York, 2 vols., 1223 pp.

1907. *Fishes.* New York, 789 pp.

1929. *Manual of the Vertebrate Animals,* 13th ed. New York, 446 pp.

JORDAN, D. S., and B. W. EVERMANN. 1896. "The Fishes of North and Middle America." *Bull. U. S. Nat. Museum,* Vol. 47, 3313 pp.

*JORDAN, D. S., and B. W. EVERMANN. 1902. *American Food and Game Fishes.* New York, 572 pp.

JORDAN, D. S., B. W. EVERMANN, and H. W. CLARK. 1930. "Check List of the Fishes and Fishlike Vertebrates of North and Middle America North of the Northern Boundary of Venezuela and Colombia." *Rept. of the U. S. Comm. Fish.* for 1928, Part II, Doc. No. 1055, 670 pp.

KENDALL, W. C. 1931. "Conflicting Classification of Game Fishes and the Status of the Steelhead Trout." Mimeographed Memorandum I-127, U. S. Bur. Fish., 4 pp.

1935. "The Fishes of New England. The salmon family. Part 2.—The salmons." *Mem. Boston Soc. Nat. Hist.*, Vol. 9, No. 1, 166 pp.

KENDALL, W. C., and W. A. DENCE. 1929. "The Fishes of the Cranberry Lake Region." *Roosevelt Wild Life Bull.*, Vol. 5, No. 2, pp. 219-309.

*KYLE, HARRY M. 1926. *The Biology of Fishes.* New York, 396 pp.

LEGER, L. 1910. "Principes de la Methods Nationelle du Peuplement des Cours d'eau à Salmonides." *Travaux du Laboratoire de Pisciculture de l'Université de Grenoble,* Fasc. 1, p. 531.

LEONARD, J. W. and DAVID S. SHETTER. 1936. "Studies on Merganser Depredations in Michigan Trout Waters." *Trans. Amer. Fish. Soc.*, Vol. 66, pp. 335-337.

LEOPOLD, ALDO. 1933. *Game Management.* New York, 481 pp.

1937. "The Research Program." *Trans. Sec. N. Amer. Wildlife Conf.*, p. 194.

LORD, RUSSELL F. 1935a. "Hatchery Trout Go Wild Overnight." *Amer. Game,* March-April and May-June issues.

1935b. "The 1935 Trout Harvest from Furnace Brook, Vermont's 'Test Stream.' " *Trans. Amer. Fish. Soc.*, Vol. 65, pp. 224-233.

MARSH, M. C., and F. P. GORHAM. 1904. "The Gas Disease in Fishes." *Rept. U. S. Comm. Fish.,* (1905) pp. 343-376.

MATHER, FRED. 1900. *Modern Fishculture in Fresh and Salt Water.* New York, 333 pp.

MEEHAN, WM. E. 1913. *Fish Culture.* New York, 287 pp.

*MORGAN, ANN HAVEN. 1930. *Field Book of Ponds and Streams.* New York, 448 pp.

*MOTTRAM, J. C. 1926. *Trout Fisheries, Their Care and Preservation.* London, 182 pp.

MUNROE, J. A. 1923. "A Preliminary Report on the Relation of Various Ducks and Gulls to the Propagation of Sockeye Salmon at Henderson Lake, Vancouver Id., B.C." *Canadian Field Naturalist,* Vol. 37.

NEEDHAM, JAMES G., and REED O. CHRISTENSON. 1927. "Economic Insects in Some Streams of Northern Utah." *Utah Agri. Exper. Sta. Bull.* 201, 36 pp.

*NEEDHAM, JAMES G., and J. T. LLOYD. 1930. *The Life of Inland Waters.* Springfield, Ill., 438 pp.

NEEDHAM, JAMES G., and HORTENSE BUTLER HEYWOOD. 1929. *A Handbook of the Dragonflies of North America.* Springfield, Ill., 378 pp.

NEEDHAM, JAMES G., and PAUL R. NEEDHAM. 1930. *A Guide to the Study of Fresh-Water Biology*. Springfield, Ill., 88 pp.

NEEDHAM, J. G., J. R. TRAVER and YIN-CHI HSU. 1935. *Biology of the May-flies*. Ithaca, N.Y., 759 pp.

NEEDHAM, P. R. 1927. "A Quantitative Study of the Fish Food Supply in Selected Areas." A Biological Survey of the Oswego River System. N. Y. State Conser. Dept. Supp. to 17th *Ann. Rept.*, pp. 192-206.

1928a. "A Net for the Capture of Stream Drift Organisms." *Ecology*, Vol. 9, pp. 339-342.

1928b. "Quantitative Studies of the Fish Food Supply in Selected Areas." A Biological Survey of the Erie-Niagara System. N. Y. State Conser. Dept., Supp. to 18th *Ann. Rept.*, pp. 220-232.

1930. "Studies on the Seasonal Food of Brook Trout." *Trans. Amer. Fish. Soc.*, Vol. 60, pp. 73-88.

1934. "Quantitative Studies of Stream Bottom Foods." *Trans. Amer. Fish. Soc.*, Vol. 64, pp. 238-247.

1937. "Methods of Measuring Anglers' Catches in Inland Waters." *Copeia*, No. 1, pp. 41-48.

NEEDHAM, P. R., and A. C. TAFT. 1934. "Observations on the Spawning of Steelhead Trout." *Trans. Amer. Fish. Soc.*, Vol. 64, pp. 332-338.

NEEDHAM, P. R., and H. A. HANSON. 1935. "A Stream Survey of the Waters of the Sierra National Forest, California, 1934." Mimeographed, U. S. Bur. Fish., 52 pp.

NERESHEIMER, E. 1937. *Die Lachsartigen (Salmonidae) Part I. Handbuch der Binnenfischerei Mitteleuropas*. Vol. III, No. 5, Stuttgart, pp. 219-370.

NESBIT, ROBERT A. 1933. "A New Method of Marking Fish by Means of Internal Tags." *Trans. Amer. Fish. Soc.*, Vol. 63, pp. 306-307.

NESBIT, ROBERT A. and J. ARTHUR KITSON. 1937. "Some results of Trout Tagging in Massachusetts." *Copeia*, No. 3, Nov. 19, pp. 168-172.

NORRIS, THADDEUS. 1868. *American Fish-Culture*. Philadelphia, 304 pp.

ODELL, THEODORE T. 1930. "The Relative Abundance of Fish of Some Lakes and Ponds of the St. Lawrence Watershed." A Biological Survey of the St. Lawrence Watershed, N. Y. State Conser. Dept., Supp. to 20th *Ann. Rept.*, pp. 95-108.

PATE, V. S. L. 1931. "Studies on the Fish Food Supply in Selected Areas." A Biological Survey of the Oswegatchie and Black River Systems, N. Y. State Conser. Dept., Supp. to 21st *Ann. Rept.*, pp. 133-149.

1932. "Studies on Fish Food in Selected Areas." A Biological Survey of the Upper Hudson Watershed, N. Y. State Conser. Dept., Supp. to 22nd *Ann. Rept.*, pp. 130-156.

1933. "Studies on the Fish Food Supply in Selected Areas of the Raquette Watershed." A Biological Survey of the Raquette Watershed. N. Y. State Conser. Dept., Supp. to 23rd *Ann. Rept.*, pp. 136-157.

*Person, H. S. 1936. *Little Waters.* Soil Conservation Service, Resettlement Administration, Rural Electrification Administration, November, 1935, rev. 1936, 82 pp.

Platts, W. Carter. (not dated). *Trout Streams, Their Management and Improvement.* London, 177 pp.

Plehn, M. 1924. *Praktikum der Fischkrankheiten.* Stuttgart, 178 pp.

Powers, E. B. 1934. "Certain Conditions of Existence of Fishes, Especially as Concerns Their Internal Environment." *Ecology,* Vol. 15, pp. 69-79.

Pratt, H. S. 1933. *Manual of the Common Invertebrate Animals Exclusive of Insects,* rev. ed. Philadelphia, 854 pp.

Regan, C. T. 1914. "The Systematic Arrangement of the Fishes of the Family Salmonidae." *Ann. Mag. Nat. Hist.,* Vol. 13, 8 Ser., pp. 405-408.

*Rhead, Louis. 1916. *American Trout-Stream Insects.* New York, 177 pp.

Ricker, William E. 1932. "Studies of Speckled Trout (Salvelinus fontinalis) in Ontario." *Univ. of Toronto Studies,* Pub. Ontario Fish. Research Lab., No. 44, pp. 69-110.

*Ronalds, Alfred. 1856. *The Fly-fisher's Entomology.* Cincinnati, Ohio, 152 pp.

Schultz, Leonard P., and Students. 1935. "The Breeding Activities of the Little Redfish, a Landlocked Form of the Sockeye Salmon, *Oncorhynchus nerka.*" *Mid-Pacific Mag.,* Jan.-Mar., pp. 67-77.

Schultz, Leonard P. 1936. "Keys to the Fishes of Washington, Oregon and Closely Adjoining Regions." *Univ. Wash. Pub. Bio.* Vol. 2, No. 4, pp. 103-228.

Shetter, David S. 1936. "Migration, Growth Rate, and Population Density of Brook Trout in the North Branch of the Au Sable River, Michigan." *Trans. Amer. Fish. Soc.,* Vol. 66, pp. 203-210.

Smith, G. M. 1923. *The Fresh-Water Algae of the United States.* New York, 716 pp.

Smith, Osgood R. 1933. "The Caledonia Shrimp Dikerogammarus." *Trans. Amer. Fish. Soc.,* Vol. 63, pp. 120-128.

1936. "A Creel Census from Dry River, New Hampshire." *Trans. Amer. Fish. Soc.,* Vol. 66, pp. 313-315.

Smith, Osgood R., and P. R. Needham. 1935. "A Stream Survey in the Mono and Inyo National Forests, California, 1934." Mimeographed, U. S. Bur. Fish., 45 pp.

Snyder, John O. 1931. "Salmon of the Klamath River, California." Calif. Div. Fish and Game, *Fish Bull.,* No. 34, 129 pp.

1933. California Trout. *Calif. Fish and Game Mag.,* Vol. 19, No. 2, pp. 81-113.

1934. A New California Trout. *Calif. Fish and Game Mag.,* Vol. 20, No. 2, pp. 105-113.

Stone, Livingston. 1877. *Domesticated Trout,* 3d ed. Cambridge, Mass. 367 pp.

SURBER, EUGENE W. 1936. "Rainbow Trout and Bottom Fauna Production in One Mile of Stream." *Trans. Amer. Fish. Soc.*, Vol. 66, pp. 193-202.

TAFT, A. C., and LEO SHAPOVALOV. 1935. "A Biological Survey of Streams and Lakes in the Klamath and Shasta National Forests of California, 1934." Mimeographed, U. S. Bur. Fish., 71 pp.

TARZWELL, CLARENCE M. 1936. "Experimental Evidence on the Value of Trout Stream Improvement in Michigan." *Trans. Amer. Fish. Soc.*, Vol. 66, pp. 177-187.

U. S. COMMISSION OF FISH AND FISHERIES. 1900. *A Manual of Fish-Culture*, rev. ed., 340 pp.

VAN OOSTEN, JOHN. 1928. "Life History of the Lake Herring (*Leucichthys artedi Le Seuer*) of Lake Huron as Revealed by Its Scales, With a Critique of the Scale Method." *Bull. U. S. Bur. Fish.*, Vol. XLIV, Doc. No. 1053, (1929), pp. 265-428.

*VIOSCA, PERCY, JR. 1937. *Pondfish Culture*, New Orleans, 260 pp.

*WALFORD, LIONEL A. 1937. *Marine Game Fishes of the Pacific Coast: Alaska to the Equator*. Berkeley, Calif., 205 pp.

*WALTON, IZAAK. 1759. *The Compleat Angler*. London. 340 pp.

WARD, HENRY B., and GEORGE C. WHIPPLE. 1918. *Fresh-Water Biology*. New York, 1111 pp.

*WATER POLLUTION, SPECIAL ADVISORY COMMITTEE ON, 1935. "Report on Water Pollution." Nat. Resources Committee, Water Resources Section, Mimeographed, U. S. Dept. of Interior, 82 pp.

WELCH, PAUL S. 1935. *Limnology*. New York, 471 pp.

WHIPPLE, G. C. 1927. *The Microscopy of Drinking Water*, 4th ed. rev. by Fair and Whipple. New York, 586 pp.

WHITE, H. C. 1924. "A Quantitatitve Determination of the Number of Survivors from Planting 5,000 Trout Fry in Each of Two Streams." *Contr. Canad. Bio.*, Vol. 2, No. 9, pp. 135-150.

1927. "A Preliminary Report on Trout Investigations in Forbes Brook in 1925 and 1926." *Contr. Canad. Bio.*, Vol. 3, No. 15, pp. 367-375.

1929. "Trout Fry Planting Experiments in Forbes Brook, P. E. I. in 1928." *Contr. Canad. Bio.*, Vol. 5, No. 8, pp. 205-211.

1930. "Some Observations on the Eastern Brook Trout (*S. fontinalis*) of Prince Edward Island." *Trans. Amer. Fish. Soc.*, Vol. 60, pp. 101-108.

WIEBE, A. H., and ALFRED M. MCGAVOCK. 1932. "The Ability of Several Species of Fish to Survive on Prolonged Exposure to Abnormally High Concentrations of Dissolved Oxygen." *Trans. Amer. Fish. Soc.*, Vol. 62, pp. 267-274.

BIBLIOGRAPHY I

(Entries on this list were cited in the annotation. CEB)

ANDERSON, N. H. 1966. "Depressant Effect of Moonlight on Activity of Aquatic Insects." *Nature,* Vol. 209, No. 5020, pp. 319–320.

APPLEGATE, V. C., J. H. HOWELL, and J. W. MOFFETT. 1961. "Use of 3-Trifluoromethyl-4-nitrophenol as a Selective Sea Lamprey Larvicide." *Great Lakes Fishery Commission. Technical Report,* No. 1:1–35.

BRIGGS, J. D. 1953. "The Behavior and Reproduction of Salmonid Fishes in a Small Coastal Stream." *California Department of Fish and Game, Fish Bull. No. 94.* 62 pp.

BUSS, K., and R. MCCREARY. 1960. "A Comparison of Egg Production of Hatchery-Reared Brook, Brown, and Rainbow Trout." *Prog. Fish Cult.,* Vol. 22, No. 1, pp. 7–10.

BUTLER, R. L., and D. P. BORGESON. 1965. "California 'Catchable' Trout Fisheries." *California Department of Fish and Game, Fish Bull. 127.* 57 pp.

CALHOUN, A. 1966. "Habitat Protection and Improvement." *In: Inland Fisheries Management,* A. CALHOUN, Ed. *California Department of Fish and Game.* pp. 40–48.

CHADWICK, H. K. 1966. "Fish Marking." *In: Inland Fisheries Management,* A. CALHOUN, Ed. *California Department of Fish and Game.* pp. 19–40.

CHAPMAN, D. W. 1962. "Aggressive Behavior of Juvenile Coho Salmon as a Cause of Emigration." *J. Fish. Res. Bd. Can.,* Vol. 19, pp. 1047–1081.

CLAY, C. H. 1961. *Design of Fishways and Other Fish Facilities,* Dept. Fisheries, Ottawa, Canada. 301 pp.

COBLE, D. W. 1961. "Influence of Water Exchange and Dissolved Oxygen in Redds on Survival of Steelhead Trout Embryos." *Trans. Am. Fish. Soc.,* Vol. 90, No. 4, pp. 469–474.

COCHE, A. G. 1967. "Production of Juvenile Steelhead Trout in a Freshwater Impoundment." *Ecological Monographs,* Vol. 30, pp. 201–228.

COOPER, E. L. 1959. "Trout Stocking as an Aid to Fish Management." *Penn. State Univ. Coll. of Ag. Bull.,* No. 663. 21 pp.

DEWITT, J. W. 1969. "The Pond, Lagoon, Bay, Estuary and Impoundment Culture of Anadromous and Marine Fishes, with Emphasis on the Culture of Salmon and Trout, Along the Pacific Coast of the United States." *Report of Technical Assistance Project, U. S. Dept. Comm. Econ. Dev. Adm.* 36 pp.

DOUDOROFF, P., B. G. ANDERSON, G. E. BURDICK, P. S. GALTSOFF, W. B. HART, R. PATRICK, E. R. STRONG, E. W. SURBER, and W. M. VANHORN. 1951. "Bioassay Methods for the Evaluation of Acute Toxicity of Industrial Wastes to Fish." *Sewage and Industrial Wastes,* Vol. 23, No. 1, pp. 1380–1397.

DOUDOROFF, P., and D. L. SHUMWAY. 1967. "Dissolved Oxygen Criteria for the Protection of Fish." *Am. Fish. Soc. Spec. Publ. No. 4,* pp. 13–19.

GILDERHUS, P. A., B. L. BERGER, and R. E. LENNON. 1969. "Field Trials of Antimycin A as a Fish Toxicant." *Investigations in Fish Control, No. 27,* U. S. Bureau of Sport Fisheries and Wildlife. 21 pp.

HAZZARD, A. S. 1954. "Problems of Trout Management." *Mich. Dept. Cons. Fish. Div. Pamphlet. No. 13,* 26 pp.

HUNT, E. O., and A. I. BISCHOFF. 1960. "Inimical Effects on Wildlife of Periodic DDD Applications to Clear Lake." *California Fish and Game,* Vol. 46, No. 1, pp. 91–106.

HYNES, H. B. N. 1965. "The Significance of Macroinvertebrates in the Study of Mild River Pollution." *Trans. 3rd Seminar on Biological Problems in Water Pollution. Public Health Service Publ. No. 999–WP–25.* pp. 235–240.

JOHNSON, R. C. 1966. "The Effect of Artificial Circulation on Production of a Thermally Stratified Lake." *Wash. Dept. Fisheries Research Papers,* Vol. 2, No. 4, pp. 5–15.

KATZ, M., and W. C. HOWARD. 1955. "The Length and Growth of O-Year Class Creek Chubs in Relation to Domestic Pollution." *Trans. Am. Fish. Soc.,* Vol. 84, pp. 228–238.

KOSKI, R. 1969. "All About Fish Stocking." *Oregon State Game Commission Bulletin,* June, 1969. Vol. 24, No. 6, pp. 3–6.

MCNEIL, W. J. 1966. "Effect of the Spawning Bed Environment on Reproduction of Pink and Chum Salmon." *U. S. Fish and Wildlife Service Fish. Bulletin 64,* pp. 495–523.

MACPHEE, C., and R. RUELLE. 1968. *Fish Culture by Squawfish Population Eradication.* U. S. Patent Office 3,389,685.

NEUHOLD, J. M., and K. H. LU. 1957. "Creel Census Method." *Utah State Department of Fish and Game,* Publ. No. 8, 36 pp.

OVERTON, W. S., and D. E. DAVIS. 1969. "Estimating the Numbers of Animals in Wildlife Populations." *In: Wildlife Management Techniques,* 3rd ed. rev. R. H. GILES, Ed. The Wildlife Society. pp. 403–455.

PATRICK, R., and M. H. HOHN. 1956. "The Diatometer—A Method for Indicating the Condition of Aquatic Life." *Proc. American Petroleum Inst. Sect. 3,* 36, pp. 332–338.

PHILLIPS, R. W. 1965. "Effect of Fine Materials on Salmon and Trout Redds." *In: Proceedings of Meeting on Erosion and Sedimentation in the Northwest, 1964-65 Flood Season,* U. S. D. A. Soil Conservation Service. Portland, Oregon.

PHINNEY, H. K., and C. A. PEEK. 1961. "Klamath Lake, an Instance of Natural Enrichment." *In: Algae and Metropolitan Wastes, U.S.P.H.S.* Robert A. Taft Sanitary Engineering Center. Tech-report W 61-3. pp. 22–27.

PRESSEY, R. T., and W. E. SMITH. 1958. "Hatchery and Fish Farm Relationships." *In: Fish Farming, Fisheries Management,* Washington Dept. Fisheries, Olympia. pp. 88–96.

RASMUSSEN, D. H. 1960. "Preventing a Winterkill by Use of a Compressed Air System." *Prog. Fish. Cult.,* Vol. 22, No. 4, pp. 185–187.

REGIER, H. A., and D. S. ROBSON. 1967. "Estimating Population Number and Mortality Rates." *In: The Biological Basis of Freshwater Fish Production,* S. D. GERKING, Ed. Blackwell. pp. 31–66.

RICKER, W. E. 1958. "Handbook of Computations for Biological Statistics of Fish Populations." *Fish. Res. Bd. Can. Bull. 119.* 300 pp.

ROBERTSON, O. H. 1956. "A Study of the Cause of Death of the Pacific Salmons After Spawning." *Year Book of the American Philosophical Society.* pp. 215–218.

ROBERTSON, O. H., and B. C. WEXLER. 1960. "Histological Changes in the Organs and Tissues of Migrating and Spawning Pacific Salmon (Genus *Oncorhynchus*)." *Endocrinology,* Vol. 66, pp. 222–239.

ROUNSEFELL, G. A., and J. L. KASK. 1946. "How to Mark Fish." *Trans. Am. Fish. Soc.,* Vol. 73:320–363.

SENN, H. G., and R. E. NOBLE. 1968. "Contribution of Coho Salmon, *Oncorhynchus kisutch,* from a Columbia River Watershed Hatchery." *Washington Department of Fisheries. Fish. Res. Pap.,* Vol. 3, No. 1, pp. 51–62.

SPORT FISHING INSTITUTE. 1964. "Most Fishing is for Fun—What Else?" *Sport Fishing Inst. Bull. No. 150,* pp. 1–2.

SHUMWAY, D. L., C. E. WARREN, and P. DOUDOROFF. 1964. "Influence of Oxygen Concentration and Water Movement on the Growth of Steelhead Trout and Coho Salmon Embryos." *Trans. Am. Fish. Soc.,* Vol. 93, No. 4, pp. 342–356.

VINCENT, R. E. 1960. "Some Influences of Domestication Upon Three Stocks of Brook Trout (*Salvelinus fontinalis* (Mitchell))." *Trans. Am. Fish. Soc.,* Vol. 89, No. 1, pp. 35–52.

WAGNER, H. H. 1968. "Effect of Stocking Time on Survival of Steelhead Trout, *Salmo gairdnerii,* in Oregon." *Trans. Am. Fish. Soc.,* Vol. 97, No. 4, pp. 374–379.

WAGNER, H. H. 1969. "Effect of Stocking Location of Juvenile Steelhead Trout, *Salmo gairdnerii,* on Adult Catch." *Trans. Am. Fish. Soc.,* Vol. 98, No. 1, pp. 27–34.

WARREN, C. E., J. H. WALES, G. E. DAVIS and P. DOUDOROFF. 1964. "Trout Production in an Experimental Stream Enriched with Sucrose." *J. Wildlife Management,* Vol. 28, No. 4, pp. 617–660.

WATERS, T. F. 1969. "Invertebrate Drift-Ecology and Significance to Stream Fishes." *Symposium on Trout and Salmon in Streams,* University of British Columbia. T. G. NORTHCOTE, Ed. pp. 121–134.

WHITE, R. S., and O. M. BRYNILDSON. 1967. "Guidelines for Management of Trout Stream Habitat in Wisconsin." *Wisc. Dept. of Nat. Res., Div. of Cons. Tech. Bull. 29.* 65 pp.

WORLUND, D. D., R. J. WAHLE, and P. D. ZIMMER. 1969. "Contribution of Columbia River Hatcheries to Harvest of Fall Chinook Salmon (*Oncorhynchus tshawytscha*)." *U. S. Fish and Wildlife Service Fish. Bull.,* Vol. 67, No. 2, pp. 361–391.

BIBLIOGRAPHY II

(This list contains a few general references on subjects covered in this book, and complements those cited.)

ALLEN, K. R. 1951. "The Horokiwi Stream, a Study of a Trout Population." *New Zealand Mar. Dept., Fish. Bull. No. 10.* 238 pp.

AMERICAN FISHERIES SOCIETY. 1960. *A List of Common and Scientific Names of Fishes From the United States and Canada,* 2nd ed., Sp. Pub. No. 2. 102 pp.

DAVIS, H. S. 1953. *Culture and Diseases of Game Fishes,* U. of Calif. Press. 332 pp.

FROST, W. E., and M. E. BROWN. 1967. *The Trout,* Collins, London. 286 pp.

HOBBS, D. F. 1948. "Trout Fisheries in New Zealand, Their Development and Management." *New Zealand Mar. Dept. Fish. Bull. No. 9.* 173 pp.

KENDALL, W. C. 1924. "The Status of Fish Culture in Our Inland Public Waters, and the Role of Investigation in the Maintenance of Fish Resources." *Roosevelt Wild Life Bull.* Vol. 2, No. 3, Syracuse U. pp. 199–351.

LAGLER, K. F. 1956. *Freshwater Fishery Biology,* 2nd ed. Brown. 421 pp.

MACAN, T. T. 1963. *Freshwater Ecology,* Wiley. 338 pp.

ROUNSEFELL, G. A., and W. H. EVERHART. 1953. *Fishery Science, Its Methods and Applications,* Wiley. 444 pp.

INDEX

References to illustrations are in boldface type